Proc IRE Vol 40 pp 1361-1364 Nov 1952
Vol 46 pp 1229-1235 Jun 1958

Field-Effect Transistors

*Physics, Technology
and Applications*

PRENTICE-HALL ELECTRICAL ENGINEERING SERIES

*This title is also in the Prentice-Hall International Series in Electrical Engineering. Prentice-Hall, Inc.; Prentice-Hall International, Inc., United Kingdom and Eire; Prentice-Hall of Canada, Ltd., Canada.

William L. Everitt, *Editor*

CONTRIBUTORS

Schuyler M. Christian, *RCA Laboratories, Princeton, N.J.*
David M. Griswold, *Radio Corporation of America, Somerville, N.J.*
Fred P. Heiman, *RCA Laboratories, Princeton, N.J.*
Steven R. Hofstein, *RCA Laboratories, Princeton, N.J.*
Harwick Johnson, *Laboratories RCA Zurich, Switzerland*
Paul E. Kolk, *KMC Semiconductor Corp., Long Valley, N.J.*
Dietrich Meyerhofer, *RCA Laboratories, Princeton, N.J.*
A. Karl Rapp, *RCA Laboratories, Princeton, N.J.*
Akos G. Revesz, *RCA Laboratories, Princeton, N.J.*
Albert Rose, *RCA Laboratories, Princeton, N.J.*
J. Torkel Wallmark, *Chalmers University, Gothenburg, Sweden*
Paul K. Weimer, *RCA Laboratories, Princeton, N.J.*
Karl H. Zaininger, *RCA Laboratories, Princeton, N.J.*

Field-Effect Transistors

Physics, Technology and Applications

EDITORS

J. Torkel Wallmark
Chalmers University
Gothenburg, Sweden

Harwick Johnson
Laboratories RCA , Ltd.
Zürich, Switzerland

Prentice-Hall, Inc., *Englewood Cliffs, New Jersey*

SERIES IN SOLID STATE PHYSICAL ELECTRONICS
Nick Holonyak, Jr., *Editor*

GENTRY, ET AL. *Semiconductor Controlled Rectifiers:*
Principles and Applications of p-n-p-n Devices
NUSSBAUM *Electromagnetic and Quantum Properties*
of Materials
NUSSBAUM *Semiconductor Device Physics*
ROBERTS & VANDERSLICE *Ultrahigh Vacuum and Its Applications*
WALLMARK & JOHNSON, EDS. *Field-Effect Transistors:*
Physics, Technology and Applications

PRENTICE-HALL INTERNATIONAL, INC., *London*
PRENTICE-HALL OF AUSTRALIA, PTY., LTD., *Sydney*
PRENTICE-HALL OF CANADA, LTD., *Toronto*
PRENTICE-HALL OF INDIA (PRIVATE) LTD., *New Delhi*
PRENTICE-HALL OF JAPAN, INC., *Tokyo*

....the hope of discovery of a purely electronic, rather than thermal, semiconductor amplifier was bolstered by the discovery of what might be called an *existence theorem,* to use a mathematical term, that such an amplifier was possible, or at least not contradictory to the theories of semiconductors and statistical mechanics. The particular device...consists of a very thin layer of semiconductor placed on an insulating support. This layer of semiconductor constitutes one plate of a parallel-plate capacitor, the other being a metal plate in close proximity to it. If this capacitor is charged, as shown in part (c), with the metal plate positive, then the additional charge on the semiconductor will be represented by the increased number of electrons. At room temperature, in germanium, a negligible number of these electrons will be bound to the donors.... Consequently, the added electrons should be free to move and should contribute to the conductivity of the semiconductor. In this way, the conductivity in the semiconductor can be modulated, electronically, by a voltage put on the capacitor plate. Since this input signal requires no power if the dielectric is perfect, power gain will result.

W. Shockley, *Electrons and Holes in Semiconductors*

Foreword

While history in the large has a discernible and rational drift, its smaller movements often have an aimless character not unlike the random excursions of an electron drifting through a lattice in a weak electric field. A given point may be repeatedly traversed before it takes its place in an "ordered" train of events. The ordering is born of a *post hoc* logic rather than of the detailed chronology of events.

The early 1930's saw a literal burst of understanding of the properties of semiconductors in the now familiar terms of band theory. The treatises by Sommerfeld and Bethe, by Frohlich, and by Wilson, all in the 1930's, are still classics in the field. Almost two decades were to pass before these early concepts were to seriously invade our technology.

One of the more elementary conclusions that might have been drawn from these works was that the conductivity of a semiconductor could be modulated by the application of an electric field to it as one plate of a capacitor. The increase or decrease in charge would then represent a corresponding increase or decrease in available free carriers. Such a proposal or conclusion played no conspicuous role in the scientific literature. The patent literature, on the other hand, has at least two examples that assert by appeal to experiment the modulation of the conductivity of a semiconductor by an applied field. One arrangement was described by Lilienfeld (1930) and a second by Heil (1934). Lilienfeld's own interpretation shows a clear lack of understanding of the mechanism responsible for the modulation. Heil, on the other hand, offered no explanation. However, the drawing that accompanies Heil's proposal has a distinctly modern flavor.

Parenthetically, in time as well as logic, both Schottky (metal-semiconductor rectifier) and Mott (space-charge-limited currents in insulators) showed that the conductivity of a semiconductor or insulator could be modulated by an applied field. But their applied fields were collinear with the currents. A third electrode was still needed to adapt these effects to the design of solid-state triodes.

The next event in this sequence was the publication in the late 1940's by Shockley and Pearson of the modulation of conductivity by the field effect. They found, however, that only some ten per cent of the induced charge was free to contribute to a change in conductivity. The remainder, as pointed out by Bardeen in one of his classic papers, was immobilized in surface states. For some years the major impact of this work was to provoke an extensive scientific exploration of surface states and their dependence on ambients.

We must recognize here that the early proposals for field-effect triodes could readily be expected to yield current and power gains but not, necessarily, voltage gains. It remained for Shockley to show analytically and for Dacey and Ross to show experimentally that voltage gains were, in fact, obtainable owing to the pentode-like characteristics of the collector current versus collector voltage.

Meantime, the publications by Brattain and Bardeen and by Shockley on the bipolar transistor overshadowed the field-effect device and absorbed most of the technological effort of the next decade. It is only recently that a significant effort has been refocused on the field-effect transistor. This refocusing has stemmed largely from the work of Weimer on cadmium sulphide and of Hofstein and Heiman on silicon.

It is easy in retrospect to see the ironies of this train of events. First, the "existence proof" by Shockley and Pearson that an electric field could modulate the conductivity of a semiconductor had already been in existence and generally ignored for some twenty years prior to their work.

Second, by launching the transistor in the direction of a bipolar device rather than a unipolar field-effect device, the more difficult and hazardous path was chosen. It is by now well-known that the achievement of the high purities needed in the bipolar transistor to yield their long free-pair lifetimes was an almost unique accomplishment in that it was confined to germanium and silicon. In none of the many compound materials explored have pair lifetimes even approaching 100 microseconds been attained. The field-effect device, by contrast, does not depend upon free pairs and hence can make use of a wide variety of materials far less refined than transistor-quality germanium and silicon. Moreover, the achievements of high grid (gate) impedance and a linear voltage response both come naturally and easily to the field-effect triode. Their realization in the bipolar transistor is a far more difficult task.

The other face of this ironic coin is that the exceptional degree of purity and control required for the bipolar transistor seeded a revolution in the scientific effort to explore the electronic properties of semiconductors. The idealized models on which physical theory thrives were actually fabricated thanks to the painstaking efforts of chemists and metallurgists. It is perhaps no exaggeration to suggest that if chance had favored the field-effect transistor over the bipolar transistor, the flowering of the science of the solid state would have been postponed by a good decade.

Now that attention has been refocused on the field-effect transistor, one can reasonably hope that the science of semiconductor-insulator interfaces and of thin insulating films will enjoy a comparable prosperity and will help to fertilize a host of allied fields.

ALBERT ROSE

Editors' Preface

It is the purpose of this book to assist physicists, device engineers, and applications engineers interested in field-effect transistors by presenting all essential information on the field-effect transistor in one place and in easily accessible form. This broad coverage is particularly desirable since the building of integrated circuits, in which field-effect transistors appear destined to play an important role, requires the collaboration of many different groups of specialists, each with a need to understand the problems of the others.

An attempt has been made to cover all important aspects related to the field-effect transistor, whether it be surface physics, device fabrication, or electronic circuit theory. Thus, the basic developments in understanding and technology, which gave rise to the rapid advances in this area, are discussed as well as the limitations imposed by physical processes. This enables the reader to make an independent judgement of the evaluation and utilization of this device. Because the insulated-gate field-effect transistor holds promise of greater versatility than the junction-gate field-effect transistor, most of the book is devoted to the former. In some cases the junction-gate construction is advantageous and a brief treatment of it is included. Much of the text is applicable to both.

In the development of field-effect transistors, particularly in the various forms of insulated-gate devices, scientists of the RCA Laboratories have played a leading role. It is natural that this first book on the subject should be put together by a team of scientists from RCA.

An effort has been made to make the book easily understood. The newspaper technique of three easy steps has been used: first a short summarizing story, then a more complete one, and finally the details of treatment in depth. A short section called "Terminology" is planned to be helpful to the reader making his first acquaintance with field-effect devices. The first chapter, "Introduction to Field-Effect Transistors," gives a brief but fairly complete summary of the field. The following eleven chapters each treat, in depth, one aspect of field-effect transistors. These discussions range from the physics of semiconductor surfaces and insulators to the growth of oxide films, and through many device considerations to the use of field-effect transistors in electronics including integrated circuits.

In addition to the pertinent references at the end of each chapter, a chronological bibliography on field-effect transistors is included at the end of the book. A notable feature not often found in books is a section of this bibliography devoted to the patent literature of field-effect transistors. This will be valuable to research-and-development groups concerned with new versions of the device or its applications, or to those interested in tracing the history of the device. The editors are grateful to Leroy Greenspan of RCA Laboratories for this bibliography.

The reader will find that the book stresses explanations, techniques and examples rather than specific instructions of how to build a specific circuit with a specific transistor. There are three reasons for this. The writers believe that information developed in the understanding of the topic has a greater long lasting utility. Second, only a few commercial insulated-gate transistors are currently available and even these can be expected to be displaced by devices with improved characteristics. Finally, the increasing role of integrated circuits demands that the transistor and circuit be designed and constructed together.

The timeliness of this book has been enhanced by the inclusion of very recent developments. This has been made possible through the cooperation of many individuals and institutions. To their colleagues in the Radio Corporation of America the authors are grateful for many fruitful discussions and helpful suggestions as well as the many technical contributions acknowledged in the references. Some of the work on insulated-gate transistors stems from RCA Laboratories work supported in part by the U.S. Air Force Cambridge Research Laboratories, the U.S. Air Force Wright-Patterson Aeronautical Systems Div., and the U.S. Army Ft. Monmouth Signal Laboratory. Figures 9–23, 9–24, 9–25, 9–27, and 9–28 are reprinted with the permission of the publisher from the 1964 Digest of Technical Papers, International Solid-State Circuits Conference. Figures 9–6, 9–10, 9–12, 9–13, 9–30, 9–31, and 9–32 are reprinted from the Proceedings of the IEEE. Permission for the reduction of other figures was graciously given by Academic Press (Physics of Thin Films), RCA Review, and Journal of Applied Physics.

The authors and editors are grateful to the Radio Corporation of America for the use of facilities at Princeton, Somerville, and Zürich in the preparation of the manuscript and to Chalmers Institute of Technology at Gothenburg.

J. TORKEL WALLMARK
HARWICK JOHNSON

Contents

Common Symbols and Constants

A voltage gain; also area

b ratio of electron-to-hole mobility; at room temperature, germanium, 2.05; silicon, 2.81

C_d drain capacitance

C_g gate capacitance

C_{gd} capacitance between gate and drain

C_{gs} capacitance between gate and source

C_i capacitance per unit area across the insulator. Also input capacitance

C_{is} total semiconductor surface capacitance per unit area

C_s semiconductor space-charge layer capacitance per unit area

d channel depth (perpendicular to current and surface; z-direction) See Figs. 1 and 2

     thickness of the insulator

E_c energy at the conduction-band edge

E_F energy at the Fermi level

E_i Fermi level for an intrinsic semiconductor

E_t energy of trap (or recombination) center

E_v energy at the valence-band edge

f frequency

g_m transconductance

g_s surface conductance

h Planck's constant $= 6.62 \times 10^{-34}$ J sec (joule sec)

$\hbar$ $= h/2\pi = 1.05 \times 10^{-34}$ J sec

I_d drain current

I_{do} drain current at zero gate voltage

I_g gate current

I_s source current

k Boltzmann's constant $= 1.38 \times 10^{-23}$ J/°K (joule/K°)

l channel length (in direction of current; x-direction). See Figs. 1 and 2 (in some cases, such as high-frequency considerations, the effective channel length is only that part of the distance from source to drain covered by the gate)

m mass of the electron, 9.11×10^{-31} kg

m_e^* effective mass of electrons; silicon, $m_e^*/m = 1.10$; germanium, $m_e^*/m = 0.55$

m_h^* effective mass of holes; silicon, $m_h^*/m = 0.57$; germanium, $m_h^*/m = 0.37$

n density of electrons

n_b density of electrons in the bulk

N_A density of acceptors

N_C density of states in conduction band

N_D density of donors

intrinsic density at room temperature of electrons (holes) silicon, 1.4×10^{10}; germanium, 2.4×10^{13}

n_s density of electrons at the surface

N_v density of states in valence band

p density of holes

p_b density of holes in the bulk

p_s density of holes at the surface

q magnitude of the charge of the electron $= 1.60 \times 10^{-19}$ coulomb

R_L load resistance

T absolute temperature

u normalized electrostatic potential, $q\phi/kT$

v normalized electrostatic potential with respect to bulk

$\bar{v}$ thermal velocity
germanium:
electrons 6.5×10^6 cm/sec, reached at 3000 v/cm
holes 6×10^6 cm/sec, reached at 9000 v/cm
silicon:
electrons 8.5×10^6 cm/sec, reached at 15,000 v/cm
holes 5×10^6 cm/sec, reached at 20,000 v/cm

V_d drain voltage (with respect to source)

V_g gate voltage (with respect to source)

V_p pinch-off voltage (gate voltage at which drain current starts to flow)

V_s source voltage. Also potential at the surface with respect to bulk

w channel width (perpendicular to current, parallel to surface; y-direction). See Fig. 1

x direction parallel to current, parallel to surface, see Fig. 1

y direction normal to current, parallel to surface, see Fig. 1

z direction normal to current, normal to surface, see Fig. 1

ϵ_i permittivity of the insulator

ϵ_s permittivity of the semiconductor

ϵ_o permittivity of free space $= 8.85$ 10^{-12} F/m

κ dielectric constant $= \epsilon/\epsilon_0$; silicon, 12; germanium, 16; vacuum evaporated SiO, 5.0; SiO_2 thermally grown in dry O_2, 3.8; SiO_2 thermally grown in steam, 4.5;

λ Debye length

λ_i Debye length in the insulator

μ_h mobility of holes, in pure material at room temperature;
silicon, $480 \text{ cm}^2\text{V}^{-1}\text{sec}^{-1}$
germanium, $1900 \text{ cm}^2\text{V}^{-1}\text{sec}^{-1}$

μ_n mobility of electrons, in pure material at room temperature;
silicon, $1350 \text{ cm}^2\text{V}^{-1}\text{sec}^{-1}$
germanium, $3900 \text{ cm}^2\text{V}^{-1}\text{sec}^{-1}$

ρ charge density

σ conductivity

σ_b bulk conductivity

σ_h capture cross section for holes

σ_n capture cross section for electrons

σ_s surface conductivity

τ_r dielectric relaxation time of the semiconductor

ϕ macroscopic electrostatic potential in the semiconductor

ϕ_b bulk macroscopic electrostatic potential

surface macroscopic electrostatic potential

χ electron affinity of semiconductor

ω angular frequency $= 2\pi f$

Terminology

Transistors may be divided into two classes, i.e., bipolar transistors (conventional) and unipolar transistors. In bipolar transistors both positive and negative free carriers take part in the functioning of the device; hence the term *bipolar*. Thus, in bipolar devices the charge of excess minority carriers injected into the base region is compensated by an equal charge of majority carriers so that electrical neutrality in the base region is maintained. On the other hand, in unipolar devices the current is carried only by the free majority carriers in the conducting channel and no essential role is played by the small number of minority carriers; hence the term *unipolar*. Charge neutrality is not necessarily maintained in the channel itself, but charge balance prevails over a larger region including the adjacent control electrodes.

The *field-effect transistor* is a type of unipolar device in which the number of carriers available to carry current in the conducting region is controlled by application of an electric field to the surface (or junction interface) of the semiconductor. In the field-effect transistor, Fig. 1, electrons flow from a *source*, consisting of an ohmic contact, through a conducting *channel* of semiconductor material to a *drain*, also consisting of an ohmic contact. The channel has a *length* in the direction of the current (from drain to source), a *width* perpendicular to the current and parallel to the surface, and a *depth* perpendicular to the current and perpendicular to the surface. The conductivity of the channel can be influenced by charge on a *gate* which may have either of two forms. In the *insulated gate* transistor, the gate is one electrode of a capacitor which is separated by a thin insulator from the channel which forms the other electrode of the capacitor. Positive charge on the gate induces an equal amount of negative charge in the channel, enhancing its conductivity.

POSITIVE

Negative charge on the gate detracts an equal amount of negative charge from the channel, reducing its conductivity. In the *junction gate* transistor, the gate is a layer of semiconductor of a conductivity type (*p*-type) opposite to that of the channel (*n*-type). The junction gate is reverse biased with respect to the channel forming an insulating depletion layer which encroaches upon the conducting channel, effectively limiting its dimensions. A more negative voltage on the gate will further reduce the channel, reducing its conductance; a less negative voltage will let the channel expand, increasing its conductance. At a particular voltage, the *pinch-off voltage*, the channel conductance is ideally reduced to zero.

The device may be constructed by two alternatives so that the *conductance of the channel is high* when the gate voltage is equal to the source voltage. First, the substrate material may have high conductivity as in Fig. 1. Second, the substrate may have low conductivity, but a

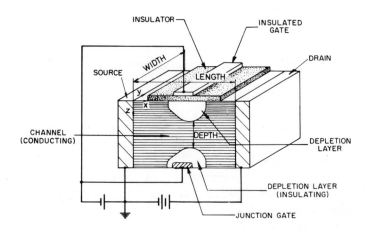

Figure 1. Schematic drawing of a depletion field-effect transistor. The principle of operation is illustrated by an insulated gate at the top and by a junction gate at the bottom of the structure.

conducting channel may be created by building in a positive charge in, or on the insulator or at the interface. Then the gate may be run negative to deplete the conductance of the channel—*depletion-type* transistor. This can be done with both the insulated gate and the junction gate. The insulated gate may even be run positive in depletion units, enhancing the initially high conductance still further. A depletion-type transistor is shown schematically in Fig. 1, equipped with both an insulated gate (on top) and a junction gate (on bottom).

If the device is constructed so that the *conductance of the channel is low* when the gate voltage is equal to the source voltage (ground), the gate is usually run positive in order to enhance the current of useful levels — *enhancement-type* transistor. In practice, this can be done only with the insulated gate; the junction gate would draw a large current because it would be biased in the forward direction, leading to a different and less desirable mode of operation, *unijunction device*. An enhancement-type transistor is shown schematically in Fig. 2, equipped with both an insulated gate (on top) and a junction gate (on bottom).

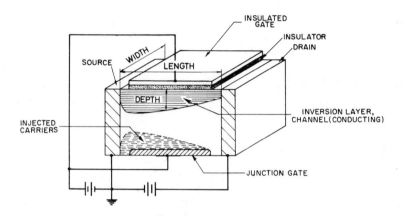

Figure 2. Schematic drawing of an enhancement field-effect transistor. The principle of operation is illustrated by an insulated gate at the top and by a junction gate at the bottom of the structure.

Instead of electrons, holes may be substituted in this description, provided that the polarities of the voltages and charge carriers are reversed at the same time.

1

Introduction to Field-Effect Transistors

J. Torkel Wallmark

This introduction presents the material of the book in a condensed form, free of mathematics and technical details. It is intended to fill two functions. First, it ties together and sets into proper perspective the various parts of the book. Second, it presents the highlights of the subject to those readers who are not at the moment interested in the full details.

The field-effect transistor has a long history, much longer than that of the conventional bipolar transistor. Some of the early attempts by J. Lilienfeld and O. Heil are referenced in the bibliography.[1] Of particular interest is a patent by Heil[2] from which Fig. 1–1 has been borrowed.

The light area marked 3 in Fig. 1–1 is described as a thin layer of a semiconductor such as tellurium, iodine, cuprous oxide, or vanadium pentoxide; 1 and 2 designate ohmic contacts to the semiconductor. A thin metallic layer marked 6, immediately adjacent to but insulated from the semiconductor layer, serves as control electrode. Heil describes how a signal on the control electrode modulates the resistance of the semiconductor layer so that an amplified signal may be observed by means

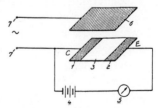

Figure 1–1. Drawing from British Patent 439,457, inventor: O. Heil.

of the current meter, marked 5. In modern terminology, one might describe this device as a unipolar field-effect transistor with insulated gate.

1

In 1952 Shockley[3] described a unipolar field-effect transistor with a control electrode consisting of a reverse-biased junction, as shown in Fig. 1–2. Such transistors were subsequently built and tested by Dacey and Ross[4] who also added an analytical treatment of the performance limits of such devices in 1955. A summary of this work is found in the last part of Chapter 5. Until recently, however, the field-effect transistor remained in the laboratory stage of development.

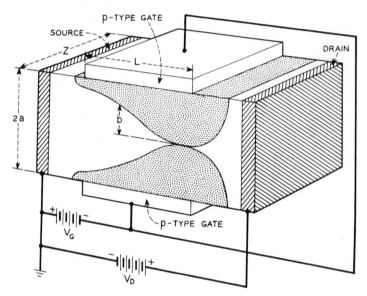

Figure 1–2. Schematic diagram of a unipolar field-effect transistor according to Shockley.

Three factors have contributed to make the unipolar field-effect transistor emerge from its previous obscurity. First, the understanding of semiconductor physics and the related advance of semiconductor technology now make it possible to fabricate devices with predictable performance. Features of this physical understanding which are particular to field-effect transistors and not usually found in textbooks are treated in Chapters 2–4. Second, there are new technological features, such as the insulated-gate construction and fabrication by evaporation described in Chapter 9, and particularly the insulated-gate construction on silicon (Fig. 1–3) described in Chapter 8. The third factor is the very considerable extent to which transistorization of electronic equipment has now progressed. In this situation it becomes increasingly annoying to find a number of functions where the bipolar transistor falls far short of devices such as electron tubes, making complete transistorization impractical or uneconomical. Therefore, a need has arisen for a transistor with the characteristics of the field-effect transistor to complement the bipolar transistor in particular applications, such as described in Chapters 10–12.

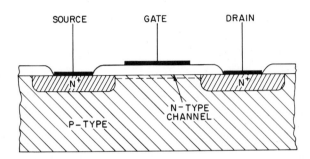

Figure 1–3. Schematic diagram of an insulated-gate field-effect transistor.

1–1 ACTIVE DEVICE CHARACTERISTICS

1. Input impedance

The most obvious feature of the field-effect transistor is its high input impedance. The saturation current drawn by the reverse-biased gate of a germanium field-effect transistor with typical resistivity and dimensions is about $1\mu a$, corresponding to an input resistance of the order of 1 megohm at the operating point at room temperature. For a silicon transistor, the current is about 10^3 times smaller and the input resistance is, consequently, about 10^9 ohms at room temperature. The saturation current increases by about one order of magnitude for a rise in temperature of 30–50°C. Therefore, when appreciable power is dissipated or the cooling is insufficient, the input resistance may decrease. In contrast, the insulated-gate field-effect transistor has a gate input resistance of 10^9 to 10^{15} ohms. The latter value is so high that when a charge is deposited on the gate, it takes at least several days to detect the leakage of charge by observing the change in current on the output side. The physics underlying this high input resistance is given in Chapter 3.

Associated with the junction gate is an input capacitance which has a value of 20–100 pf at a transconductance of 1000–3000 μmhos for such field-effect transistors now commercially available. This capacitance can be made considerably smaller for the insulated gate than for a reverse-biased junction, and it is typically 1–5 pf for the same transconductance. A breakdown of the factors that contribute to this capacitance is obtained from the equivalent circuit for such a transistor shown in

Fig. 1–4. The capacitances in the stem between leads and the contact areas amount to about 0.4 pf. In the device itself, the capacitance between drain and gate (feedback capacitance) is less than 0.1 pf while

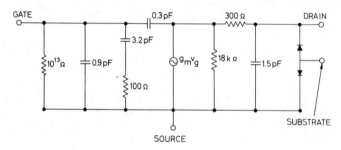

Figure 1–4. Equivalent circuit of an experimental insulated-gate field-effect transistor.

the gate-to-source capacitance is about 3 pf for a device with a transconductance of 1500 μmhos. A detailed treatment of the gate capacitance is found in Chapter 2; the drain capacitance is covered in Chapter 5

2. Current voltage characteristics

Current-voltage characteristics obtained on a curve tracer for four different field-effect transistors are shown in Fig. 1–5: (a) a silicon junction device; (b) a silicon insulated-gate depletion type; (c) an evaporated cadmium sulfide device; and (d) a silicon insulated-gate enhancement type. For comparison, all devices were operated with positive and negative drain voltage and with positive and negative gate voltage, although the junction input device is not designed for the dual mode of operation. When the gate has no bias ($V_g = 0$) transistors (a) and (b) draw a large drain current, while transistors (c) and (d) draw negligible current, typically less than 1μa. When the gate is biased positively, transistor (a) quickly saturates at the same time that the gate resistance becomes very low. In Fig. 1–5, this results in an apparent voltage offset at $I_d = 0$, because of the construction of the curve tracer. When V_d is negative, the point at which the gate becomes forward biased shows as a break where the slope of the curve changes abruptly. The decrements in drain current for increments in negative gate voltage decrease rapidly in case (a), which may also be expressed as a transconductance that varies strongly with gate bias. In cases (b), (c), and (d) the decrements in drain current for the same increments in gate voltage are uniform over a large range; in other words, the transconductance is nearly constant over a large range of current. The design theory for obtaining various characteristics is given in Chapter 5.

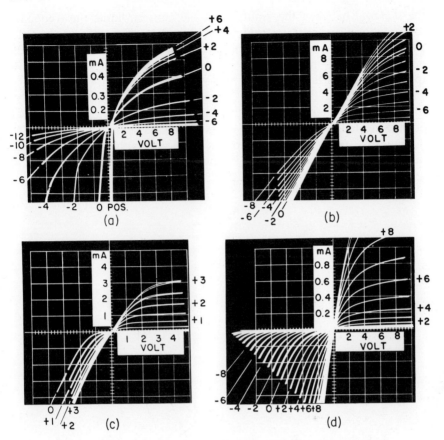

Figure 1-5. Curve-tracer pictures of drain current vs. voltage with gate voltage as parameter for several field-effect transistors: (a) silicon, junction gate; (b) silicon, insulated gate, depletion mode; (c) cadmium sulfide, insulated gate, enhancement mode; and (d) silicon, insulated gate, enhancement mode.

3. Frequency response

The frequency response of field-effect transistors has been analyzed by Dacey and Ross,[4] who concluded that the response would be limited in germanium by the fact that the carrier mobility saturates beginning at a critical field of about 10^3v/cm. Higher fields would require such excessive power dissipation that it would be difficult to remove the generated heat. A comparison, based on this finding, between field-effect transistors and bipolar transistors was made by Early[5] and indicated a superiority in frequency response of the bipolar transistor over the field-effect transistor by a factor of ten. However, a later analysis by Rose[6] has indicated that the same physical phenomenon, the dielectric relaxation time of the material between the emitter and the control, limits the frequency response of all solid-state triodes — bipolar, field-effect transistors, field-emission triodes, and space-charge limited triodes. If, instead of the critical velocity, the thermal velocity is accepted as an upper limit to the velocity of the carriers in field-effect transistors, the frequency response is indeed the same for bipolar transistors and the field-effect transistors. In Chapter 5 the factors that limit the frequency response will be investigated. Practical figures are given in Chapter 8.

Figure 1–6 shows the transconductance versus the total gate capacitance with source and drain grounded for a number of commercial

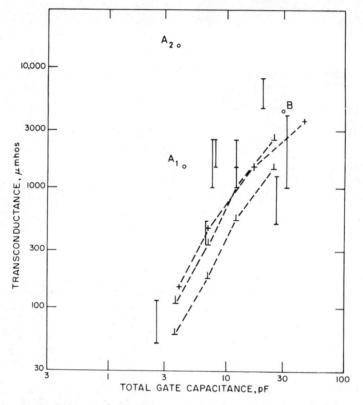

Figure 1-6. Transconductance vs. total gate capacitance for field-effect transistors. The dashed lines connect selections of commercial units from the same group. The vertical bars represent the manufacturer's tolerance limits. (A) indicates experimental silicon insulated-gate units; (B) indicates experimental cadmium-sulfide insulated-gate unit.

field-effect transistors. For good high frequency performance, the transistor should be located in the upper left-hand corner of Fig. 1–6. Also shown are values for insulated-gate field-effect transistors. (A) denotes silicon units, which have a higher frequency response than the other field-effect transistors which all have junction input; and (B) denotes laboratory results for evaporated cadmium sulfide units. The difference in frequency response reflects the fact that carrier mobility in cadmium sulfide is lower than in silicon.

The insulated-gate field-effect transistor exhibits a higher trans-conductance-to-capacitance ratio than junction-input types because it is easier to fabricate a short gate with the insulated-gate technology than with junction-gate technology. Because the field-effect transistor is a majority-carrier device, it does not exhibit carrier storage in switching applications. The switching speed is determined entirely by the RC time constant of the gate capacitance charging through the channel resistance. With a low impedance driver, switching times as low as a fraction of a nanosecond have been observed, but for one field-effect unit driving another, switching times of 10–20 nsec are more realistic. An analysis of the switching behavior is given in Chapter 12.

4. Bilateral symmetry, offset voltage

Many field-effect transistors are at the present time made symmetrical with source and drain interchangeable. Bipolar transistors can also be made symmetrical but not without a sacrifice in performance. It is believed that the same will prove true for the field-effect transistor. For example, the source series resistance gives a strong negative feedback and also contributes to the noise of the unit far more than the drain series resistance. It is therefore advantageous to offset the gate towards the source electrode, gaining performance but sacrificing symmetry.

In contrast to bipolar transistors, the field-effect transistor has no voltage offset. Figure 1–7 shows the central portion of the current-voltage characteristics greatly magnified. For both positive and negative voltages sufficiently small compared to the pinch-off voltage, the curves are approximately linear. The resistance values obtained range from a minimum of $1/g_m$ (i.e., about a few hundred ohms) to the resistance of a reverse-biased junction (the drain junction) of about a few hundred megohms. The absence of a voltage offset and the symmetry are particularly useful in chopper applications as described in Chapter 10.

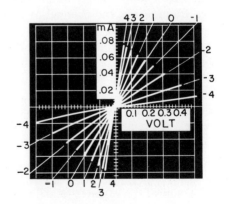

Figure 1–7. Curve-tracer picture of drain current vs. drain voltage with gate voltage as parameter for low drain voltages.

5. Radiation tolerance

Because the field-effect transistors are majority-carrier devices, lifetime degradation is immaterial, and these transistors may therefore be expected to tolerate higher radiation doses than bipolar transistors. Dosages up to a value where either mobility or doping level changes are tolerable. These are generally more than ten times the dose for which lifetime begins to deteriorate. It is found that field-effect transistors of silicon tolerate about three hundred times higher radiation dosages than bipolar transistors of comparable dimensions. Bipolar transistors are made radiation-immune by the use of semiconductor material in which the lifetime is initially very short, and by making the base region very narrow. However, the same method may be adapted to field-effect transistors if material with initially low mobility and high doping level is used. Therefore, it seems probable that the potential advantage of about 100–1000 times in radiation tolerance will remain. A more detailed treatment is found in Chapter 7.

6. Noise behavior

While the main noise source in bipolar transistors is the shot noise connected with the flow of minority carriers, the main source of noise in field-effect transistors is the thermal noise in the output resistance. At low frequencies, $1/f$ noise occurs. In field-effect transistors with junction input, the $1/f$ noise is greater than the thermal noise below about 100 cps. In insulated-gate transistors the $1/f$ noise is, as yet, quite large, and it exceeds thermal noise at frequencies as high as several mc/sec. Whether or not this may be improved in the future is not yet known. At high frequencies, the channel-to-gate feedback capacitance causes thermal noise to be fed back to the gate and be amplified. In the source end of the channel, a source resistance constitutes an unbypassed resistance, the thermal noise of which appears in the input and becomes amplified. Since a resistance in the drain lead does not have this disadvantage, it may be desirable to offset the gate toward the source. If the gate insulation is defective, the corresponding leakage current through the oxide gives rise to very strong noise. Also, leakage current from drain to source through, on the surface of, or outside the semiconductor gives noise.

The noise figure of a field-effect transistor is only a few tenths of 1 db at moderate frequencies and with sufficiently high input resistance, e.g., 3 megohms. As a simple rule of thumb summarizing the noise performance, the field-effect transistor gives the best signal-to-noise ratio when the signal impedance is high ($> 10^4$ ohms), but the bipolar transistor gives the best signal-to-noise ratio when the signal impedance is low ($< 10^4$).

The noise performance of the field-effect transistor is important enough to warrant a separate treatment which is found in Chapter 6.

7. Choice of semiconductor material

Another consequence of majority-carrier conduction is the large number of semiconductor materials which are potentially useful for field-effect transistors but not for bipolar transistors. This is borne out by Table 1–1, which shows the semiconductors that have been used

Table 1–1 Semiconductors Potentially Useful for Field-Effect Transistors

Designation (periodic table)	Type of semiconductor
I–V	Cs_3Sb*
I–VI	Cu_2O†
II–IV	Mg_2Sn* Mg_2Si*
II–VI	CdS† CdTe* ZnO† ZnS† CdSe†
III–V	GaAs*†‡ GaSb* GaP*† AlSb* InSb* InP*‡ InAs*
IV	Ge*†‡ Si*†‡ SiC*†
IV–VII	PbS*‡ PbSe* PbTe* TiO_2†
V–VI	Bi_2Te_3*
VI	Te*
VI–VIII	NiO†

*Junction formation possible.
†Resistivity sufficient for unipolar transistors.
‡Semiconductors with lifetime sufficient for bipolar transistors.

for bipolar transistors (marked ‡) as well as some of the common semi-conductors that are potentially useful for field-effect transistors. The conditions for usefulness are either (1) that both p- and n-type materials can be made, so that a channel can be properly isolated from the bulk or from the gate (marked *), or (2) that the resistivity can be made sufficiently high to prevent an induced channel on the surface from being shunted by conduction through the bulk (marked †). The Shockley-type field-effect transistor is an example which requires the first condition, while the insulated-gate field-effect transistor is an example which requires the second. While very few semiconductor materials are, at the present time, useful for bipolar transistors, the opposite is true of field-effect transistors. Therefore, to make transistors for special purposes requiring a particular semiconductor, it will frequently be necessary to resort to field-effect structures.

Consider, for example, the necessity for using wide-bandgap materials such as silicon carbide or gallium arsenide in transistors for high-temperature operation. Or consider the fabrication of transistors by evaporation or plating, in which case the short lifetime in the semi-conductor may not permit bipolar principles to be used. A final example is that the use of the thin-film structure may permit fabrication of high-frequency performance transistors from semiconductors with extremely high mobility, such as InSb or InAs, without the need for a reduction of dimensions.

One factor that has not been discussed, although of central importance in insulated-gate field-effect transistors, is the surface. Whether all the listed semiconductors can be given a surface sufficiently free of traps for satisfactory transistor performance is not yet known.

8. Thermal stability

The temperature dependence of the characteristics of field-effect transistors is related to the majority carrier mobility. For silicon in the resistivity range used for field-effect transistors, the mobility is proportional to the (absolute temperature)$^{-3/2}$ characteristic of lattice scattering. This relation is shown in Fig. 1–8 as a dashed line. The same figure shows curves of g_m versus temperature taken from data sheets for four different makes of silicon field-effect transistors which, within the accuracy of the data, all fall on this line. The same temperature dependence is obtained for the current at constant voltages. Figure 1–8 also shows data for a thin-film transistor of evaporated cadmium sulfide. In this case the temperature dependence is much larger, and the temperature coefficient is positive instead of negative. The evaporated cadmium sulfide layer is known to consist of many small crystallites with a large number of defects and grain boundaries. Therefore, there are large numbers of surface states to induce bending of the bands which may result in a surface channel charge which increases with temperature. In addition to lattice scattering, there may be a considerable amount of surface and defect scattering having a different temperature dependence.

In the case of the silicon insulated-gate field-effect transistor also shown in Fig. 1–8, the temperature dependence is very small. This is

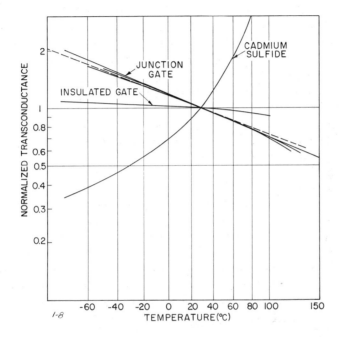

Figure 1–8. Transconductance vs. temperature for (a) silicon, junction gate, (b) silicon, insulated gate, and (c) cadmium sulfide, insulated gate.

ascribed to a fortuitous balance of effects with opposite temperature dependence, namely, the lattice scattering with negative temperature coefficient, and induced channel charge density and surface scattering with positive temperature coefficient. If this is so, it should be possible to accomplish an even closer balance for specific purposes, perhaps to the point where active devices may be obtained with the same small temperature coefficient that usually characterizes passive components, i.e., a few hundred parts per million per degree centigrade.

Another aspect of thermal stability is freedom from thermal runaway in field-effect transistors. In bipolar transistors the collector current increases with increasing temperature to the point where thermal runaway takes place and the transistor is destroyed. This is particularly troublesome in power transistors. In field-effect transistors (although at the present time not in thin-film transistors), the current decreases with increasing temperature, reducing the dissipated power and preventing thermal runaway.

9. Remote cutoff

One of the major drawbacks of transistors compared to electron tubes has been the difficulty of constructing the transistor equivalent of variable-μ tubes needed in applications requiring automatic gain control. The performance of conventional transistors in such circuits has been poor, resulting in severe cross modulation in which the signal is modulated by other unwanted signals adjacent in frequency. Here, the field-effect transistor excels with a performance rivaling that of electron tubes, as described in Chapter 11.

1–2 CHARACTERISTICS OF FIELD-EFFECT TRANSISTORS IN INTEGRATED CIRCUITS

10. Geometrical considerations

Bipolar transistors are difficult to incorporate into integrated circuits, partly because the current flow is perpendicular to the surface while the preferred circuit construction is in the plane of the surface, and partly because the carrier lifetime must be maintained. In contrast, the field-effect transistor is naturally a plane surface device with no requirement on carrier lifetime and which can be easily used in integrated circuits. An integrated circuit using sixteen field-effect transistors is shown in Fig. 1–9.

Figure 1–9. Integrated circuit using four rows of interconnected field-effect transistors.

The transistors are aligned in four rows of four each with one source (or drain) in common for each neighboring pair of units. The interconnections are deposited on the surface of the silicon wafer and are insulated from the active parts by an oxide layer. Another attractive feature of the field-effect transistor in this application is that a transistor is, in effect, a resistor and may with advantage be used as such in circuits. Such "resistors" are highly nonlinear, a characteristic that is usually advantageous in digital circuits. More detailed considerations are found in Chapters 8 and 9.

11. Digital circuit features

Another feature useful in digital circuits is the fact that an enhancement-type field-effect transistor is in itself an inverter. Figure 1–10a shows a transistor stage with a *low* input (no or negligible current flowing

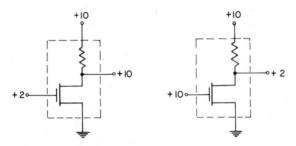

Figure 1–10. Field-effect transistor inverter circuit (a) with "off"- and (b) with "on"-signal at the input.

through the device) and, therefore, a *high* output. With a high input, as shown in Fig. 1–10b, considerable drain current flows and the output is low. The voltages are identical and of the same polarity, so that direct coupling may be used.

A unique circuit that uses pairs of field-effect transistors with complementary symmetry and makes logic possible without drawing current except during switching is shown in Fig. 1–11. When the input potential is high, the top unit is cut off and the output potential is high. When the input is low, the bottom unit is cut off and the output is low. In neither position does the pair draw current since one unit in

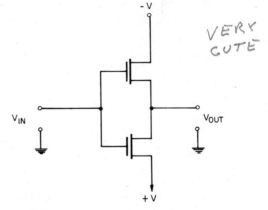

Figure 1–11. Electronic switch with single-pole, double-throw action, which dissipates negligible power except when switched.

the series chain is always cut off. Only in the transition between states is current drawn. Digital circuit applications are found in Chapter 12.

3. Application of redundancy

In large integrated circuits, the larger the circuit the more and more attractive the use of redundancy becomes. One of the simplest ways to introduce redundancy is through the use of series-parallel four-groups, as shown in Fig. 1–12a. Each element is replaced by a group of four identi-

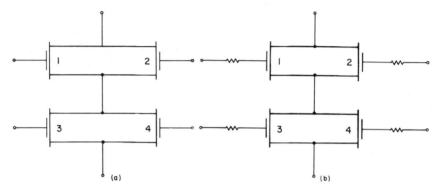

Figure 1–12. (a) Redundant four-group, and (b) redundant four-group with gate resistors.

cal elements, and the four-group performs the intended circuit function even if one, two, or even three of the elements in the group become faulty. With conventional bipolar transistors, such four-groups are not very efficient because a short circuit between input and output allows current flow between adjacent four-groups and interferes with the functioning of the redundancy. With field-effect transistors, however, redundancy in the form of four-groups is quite effective. Because of the high input resistance, there can be introduced in the gate lead a resistor large enough to protect against excessive current and, at the same time, small enough not to reduce the speed of the circuit appreciably. A typical value may be 10^4 ohms. A redundant circuit of this type is shown in Fig. 1–12b.

4. Multiple units

Special advantages may be obtained if the functions of two or more units are combined in a manner analogous to that in which special advantages were obtained in electron tubes by the introduction of more than one grid. Figure 1–13 shows a simple combination of two series-connected units which reduces the feedback capacitance. Just as extra grids in electron tubes offer better performance and lower cost than the use of multiple units, so the combination of two or more field-effect units in one structure may be cheaper and better than the use of several separate units.

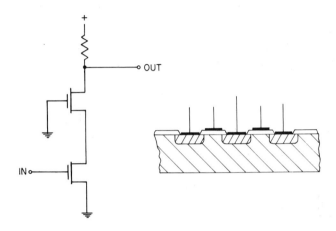

Figure 1-13. Field-effect transistor cascode.

Of special interest is the combination of a bipolar and a field-effect transistor. In this unit, shown in Fig. 1-14, the extra field-effect electrode controls the surface potential of the base region and thereby the surface recombination velocity. When the field-electrode potential is positive, the surface potential is also positive and the surface recombination is consequently high. The base bias current is therefore used up for recombination of injected carriers under the field electrode and little is left for biasing the emitter. Hence the injected current is low. On the other hand, when the field-electrode potential is negative with respect to the base, the surface recombination is low

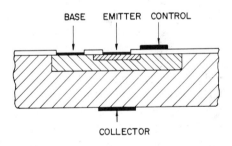

Figure 1-14. Semiconductor tetrode using *n-p-n* transistor.

and all the base bias current is available for injecting carriers from the emitter. Then the current transfer ratio is high.

The tetrode combines the advantages of a bipolar and a field-effect transistor. However, the device requires that the bipolar characteristics and the field-effect characteristics be controlled at the same time on the same unit.

REFERENCES

1. V. E. Bottom, *Physics Today* **17**, 24 (Feb., 1964).
   J. B. Johnson, *Physics Today* **17**, 60 (May, 1964).

2. O. Heil, Brit. Pat 439, 457, (Sept. 26, 1939).

3. W. Shockley, *Proc. IRE* **40**, 1365 (1952).

4. G. C. Dacey and I. M. Ross, *Proc. IRE* **41**, 970 (1953).

5. J. M. Early, *Proc. IRE* **46**, 1924 (1958).

6. A. Rose, *RCA Rev.* **24**, 627 (1963).

2

Semiconductor Surface Physics

Karl H. Zaininger

2–1 INTRODUCTION AND HISTORICAL REVIEW

1. Ideal and actual surfaces; surface states

In the derivation of the band theory of solids, a *perfect* crystal is assumed. This implies that the crystal is of infinite extent in all directions. The effects of imperfections are taken into account as perturbations on the results obtained for the perfect crystal. An imperfection is defined as any cause of a disturbance in the perfect periodicity of the potential inside a solid. Such imperfections introduce localized electronic energy states which can be either in an allowed or a forbidden band.

A real crystal is finite and this makes the surface an unavoidable imperfection. There is some ambiguity as to what is meant by the surface of a solid. One can define the surface in the manner of Gibbsian thermodynamics as a dividing *plane* between two bulk phases. Surface quantities are then defined as the excess over the value characteristic of the bulk, and are always given per unit area. In reality, however, the surface must generally be considered as a *region* because the mutual interaction of the two phases is not localized in a plane. The surface, in this sense, is that region in which a given property departs from the value characteristic of the bulk. Depending on the material and the nature of the interactions, this surface region can vary considerably in extent. In practice, both of these definitions are used and one must be careful to realize which one is implied.

Surfaces may be classified as ideal or actual surfaces. An *ideal surface* is a planar surface obtained, in principle, by cleaving a crystal in perfect vacuum along a perfect plane, and assuming that the *surface* atoms are still at the exact positions they had before cleaving. These ideal surfaces are normally the starting point for theoretical investigations. *Actual surfaces* are those which can, in practice, be obtained in the laboratory. They fall into three different groups:

1. *Atomically clean surfaces* are produced by high-vacuum techniques involving methods such as surface sputtering by ion bombardment, surface evaporation by high-temperature heating, field desorption and field evapo- ration, chemical reduction at elevated temperatures, and cleavage. These surfaces differ from the ideal in several respects, including the fact that they are not completely planar. However, they are essentially free of all ad- sorbed materials and must be maintained in an ultrahigh vacuum for physical measurements.

2. *Real surfaces* are prepared by various device fabrication techniques involving chemical etching and/or other "magical" and mostly proprietary prescriptions. They are normally covered with residual chemicals and gases adsorbed from the ambient.

3. *Solid-solid interfaces* are formed when two solids are brought into contact. The interface is defined as the region containing the surface regions in both phases.

A major imperfection, such as the surface, will manifest itself in local- ized electronic energy states. Since these states are localized at the surface, they are called *surface states*.

2. Development of the theory of surface states

Stationary electronic states within the forbidden energy gap, located at the boundary of an otherwise perfect crystal, and due to the termina- tion of the periodic potential within the solid, were predicted originally by Tamm.[1] In 1939 Shockley[2] found the conditions under which these surface states are occupied in a normal crystal, and Pollard[3] presented an argument for surface levels associated with adsorbed atoms. The modern theory of surface states in semiconductors, and especially its application to metal-semiconductor contacts, is due to Bardeen[4] who postulated the presence of large densities of surface states on germanium and silicon to explain why metal-semiconductor contacts are almost independent of bulk properties.

Since the now famous *field-effect* experiment of Shockley and Pearson[5] supplied experimental evidence for the existence of surface states, many theoretical and experimental investigations have been carried out to gain increased understanding of the properties associated with these states. The discovery of transistor action by Bardeen and Brattain[6] gave more impetus to intensive surface studies. Very rapid and spectacular advances were achieved and, by 1955, the basic picture of a germanium surface had emerged. This was described by Garrett and Brattain[7] and a review of germanium surface phenomena was given by Kingston.[8] This picture was subject to further refinement and the additional work has resulted in a great increase in the fundamental knowledge and understanding of semiconductor surface physics.[9-14] An extensive treatment of the entire subject of semiconductor surfaces, including a discussion of all pertinent experimental results, has recently been published.[15]

This chapter reviews the physics of semiconductor surfaces with particular emphasis on the electrical aspects which are needed for an understanding of the field-effect transistor. It is sufficiently detailed so that effects which influence frequency response, hysteresis, and distortion may be understood. In particular, illuminating results from MOS capacitance measurements[16-26] are included.

2-2 THE SEMICONDUCTOR SURFACE IN THE ABSENCE OF SURFACE STATES

1. Statement of assumptions

Several surface systems may be considered depending on the material adjacent to the semiconductor surface, e.g., the gas or vacuum-semiconductor system, the metal-semiconductor system,[27, 28] the insulator-semiconductor system, or the metal-insulator (oxide)-semiconductor (MOS) system. This chapter is restricted to the gas-semiconductor and the MOS systems.

In the subsequent discussion the following assumptions are made unless specified otherwise:

1. The temperature is room temperature, so that all shallow donors and acceptors are ionized.

2. The semiconductor is nondegenerate, so that the edge of the bands never get closer than about $2kT$ to the Fermi level, and Maxwell-Boltzmann statistics can be applied.

3. The donor and acceptor concentrations in the semiconductor are uniform and constant throughout, up to the interface.

4. There is no trapped charge other than ionized donors or acceptors within the semiconductor space charge region.

5. The crystal is semi-infinite, homogeneous, and in thermal equilibrium. The surface is represented by a plane $z = 0$ and the bulk is at positive values of z. Surface conditions are uniform in planes normal to z.

2. Carrier densities and band model for a semiconductor surface

The concentrations of free electrons, n, and of free holes, p, in the semiconductor bulk in thermal equilibrium are given by the following expressions:

$$n = N_c e^{-(E_c - E_F)/kT} = n_i e^{(E_F - E_i)/kT} = n_i e^{q\phi/kT} \tag{2-1}$$

and

$$p = N_v e^{+(E_v - E_F)/kT} = n_i e^{(E_i - E_F)kT} = n_i e^{-q\phi/kT} \tag{2-2}$$

From this one can obtain the product of the electron and hole densities:

$$np = n_i^2 = N_c N_v e^{-(E_c - E_v)/kT} \tag{2-3}$$

which is constant for a given temperature, and where the macroscopic† electrostatic potential, ϕ, in the semiconductor is defined by:

$$q\phi = (E_i - E_F) \tag{2-4}$$

Here n_i is the free electron (or hole) density in an intrinsic semiconductor, N_c and N_v are the effective densities of states in the conduction and valence bands, respectively, q is the magnitude of the electronic charge, E_c is the conduction band energy, E_v the valence band energy, E_F the energy at the Fermi level, and E_i the Fermi energy for intrinsic material. E_i is given by Eq. (2–7). Figure 2–1 shows an energy band diagram

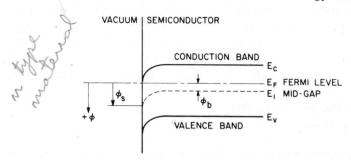

Figure 2–1. Energy-level diagram indicating the various parameters used to characterize the surface.

indicating the various energy levels. Notice that the reference for the electrostatic potential, ϕ, has arbitrarily been chosen to be that of the Fermi level.

†The periodic fluctuations around the neighborhood of atoms and ions are neglected.

The effective densities of states for silicon and germanium at room temperature are:

$$N_{c,v} = 2.5 \times 10^{19}\left(\frac{m^*_{e,h}}{m}\right)^{3/2} \text{cm}^{-3} \qquad (2\text{-}5)$$

where $m^*_e/m = 0.55$ in germanium and 1.10 in silicon and $m^*_h/m = 0.37$ in germanium and 0.57 in silicon.

The Fermi energy, E_i, for an intrinsic material where

$$n = p = n_i \qquad \text{and} \qquad E_F = E_i \qquad (2\text{-}6)$$

is:

$$E_i = \tfrac{1}{2}(E_c - E_v) + \tfrac{1}{2}kT\ln\left(\frac{N_v}{N_c}\right) = \tfrac{1}{2}(E_c - E_v) + \tfrac{3}{4}kT\ln\left(\frac{m^*_h}{m^*_e}\right) \qquad (2\text{-}7)$$

This intrinsic level is slightly displaced from the middle of the forbidden gap due to the difference between the effective masses of holes and electrons.

In the bulk of the material, far from the surface, the energy bands are assumed to be flat. The value of the electrostatic potential in this region is called the *bulk potential, ϕ_b.* It can be used to express the free carrier densities in the bulk as:

$$n_b = n_i e^{q\phi_b/kT} \qquad (2\text{-}8)$$

and

$$p_b = n_i e^{-q\phi_b/kT} \qquad (2\text{-}9)$$

The bulk densities n_b and p_b, or ϕ_b (and thereby the Fermi level, E_F) are determined by the doping of the material. The electrostatic potential at the surface is called the *surface potential*† and is designated by ϕ_s. The free carrier densities at the surface are given by:

$$n_s = n_i e^{q\phi_s/kT} = n_b e^{q(\phi_s - \phi_b)/kT} \qquad (2\text{-}10)$$

and

$$p_s = n_i e^{-q\phi_s/kT} = p_b e^{-q(\phi_s - \phi_b)/kT} \qquad (2\text{-}11)$$

The potential, with respect to bulk potential, at any point in the semiconductor, is given by:

$$V \equiv \phi - \phi_b \qquad (2\text{-}12)$$

---

†In many cases, especially in electrochemistry, the bulk potential is used as reference. In that case the surface potential becomes identical with the surface barrier, defined in Eq. (2-13).

and the *surface barrier* is defined by:

$$V_s = \phi_s - \phi_b \tag{2-13}$$

It will prove convenient to define the dimensionless potentials, u and v, by the equations:

$$u \equiv \frac{q\phi}{kT} \tag{2-14}$$

and

$$v \equiv \frac{qV}{kT} \tag{2-15}$$

The electron and hole densities at every point can then be expressed as:

$$n = n_i e^u = n_b e^v \tag{2-16}$$

and

$$p = n_i e^{-u} = p_b e^{-v} \tag{2-17}$$

The value and polarity of the surface potential, ϕ_s, and the surface barrier, V_s, are convenient means of classifying the surface conditions. If $\phi_s > 0$, the surface is *n*-type, and if $\phi_s < 0$, the surface is *p*-type. In practice, the surface condition is designated as one of the following:

1. When an enhancement of majority carriers exists at the surface, one speaks of an *enhancement* or *accumulation layer*. This condition exists if $V_s < 0$ for *p*-type and $V_s > 0$ for *n*-type material.

2. When $V_s = 0$, the energy band is flat out to the surface. This is called the *flat band* condition.

3. When some of the majority carriers have been repelled from the surface and ionized (donor or acceptor) impurities are uncompensated, a *depletion layer* has been formed. This condition exists if the sign of V_s is opposite to that of ϕ_b and $|V_s| < |2\phi_b|$.

4. When the minority carrier density at the surface equals or exceeds the majority carrier bulk density, an *inversion layer* is obtained. For this condition the sign of V_s is opposite to that of ϕ_b and $|V_s| \geqslant |2\phi_b|$. The band pictures illustrating these surface layers are given in Fig. 2–2.

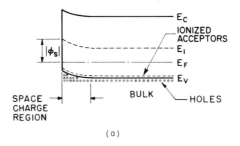

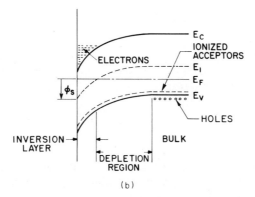

Figure 2-2. Energy level diagram for *p*-type semi-conductor (a) with accumulation layer, and (b) with inversion layer and depletion region.

3. Surface space charge; shape and extent of surface space charge region

The electrostatic potential, ϕ, within the crystal is related to the charge density, ρ, in the crystal through Poisson's equation which, in one dimension, is:

$$\frac{d^2\phi(z)}{dz^2} = -\frac{\rho(z)}{\epsilon_s} \tag{2-18}$$

where ϵ_s is the permittivity of the semiconductor, and the charge density, ρ, is given by the algebraic sum of fixed and mobile charge densities:

$$\rho = q(N_D - N_A + p - n) \tag{2-19}$$

N_A and N_D are the acceptor and donor densities, respectively, and n and p are given by Eqs. (2–1) and (2–2), or Eqs. (2–16) and (2–17).

In the bulk of the sample, where $\phi = \phi_b$, charge neutrality must exist, and:

$$N_D - N_A = n_b - p_b \tag{2-20}$$

By the use of Eqs. (2–16) and (2–17) this can be expressed as:

$$N_D - N_A = 2n_i \sinh u_b \qquad (2\text{–}21)$$

Also, in general, for any value of u, the following expression holds:

$$n - p = 2n_i \sinh u \qquad (2\text{–}22)$$

Poisson's equation takes the form:

$$\frac{d^2u}{dz^2} = \frac{1}{\lambda_i^2}(\sinh u - \sinh u_b) \qquad (2\text{–}23)$$

where λ_i, the Debye length of the semiconductor based on the intrinsic concentration n_i, is defined as:

$$\lambda_i \equiv \left(\frac{\epsilon_s kT}{2q^2 n_i}\right)^{1/2} \qquad (2\text{–}24)$$

The complicated nature of Eq. (2–23) is due to the mutual interdependence of carrier density on potential through Boltzmann's relation on the one hand, and of potential on carrier density (charge) through Poisson's equation on the other. This equation, in physical terms, requires that the electrostatic potential produce, through Boltzmann's relation, just such a total charge density, ρ, that this charge density, when used in Poisson's equation, in turn produces ϕ. The boundary condition at the surface ($z=0$) is $u=u_s$ and in the bulk ($z \to \infty$), $u=u_b$.

Equation (2–23) may be integrated† to give the electric field, $\mathscr{E}$, as:

$$\mathscr{E} = \pm\sqrt{2}\left(\frac{kT}{q\lambda_i}\right)[(u_b - u)\sinh u_b - (\cosh u_b - \cosh u)]^{1/2} \qquad (2\text{–}25)$$

The plus sign is to be used for $u < u_b$ and the minus sign for $u > u_b$. The value of the electric field at the surface is obtained by letting $u = u_s$. This results in:

$$\mathscr{E}_s = \pm\left(\frac{kT}{q\lambda_i}\right)F(u_s, u_b) \qquad (2\text{–}26)$$

†The literature concerning integration of Poisson's equation in semiconductors is voluminous and has been reviewed by McDonald.[28] References 7, 15, and 29 to 35, among others, contain useful graphs of space charge, electric field, and change in free carrier concentration for a semiconductor surface as a function of the surface potential and space-charge layer width.

where:

$$F(u_s, u_b) \equiv \sqrt{2}[(u_b - u_s) \sinh u_b - (\cosh u_b - \cosh u_s)]^{1/2} \qquad (2\text{-}27)$$

A plot of the function $F(u_s, u_b)$ for values of u_s between -24 and $+24$, and of u_b between 0 and 24 is shown in Fig. 2-3.

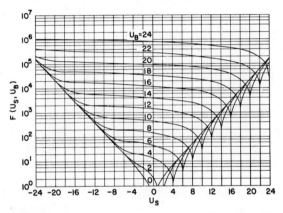

Figure 2-3. $F(u_s, u_b)$ vs. u_s for various values of u_b (after Young[34]).

To determine the total charge per unit surface area, Q_{sc}, let $u = u_s$ and use Gauss' law to get:

$$Q_{sc}(u_s) = \epsilon_s \mathscr{E}_s(u_s) = \pm C_o\left(\frac{kT}{q}\right)F(u_s, u_b) \qquad (2\text{-}28)$$

where $C_o = \epsilon_s/\lambda_i$ represents an "effective" semiconductor surface capacitance per unit area. A plot of Q_{sc} vs. V_s for p-type silicon with $N_A = 10^{14}$ cm^{-3} is shown in Fig. 2-4.

These general equations (which apply to both n- and p-type) take on more meaningful forms if expressed in terms of the effective Debye length:[15]

$$L \equiv \left[\frac{\epsilon_s kT}{q^2(n_b + p_b)}\right]^{1/2} \qquad (2\text{-}29)$$

It is this length, rather than λ_i, which characterizes the width of the space-charge region.

If an inversion layer is present at the surface, it is convenient to express the electric field at the surface in a somewhat different way. For p-type material:

$$\mathscr{E}_s = \left(\frac{kT}{q}\right)\left[\frac{1}{\lambda^2_{(n_s - n_b)}} + \frac{1}{\lambda^2_{(p_s - p_b)}} + \frac{v_s}{\lambda^2_{(N_A - N_D)}}\right]^{1/2} \qquad (2\text{-}30)$$

where the λ's are the Debye lengths [see Eq. (2–24)] based on the concentrations indicated by their subscripts.

The first term in Eq. (2–30) represents the contribution to the surface field of the n-type inversion layer and the third term that of the fixed lattice charge, $N_D - N_A$, in the depletion region. The second term corrects for the fact that the edge of the depletion region is not abrupt but extends approximately one Debye length (based on p_b).

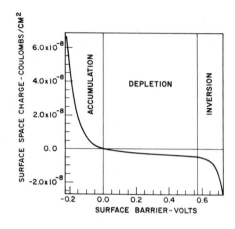

For surface potentials sufficiently high to satisfy the condition:

$$n_s = n_b e^{v_s} \gg p_b \qquad (2\text{–}31)$$

the surface field is simply:

Figure 2–4. Surface space-charge Q_{sc} as a function of the surface barrier V_s for p-type silicon. Acceptor concentration $N_A = 1 \times 10^{14}$

$$\mathcal{E}_s \cong \left[n_s \left(\frac{2kT}{\epsilon_s} \right) \right]^{1/2} \qquad (2\text{–}32)$$

For high surface potentials, there are so many mobile electrons in the inversion layer that the field at the surface is determined essentially by these electrons. Under the same assumption, Eq. (2–31), the total mobile charge in this inversion layer is given by:

$$Q_{sci} = - \epsilon_s \mathcal{E}_s = - [2kT\epsilon_s n_s]^{1/2} \equiv - 2\lambda_{n_s} q n_s \qquad (2\text{–}33)$$

where λ_{n_s} is a Debye length based on the concentration n_s. It can be shown that half of the total charge, Q_{sci}, is actually located within a distance $2\lambda_{n_s}$ of the surface.

For sufficiently intense electric fields at the surface, the bands at the semiconductor surface may be bent to the extent that degeneracy may exist. The field necessary to cause the onset of degeneracy, $\mathcal{E}_s^+$, may be found from Eq. (2–32). If n_s^+ is the electron density at the surface at the onset of degeneracy (about 3×10^{19} cm^{-3} for silicon), then:

$$\mathcal{E}_s^+ \cong \left[\frac{2kT n_s^+}{\epsilon_s} \right]^{1/2} \cong 5 \times 10^5 \frac{V}{cm} \qquad (2\text{–}34)$$

The electric field in the SiO$_2$ required to produce this situation is approximately $1.5 \times 10^6 \, V/cm$, if no surface states are present.

To obtain the shape of the potential and the extent of the space-charge region in the semiconductor surface, we rewrite Eq. (2–25) as:

$$\frac{z}{\lambda_i} = \int_{u_s}^{u} \frac{du}{F(u,u_b)} \qquad (2\text{–}35)$$

Integration of Eq. (2–35) results in the desired relationship between u and z in the form of a relation between the dimensionless quantities z/λ_i and u. For intrinsic material ($u_b = 0$) the integration can be carried out explicitly; for all other cases numerical calculations must be performed. Typical results are shown in Fig. 2–5.

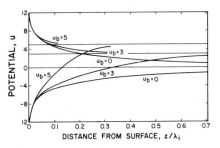

Figure 2–5. Normalized electrostatic potential vs. distance from the surface for normalized surface potential $u_s = \pm 12$ and various bulk potentials u_b.

4. Surface space-charge capacitance

Since the net charge in the semiconductor surface changes with variations in the potential across the surface layer, one can associate a differential capacitance, C_{sc}, with the semiconductor surface. This capacitance per unit area is defined as:

$$C_{sc} = \left| \frac{dQ_{sc}}{dV_s} \right| = C_o \left| \frac{dF(u_s, u_b)}{du_s} \right| \qquad (2\text{–}36)$$

where Q_{sc} is the net charge in the space-charge layer and C_o is the effective semiconductor capacitance per unit area. A plot of this surface space-charge capacitance, normalized with respect to C_o, versus the normalized surface barrier height, v_s, for various bulk potentials is shown in Fig. 2–6.

Equation (2–36) represents a differential capacitance which we can measure by superimposing a small a-c voltage upon the applied d-c bias. The measured capacitance may decrease as the frequency of the test signal increases, since the charge in the space-charge layer cannot change instantaneously.

For depletion or accumulation layers, the charge fluctuations are produced by a flow of majority carriers through the bulk of the semiconductor, and they will follow the applied voltage signal as long as:

$$\frac{1}{\omega} \gg \frac{\epsilon_s}{\sigma_b} = \tau_r \qquad (2\text{–}37)$$

where σ_b is the semiconductor bulk conductivity, and τ_r is the dielectric relaxation time of the semiconductor. For silicon with a bulk conductivity of $\sigma_b = 0.1$ (ohm-cm)$^{-1}$, $\tau_r = 10^{-11}$ sec, and it is clear that for all frequencies of practical concern the majority carriers will respond immediately.

For inversion layers the time constant is much longer, typically $0.01 - 1$ sec, and it is further described in Section 2-5.

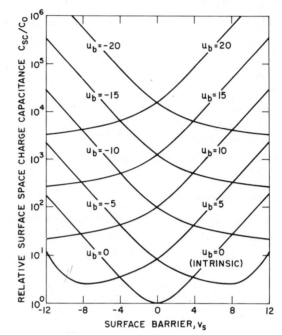

Figure 2-6. Relative surface space-charge capacitance vs. surface barrier with bulk potential, u_b, as running parameter. C_0 is 4.24×10^{-10} f cm^{-2} for silicon and 9.36×10^{-9} f cm^{-2} for germanium. The following relations hold for silicon:

$u_b = 0$	$n = 1.4 \times 10^{10}$ cm^{-3}
$u_b = 5$	$n = 2.1 \times 10^{12}$ cm^{-3}
$u_b = 10$	$n = 3.1 \times 10^{14}$ cm^{-3}
$u_b = 15$	$n = 4.6 \times 10^{16}$ cm^{-3}
$u_b = 20$	$n = 6.8 \times 10^{18}$ cm^{-3}

For negative values of u_b, the hole concentration is given by the corresponding numbers.

The general expression for the surface space-charge capacitance, Eq. (2–36), takes on specific and somewhat simpler forms for various conditions of barrier height. For p-type material with $p_b \gg n_b$ these forms are:

1. The accumulation-layer capacitance:

$$C_{sca} \cong \frac{1}{2}\left(\frac{\epsilon_s}{\lambda_p}\right)e^{-v_s/2} \tag{2-38}$$

2. The flat-band capacitance:

$$C_{scf} \cong \frac{1}{\sqrt{2}}\left(\frac{\epsilon_s}{\lambda_p}\right) \tag{2-39}$$

3. The Schottky depletion-layer capacitance:

$$C_{scd} \cong \frac{1}{2}\left(\frac{\epsilon_s}{\lambda_p}\right)v_s^{-1/2} \tag{2-40}$$

4. The inversion layer capacitance:

$$C_{sci} = \frac{1}{2}\sqrt{\frac{n_b}{p_b}}\left(\frac{\epsilon_s}{\lambda_p}\right)e^{v_s/2} \tag{2-41}$$

if the minority carriers reach equilibrium, and approximately

$$C'_{sci} = \frac{1}{2}\left(\frac{\epsilon_s}{\lambda_p}\right)v_s^{-1/2} \tag{2-42}$$

if they do not. Analogous expressions can be derived for n-type material.

5. Surface conductance

The conductivity of a semiconductor, assuming a one-dimensional geometry, is given by:

$$\sigma(z) = q[n(z)\mu_n(z) + p(z)\mu_p(z)] \tag{2-43}$$

where $\mu_n(z)$ and $\mu_p(z)$ are the electron and hole mobilities, respectively, and $n(z)$ and $p(z)$ are given by Eqs. (2–1) and (2–2), or (2–16) and (2–17). Deep inside the bulk, the mobilities and carrier densities become constant and the bulk conductivity is given by:

$$\sigma_b = q(n_b\mu_n + p_b\mu_p) \tag{2-44}$$

At the surface a more complicated situation arises due to the fact that usually $V_s \neq 0$. First, the carrier densities change to the values dictated by Eqs. (2–10) and (2–11). Second, for large (positive or negative) surface barriers, a potential well exists for one or the other type of carrier and, under certain circumstances, this can reduce the mobility at the surface. The case of a reduced surface mobility in an inversion layer will be discussed in Section 2–5.

The concept of surface conductance becomes important in field-effect devices in which charge flows parallel to the surface. Any change in the conductance of a bar of semiconductor due to a surface layer is a function of the surface barrier height, V_s, and for its evaluation it is convenient to introduce the concept of *surface excesses*,[7] defined as the additional number of *free carriers* per unit area of surface due to the presence of the surface barrier. In the simple case of equilibrium one may write for these excesses:

$$\Delta N = \int_{\infty}^{0} (n - n_b)\, dz = \int_{0}^{V_s} (n - n_b)\left(\frac{\partial s}{\partial V}\right) dV = -\int_{0}^{V_s} \frac{n - n_b}{\mathcal{E}}\, dV \tag{2–45}$$

and

$$\Delta P = \int_{\infty}^{0} (p - p_b)\, dz = -\int_{0}^{V_s} \frac{p - p_b}{\mathcal{E}}\, dV \tag{2–46}$$

The change in conductance of a bar of semiconductor, due to the surface barrier, is called the *surface conductance* and is given by:

$$g_s = q(\mu_p \Delta P + \mu_n \Delta N) \tag{2–47}$$

where it is assumed that the carrier mobilities in the space-charge layer are the same as those in the bulk. The units of g_s are those of conductance (mhos), since the conductance associated with a unit (square) area of surface is independent of the size of the square. The surface conductance g_s as a function of the dimensionless barrier height v_s is plotted in Fig. 2–7 for *n*-type, *p*-type, and intrinsic germanium at 300°K.

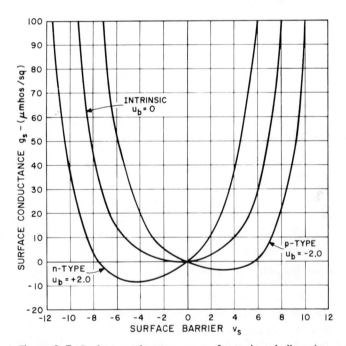

Figure 2–7. Surface conductance vs. v_s for various bulk resistivities: curve 1, 15 ohm-cm, *n*-type; curve 2, intrinsic; curve 3, 10 ohm-cm, *p*-type.

This surface conductance is in parallel with the conductance of the sample under flat-band conditions, characterized by the appropriate bulk parameters. Equations (2–45), (2–46), and (2–47) give the surface conductance as a unique function of the surface barrier. On the other hand, if the surface conductance can be measured, its value may be used to deduce the corresponding value of the surface barrier height. If the mobilities of the excess carriers are independent of the surface barrier and assumed to be equal to the bulk values, then g_s is a particularly convenient quantity for determining the surface barrier. However, if the surface mobilities differ from those characteristic of the bulk, then the surface conductance has to be used with caution.

Surfaces in either the accumulation or inversion regime exhibit a high surface conductance, due to the large number of majority or minority carriers, respectively. The surface conductance characterizing a surface depletion layer is smaller and passes through a minimum value, $g_{s\,min}$, where very few excess free carriers are present in the space-charge region.

The surface conductance is zero when:

$$\Delta N = \Delta P = 0 \tag{2–48}$$

and when:

$$\Delta P = - \left(\frac{\mu_n}{\mu_p}\right) \Delta N \tag{2–49}$$

The minimum value of surface conductance occurs when:

$$\frac{\partial(\Delta P)}{\partial u_s} = -\left(\frac{\mu_n}{\mu_p}\right)\frac{\partial(\Delta N)}{\partial u_s} \tag{2–50}$$

The exact value of $v_{s\,min}$ of the surface barrier height at which this minimum occurs can be evaluated from Eqs. (2–45) and (2–46):

$$v_{s\,min} \equiv \frac{qV_{s\,min}}{kT} \cong -2u_b - \ln\left(\frac{\mu_n}{\mu_p}\right) \tag{2–51}$$

if it is assumed that $v_s \gg 0$.

2–3 THE SEMICONDUCTOR SURFACE IN THE PRESENCE OF SURFACE STATES

1. General discussion of surface states and their experimental observation

The termination of the perfect periodicity of the crystal potential at a surface introduces localized allowed energy states, some of which may be in the forbidden gap. However, atomically clean surfaces normally do not exist because gases or other impurities are adsorbed by the dangling or unsaturated bonds at the surface, and the surface has oxidized. The term, oxide, is taken here to mean any sort of composite layer or structure that has grown onto the bulk material by virtue of interaction with the ambient. It is reasonable to expect states in the forbidden gap due to these adsorbed atoms, because the transition between the bulk and the oxide is also a disturbance of the periodicity of the lattice. The distribution and properties of these bound states are known to be a sensitive function of the chemical and mechanical treatment of the surface, and of the gaseous or liquid environment to which it is exposed.

Many experiments[15] indicate that there are two classes of surface states. States of the first class are called *slow surface states* because they exchange charge very slowly with the bulk material. The time constants of charge exchange range from a few seconds to months. These states are intimately associated with the surface chemistry and with the oxide film that is almost always present on a germanium or silicon surface. They are strongly affected by the ambient and were historically thought to be situated at the outside surface of the impurity layer on the semiconductor. The large value of the time constant was thought to be associated with the time taken by the electrons to penetrate the layer. The density of these states appears to depend on the adsorption equilibrium with the ambient, and is not a constant of the surface except in ultrahigh vacuum. These states are of great importance in device technology because they largely determine the surface potential by pinning the Fermi level at the surface trap level.

States of the second class are called *fast surface states* because they exchange charge with the bulk material with time constants ranging from milliseconds to microseconds or less. These fast states are thought to exist at or near the interface between the semiconductor and the oxide, and they are relatively unaffected by the atmospheric ambient. They are the states mainly responsible for the generation and recombination of electrons and holes at the surface.

2. Probability of occupation of surface states

The occupancy of surface states, as well as bulk impurity levels, is governed by Fermi-Dirac statistics. However, spin degeneracy has to be taken into account[†] and the probability of a trap site at energy E_t being occupied is given by:

$$f(E_t) = \frac{1}{1 + g \exp\left(E_t - E_F/kT\right)} \tag{2-52}$$

where $g = \frac{1}{2}$ for acceptors and $g = 2$ for donors.

[†]If calculations are carried out with the usual distribution function (i.e., $g = 1$), then E_t does not represent the actual energy of the trap level, but is related to the actual level, E_{act}, by $E_t = E_{act} + kT \ln g$. Since $\ln 2 = 0.7$, the error introduced is smaller than kT and is often neglected.

At equilibrium, the surface potential will adjust itself in such a way that the surface traps are filled in accordance with Eq. (2-52), and over-all charge neutrality exists. That is, the surface potential is such that it produces the necessary charge in the space-charge layer to just neutralize the charge in surface states. If Q_{ss} is the total charge in surface states, then, with no applied voltage:

$$Q_{ss} + Q_{sc} = 0 \tag{2-53}$$

An example of such an arrangement is shown in Fig. 2-8 for the case of an n-type semiconductor and surface states which are neutral when not occupied.

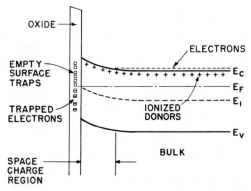

Figure 2-8. Band picture for semiconductor surface with surface states that are neutral when empty.

3. Surface state capacitance

There is a differential capacitance, C_{ss}, associated with change of charge in surface states. It is defined by:

$$C_{ss} \equiv \left| \frac{\partial Q_{ss}}{\partial V_s} \right| \tag{2-54}$$

The total surface capacitance is given by:

$$C_s \equiv \left| \frac{\partial Q_T}{\partial V_s} \right| = C_{sc} + C_{ss} \tag{2-55}$$

where $Q_T = Q_{ss} + Q_{sc}$ is the total charge at the semiconductor surface. Thus, the semiconductor surface capacitance is a parallel combination of space-charge and surface-state capacitance.

4. Physics of trapping carriers at a surface

The frequency response of surface states can be obtained by a detailed investigation of carrier trapping at the surface. It has been shown[36] that if traps and recombination centers are located in the oxide adjacent to the semiconductor, the mean time before a trap is filled, called *the response time of a trap*, τ_c, depends on the number of available charge carriers at the surface and is not an inherent property of the trap site. A complete description of a trap is given by its capture cross section, σ, its energy level, E_t, and its distance from the interface, z_t. The trap time-constant for a single trap level (or surface-state time-constant) based on a tunneling model is given by:

$$\tau_c = \frac{e^{2k_o z}}{2\bar{v}(\sigma_n n_s + \sigma_p p_s)} \tag{2–56}$$

where $\bar{v}$ is the thermal velocity (assumed equal for electrons and holes), σ_n is the capture cross section for electrons, σ_p is that for holes, and k_o is defined by the following relation:

$$k_o^2 = \left(\frac{2m^*}{\hbar^2}\right)\left(W - E_c\right) \tag{2–57}$$

Here m^* is the effective mass, and W is the height of the potential energy barrier at the surface (see Fig. 2–9).

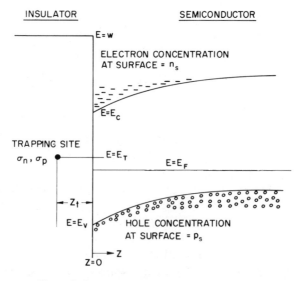

Figure 2–9. Trapping site imbedded in the insulator.

5. Frequency response of surface states

The frequency response, f, of a monoenergetic trap level localized at the interface when the level is intersected by the Fermi level is adequately described by the dimensionless function:

$$f(\omega) = \frac{1}{\sqrt{1 + (\omega\tau_c)^2}} \qquad (2\text{–}58)$$

which represents the fraction of trapped electrons that can follow an applied signal of angular frequency ω. The phase delay associated with this frequency factor will add a resistive component to the surface-state capacitance, but this has been omitted here. For the case of surface states spatially distributed through the oxide, the frequency response is complicated. See Eq. (2–69) and the discussion in Section 2–4.3.

2–4 THE SEMICONDUCTOR-INSULATOR INTERFACE

1. Definition and description of the MOS capacitor

An MOS capacitor is a structure consisting of an n-type or p-type semiconductor covered by a thin film ($50\text{Å} < d_i < 5000\text{Å}$) of insulating material (normally oxide) with a metal electrode† on top of the insulator. It will be assumed that the film is perfectly insulating (no tunnel or space-charge-limited current flow) and is characterized by a certain trap distribution. A schematic representation of such a device is shown in Fig. 2–10.

In a device such as this, the trap states located at the outside of the oxide (historically termed the slow surface states) are so

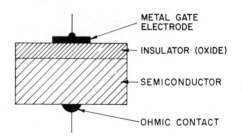

Figure 2–10. Schematic representation of an MOS capacitor.

distant from the semiconductor that carriers cannot tunnel there, and one should have only fast states. However, experiments show that charge transfer characterized by time constants similar to those of slow states is taking place at the interface. This indicates that there are states *within* the oxide which can electronically interact with the semiconductor surface.

†The metal electrode is often referred to as the gate to conform with MOS transistor terminology.

The usual distinction between fast and slow states is not applicable in the case of an MOS structure because all ranges of response time can be expected. It is best so simply speak of surface states including the effect of traps in the oxide.

If the insulating film is produced by oxidation of the semiconductor under rigorously controlled conditions, the density of what are normally called the fast surface states is substantially reduced. The electronic properties of the semiconductor surface become sensitive to the defect structure of the oxide, as is the case with a properly prepared Si-SiO$_2$ structure. Hence, the (silicon) surface potential is dependent upon imperfection sites in the oxide. The response time of the oxide-semiconductor interaction may be quite long.

2. Energy band diagram for an MOS capacitor

The band picture applicable when an external voltage, V_a, is applied to an MOS capacitor is shown in Fig. 2–11. The following relationship between the various potentials can be obtained by inspection of Fig. 2–11:

$$V_a = \phi_m + V_i - \chi + V_s - V_c \tag{2-59}$$

where: V_a = total applied voltage across the MOS capacitor, i.e., potential of the metal electrode with respect to the bulk of the semiconductor;

ϕ_m = work function of the metal;

V_i = voltage across the oxide film;

χ = electron affinity of the semiconductor; and

V_c = electrostatic potential difference between Fermi level and conduction band.

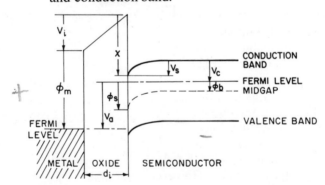

Figure 2–11. Band picture applicable to MOS structures with an applied voltage V_a. It is assumed that the semiconductor is n-type and that an accumulation layer has been formed at the interface. However, the voltage equation derived from this picture, i.e., Eq. (2–59), is generally applicable.

For convenience it is assumed that there is no contact potential between the metal and the semiconductor. A finite contact-potential difference may be absorbed in an effective applied voltage, V, without changing the essential features of the discussion. Thus:

$$V = V_a - \phi_m + \chi + V_c = V_i + V_s \qquad \text{(2–60)}$$

The assumption that the surface states are uniformly distributed spatially in the oxide means that charge resides not only at the two interfaces involved, but also in the oxide near these interfaces to varying depths, depending on the carrier concentration in the metal and semiconductor, respectively. There will be a voltage drop on the order of a few kT/q in the oxide due to these charges. This drop is negligible in most cases compared to the over-all oxide voltage; for the purpose of voltage calculations, the charges can be assumed to be located at the interface, and the electric field in the oxide may be considered uniform.

This uniform field approximation is valid only in two limiting cases, determined by the ratio of oxide thickness to the extent of the space-charge regions in the oxide. These space-charge regions exist both at the metal-SiO$_2$ and Si-SiO$_2$ interfaces. If this ratio is very large compared to unity, the two space-charge regions are widely separated and the field in the oxide is uniform over most of the oxide. There is a departure from uniformity only over the two relatively small space-charge regions. If the ratio is much smaller than unity, the two space-charge regions overlap appreciably. The integrated space charge in the oxide can be neglected with respect to the surface charge either in the metal or in the semiconductor. Thus, the field will be essentially uniform throughout the oxide. In the intermediate case, in which this ratio is of the order of unity, the assumption of uniform field is not valid. In this chapter, we are concerned with the first limiting case, i.e., with an oxide which is quite wide compared to the extent of the two space-charge regions.

3. MOS capacitance

If a voltage is applied across the device, the electric field terminates on two different kinds of charges: the charge in the semiconductor space-charge region, given by Eq. (2–28); and charge in the surface states, given by:

$$Q_{ss} = qN_{ss}$$

where N_{ss} is the density of occupied surface states per unit interface area for the particular value of ϕ_s (and V_a).

The total charge, Q_T, per unit area at the semiconductor is:

$$Q_T = Q_{sc} + Q_{ss} \qquad \text{(2–62)}$$

and it is equal and opposite in sign to the charge, Q_m, on the metal plate. If it is assumed that all the charge in the oxide is close to the semiconductor, or, more specifically, that the oxide thickness is large compared to the Debye length in the oxide, the electric field within the oxide is constant and has the magnitude V_i/d_i, where d_i is the oxide thickness. Therefore, by Gauss law:

$$|Q_m| = Q_T = C_i V_i \qquad (2\text{–}63)$$

where $C_i = \epsilon_i/d_i$ is the oxide capacitance per unit area.

The total capacitance per unit area of the MOS structure is:

$$C = \frac{\partial Q_T}{\partial V} = C_i\left(1 - \frac{\partial \phi_s}{\partial V}\right) \qquad (2\text{–}64)$$

or, using Eqs. (2–55), (2–62), (2–64), and $C_i \equiv dQ_T/dV_i$:

$$C = \frac{C_i C_s}{C_i + C_s} \qquad (2\text{–}65)$$

The total capacitance corresponds to a series combination of the oxide and the surface capacitance.

Equation (2–64) is a very instructive way of expressing the MOS capacitance because one can see immediately that the differential capacitance of an MOS structure will deviate from the oxide capacitance only to the extent that the surface potential can follow the applied signal. Neglecting the influence of surface states, one sees that if a heavy accumulation or inversion layer is present, the change in surface space charge called for by a change in applied voltage, δV, can be accomplished through a small change in surface potential, $\delta\phi_s$. For this case, $\delta\phi_s/\delta V \cong 0$ and essentially the oxide capacitance is measured. On the other hand, the presence of a significant depletion region causes the change in surface potential, $\delta\phi_s$, to be very close to δV since a small change in surface space charge accompanies the applied signal. Therefore, $\delta\phi_s/\delta V \lesssim 1$, and the measured capacitance is small compared to the oxide capacitance. The presence of surface states which are capable of following the applied signal will always lower the value of $\delta\phi_s$ required to produce a change in total semiconductor space charge and hence raise the capacitance of the MOS capacitor.

Since the oxide capacitance is constant and assumed to be frequency independent, the frequency dependence of the MOS capacitance is completely determined by the frequency dependence of the semiconductor surface capacitance. Different physical mechanisms determine the variation with frequency of C_{sc} and C_{ss}. For C_{sc} in the accumulation and depletion layer region, the necessary charge fluctuations are brought about by majority carrier flow through the bulk of the semiconductor. The response is characterized by the dielectric relaxation time (see Section 2-2.4). For C_{sc} in the inversion regime, there are several sources which can supply the minority carriers required to change the charge in the inversion layer: an electron bulk diffusion current from the reverse-biased depletion region; a volume-generated current within the depletion region; and a surface-generated current directly related to the surface states at the insulator-semiconductor interface. The surface state capacitance, on the other hand, depends upon transitions of electrons and holes between the surface states and the bulk. This is essentially a two-step process in that there is an exchange between the surface states and the conduction or valence bands at the interface, and an exchange through the accumulation or depletion layers between the interface and the bulk. The time constants characteristic of these processes depend on many parameters and can be considerable.

The complete functional form, including frequency dependence of the over-all capacitance, can be obtained if we rewrite the voltage across the device as:

$$V = V_i + V_s = V_{ss} + V_{sc} + V_s \qquad (2\text{--}66)$$

where

$$V_{ss} \equiv \frac{Q_{ss}}{C_i} = \frac{qN_{ss}}{C_i} \qquad (2\text{--}67)$$

and

$$V_{sc} \equiv \frac{Q_{sc}}{C_i} \qquad (2\text{--}68)$$

are the voltage equivalents of Q_{ss} and Q_{sc}. From Eqs. (2-28) and (2-68), V_{sc} and $\partial V_{sc}/\partial V_s$ are explicit functions of ϕ_s, provided that the frequency is low enough so that the semiconductor is in thermal equilibrium.

The situation with V_{ss} is more complex and depends on the distribution of the surface states with respect to energy and position in the oxide, $K_t(z, E_t)$. It can be shown[36] that, in general, for a tunneling model

$$\frac{\partial V_{ss}}{\partial V_s} = \frac{q^2}{C_i} \int_0^{d_i} \int_{E_{vo}}^{E_{co}} K_t(z, E_t) g(z, E_t) [1 + \omega^2 \tau_c^2(z, E_t)]^{-1/2} \left(\frac{\partial f}{\partial E_F} \right) dE_t \, dz \quad (2\text{--}69)$$

where

$$g(z, E_t) = 1 - \exp[-e^{-2K_0(z - z_m)}] \qquad (2\text{--}70)$$

is a pseudo-Fermi-function in the variable z. This function can be interpreted as the probability that a trap of energy, E_t, at z will have its thermal equilibrium occupancy. The function $f(E_t)$ is the Fermi function, and z_m is the maximum depth into the oxide to which traps can be filled within the measurement time.

Physically, this means that only those trap states which are within a few kT of the average position of the Fermi energy, E_F^0, can contribute to the surface state capacitance. States several kT above E_F^0 will never be occupied by electrons, whereas those several kT below will always be fully occupied during the period of the test signal, provided they are within a distance, z_m, of the interface.

The frequency dependence of the MOS capacitance is implied in the frequency dependence of $\partial V_{ss}/\partial V_s$. Since the small-signal time constant, τ_c, depends upon the applied bias through V_s, the frequency dependence will be a function of the bias.

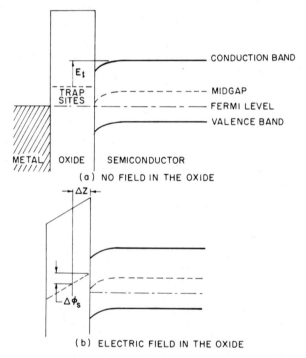

Figure 2–12. Energy-level diagram for a uniform spatial distribution of traps in the oxide. (a) No field in the oxide; (b) electric field in the oxide.

If the surface states are trap levels distributed throughout the oxide, their energy levels with respect to ϕ_s will depend both on the strength of the electric field in the oxide as well as the distance from the interface.[36] This can best be illustrated if we consider a single, uniformly distributed trap level in the oxide, as shown in Fig. 2–12a. It is clear from Fig. 2–12b that – when viewed from the semiconductor – after the field is applied, this single trap level gives rise to a uniform energy distribution of surface states which is a direct function of the electric field in the oxide.

There are $N_t \Delta z$ traps in the spatial interval Δz within the oxide. In the presence of an electric field within the oxide, these traps are spread uniformly over the energy range:

$$\Delta E = q\Delta\phi = q\,\mathcal{E}_i\Delta z \tag{2-71}$$

Therefore, the density of traps, $\mathcal{N}_{ss}$, per unit energy interval is:

$$\mathcal{N}_{ss} = \frac{N_t\Delta z}{q\Delta\phi} = \frac{N_t}{q\,\mathcal{E}} \tag{2-72}$$

For a tunneling model it can be shown that traps can be filled to a distance of about 20Å into the oxide for measurement times on the order of 2 minutes. For a maximum field in the oxide of 10^6 v/cm, the effective energy range for the states which can communicate with the semiconductor is:

$$q\Delta\phi = q\,\mathcal{E}_{i\,max}\Delta z_{max} = 0.2\ \text{ev} \tag{2-73}$$

The preceding considerations show that V_{ss} is a function of both ϕ_s and V, and its specific form depends on the particular distribution in energy of the oxide traps.

The MOS capacitance as a function of surface barrier can be obtained by use of Eq. (2–66). It is:

$$C(V_s) = C_i\left(1 - \frac{\partial V_s}{\partial V}\right) = C_i\left[\frac{(\partial V_{sc}/\partial V_s)+(\partial V_{ss}/\partial V_s)}{1+(\partial V_{sc}/\partial V_s)+(\partial V_{ss}/\partial V_s)}\right] \tag{2-74}$$

If the frequency of the a-c signal is so high that none of the surface states (trap states) can follow (i.e., $\omega \gg 1/\tau_c$), then it can be seen from Eq. (2–69) that $\partial V_{ss}/\partial V_s \to 0$. If this condition is satisfied, the MOS capacitance reduces to:

$$C = C^\infty = C_i\left[\frac{(\partial V_{sc}/\partial V_s)}{1+(\partial V_{sc}/\partial V_s)}\right] \tag{2-75}$$

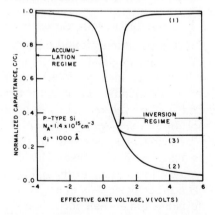

EFFECTIVE GATE VOLTAGE, V (VOLTS)

Figure 2-13. Normalized MOS capacitance vs. gate voltage for no surface states. In the inversion regime curve (1) holds if the minority carriers follow both a-c and d-c voltage; curve (2) if they cannot accumulate at the surface (Schottky depletion layer capacitance); curve (3) if they follow d-c but not a-c signals.

This high-frequency capacitance for the case of no surface states is shown in Fig. 2–13. In the inversion regime, curve (1) holds if the minority carriers reach equilibrium, curve (2) if they do not; if they can follow the applied bias, but not the a-c signal, curve (3) applies.

4. Surface conductivity in MOS structures; the field effect

The conductance of the semiconductor surface, given by Eq. (2–47), is a function of the electric field at the surface. To modulate this conductance, the electric field at the surface has to be changed. This can be done if we change the ambient in such a way that the density of surface states is altered.[37] However, a more desirable and controllable method is to apply a voltage to an MOS capacitor so that an electric field is established normal to the semiconductor surface. This method, in contrast to the gaseous ambient case, does not alter the surface states and allows the study of a particular surface in its original form. After the application of the voltage, the surface potential adjusts itself in accordance with Eq. (2–66) to maintain charge neutrality. This change in surface potential has two effects. First, the location of the Fermi level at the surface is altered and the occupancy of the surface states is changed. Second, the surface excesses of holes and electrons are changed, resulting in a change in the surface conductance. This is called the *field effect*.[15, 38] The larger the density of surface states, the larger will be V_{ss}, and the smaller V_s (and thereby V_{sc}). A small change in V_{sc} (and V_s) means a small change in the surface conductance. The presence of surface states is thus experimentally apparent as a reduction in the measured change in conductance below that expected if all the induced charge went into the space-charge region. If it is possible to apply a field high enough to change the surface conductance to its minimum value, the surface conductance and the surface potential of the initial state can be determined.

5. Hysteresis due to carrier trapping in the oxide near the interfaces

It is sometimes found that measurements of MOS capacitance under otherwise identical conditions give different results, depending on whether the bias is increasing or decreasing. These hysteresis effects are of two kinds. One effect is unstable, dependent on ambient and time, and is observed only for p-type units. It manifests itself in a gross distortion of the C vs. V curve (in the inversion layer regime) obtained with increasing bias. No shift in the location of the capacitance minimum is observed in this case. This effect can be explained by charge migration on the surface of the oxide layer and is discussed in Section 2–5.1. The other hysteresis effect is stable, independent of ambient, and manifests itself in a small horizontal shift of the C vs. V characteristic to either the left or right. This can be explained by trapping effects at the two interfaces.

If the surface states in an MOS structure are assumed to be traps uniformly distributed throughout the oxide, then it can be shown[36] that there must be a hysteresis in the MOS-capacitance vs. bias curves. The origin of this hysteresis for p-type material is as follows. The depths to which traps in the oxide can be filled, z_F, or emptied, z_E, during the time of measurement, T_m, depend for a tunneling model logarithmically upon the density of free electrons and holes at the surface, respectively. Experimentally it has been found that often an inversion layer exists at the surface of p-type samples. In such a case it is true that for any particular bias (except for a very large negative value) $n_s \gg p_s$ and $z_F > z_E$. Consequently, during the increasing bias cycle, there is a net negative charge trapped in the oxide near the oxide-semiconductor interface (see Fig. 2–14). The voltage due to this trapped charge is part of V_{ss}. Thus, for

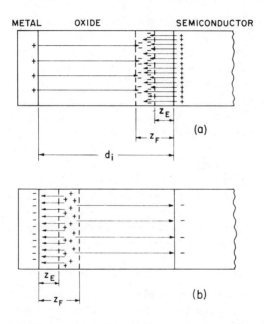

Figure 2–14. Schematic representation of electric-field lines terminating on charges trapped in the oxide. (a) Traps near the semiconductor; (b) traps near the metal.

the same applied voltage, V_{ss} will be different for increasing and decreasing bias. This requires that $V_{sc} + V_s$ must also be different, resulting in a different value of the surface capacitance, C_s. At a very large negative bias, the hole concentration is high enough to ensure that $z_E \rightarrow z_F$, that all the traps filled up to z_F will empty, and that the capacitance curves will merge.

From this reasoning it follows that the C vs. V curve for increasing bias lies to the left of that for decreasing bias. Such behavior has been observed experimentally and typical results are shown in Fig. 2–15. In this graph the capacitance minima are not idential for the two branches of the curve. This is in complete agreement with the assumption of a spatial distribution of the traps in the oxide and is explained on the basis of the field dependence of the surface state density[36] (Section 2–4.3).

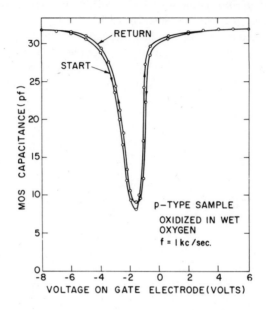

Figure 2–15. MOS capacitance vs. gate voltage, showing hysteresis because of trapping at the oxide-semiconductor interface.

For some samples, hysteresis may be in a direction opposite to that discussed before. A typical result is shown in Fig. 2–16. This behavior may be explained by interchange of charge between the metal electrode and states near the metal-oxide interface. The reasoning is similar to that used in the oxide-semiconductor case discussed earlier, except that the electric field and its influence are reduced by the geometrical factor (z/d). (See Fig. 2–14b.) The direction of the electric field at the semiconductor surface is reversed in this case because the polarity of the trapped charges injected from the metal electrode is positive. Although the free-carrier density at the metal-oxide interface is orders of magnitude higher than that at the oxide-semiconductor interface, it increases the depth into the oxide to which traps can be filled by tunneling within 2 min only by about 10Å.

Since the depth in the oxide to which traps can be filled is about the same at the metal-oxide interface as it is at the semiconductor-oxide interface, the magnitude of the hysteresis effect for the two different cases will depend primarily on the trap concentration, N_t, near the two interfaces. This explains why more curves of the type shown in Fig. 2–16 than those in Fig. 2–15 are observed experimentally. Since the oxide is always grown under controlled conditions, the density of traps at the semiconductor-oxide interface and in the oxide adjacent to that inter-

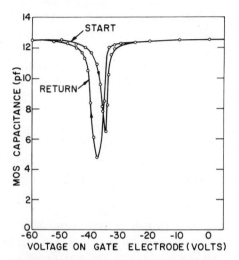

Figure 2-16. MOS capacitance vs. gate voltage showing hysteresis because of trapping at the metal-oxide interface.

face is kept low. This is not true at the metal-oxide interface. It is not always possible to evaporate the metal electrode onto a fresh and uncontaminated oxide surface, and the density of traps at or near the oxide surface may have increased considerably. Furthermore, traps at the metal-oxide interface may be introduced as a result of the evaporation process itself.

2-5 CHARACTERISTICS OF THE SURFACE INVERSION LAYER

1. Frequency response of the surface inversion layer

FIRST-ORDER ONE-DIMENSIONAL MODEL. The small-signal impedance of MOS structures has been discussed by several authors.[24, 25, 39–42] These discussions are mathematical and the results are difficult to apply to practical systems. Lehovec and Slobodskoy[25] have presented equivalent circuits which reflect the complexities of the mathematical results and are themselves as difficult to use in practice. Hofstein,[43] and Hofstein and Warfield[44] have presented an approximate analysis of the frequency response of the MOS capacitor when the surface layer is strongly inverted, with emphasis on the frequency response of the inversion layer itself. Their first-order one-dimensional analysis gives a relatively simple picture of the physical mechanisms controlling the frequency response of the inversion layer and leads to a simple equivalent circuit for the MOS capacitor in the inversion layer mode. Although this equivalent circuit is not exact, it yields numerical values for the pertinent parameters of MOS capacitors which agree with experimental results to within an order of magnitude.

There are several sources which can supply the minority carriers required to charge the inversion layer; and a current can be associated with each source. For an input signal smaller than kT/q these currents will be proportional to the signal voltage. When the surface layer is strongly inverted, these sources are:

1. Diffusion from the semiconductor bulk to the edge of the reverse-biased depletion region, and drift through this region.
2. Volume generation-recombination within the depletion region.
3. Surface generation-recombination through surface states at the insulator-semiconductor interface.

Each of these three sources can be represented by a resistance. This leads to the simplified equivalent circuit, shown in Fig. 2–17, for the input impedance of the MOS capacitor in the bias range for inversion. R_d is associated with an electron diffusion current from the bulk, R_{gD} with a volume-generated current within the depletion region; R_{gS} is associated with a surface-generated current directly related to the surface states at the insulator-semiconductor interface. C_D is the capacitance of the depletion region. For p-type silicon (10 ohm-cm) at room temperature and a minority carrier lifetime of $\tau_n = 10^{-6}$ sec these resistances are:

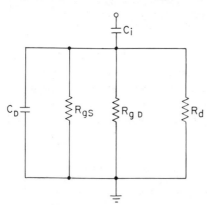

Figure 2–17. Simplified equivalent circuit for determining the frequency response of the inversion layer, including the effects of surface, bulk, and junction-generated currents.

$$R_d = 2 \times 10^8 \text{ ohm-cm}^2$$

$$R_{gD} = 5 \times 10^6 \text{ ohm-cm}^2$$

$$R_{gS} = 1 \times 10^8 \text{ ohm-cm}^2$$

For this material $C_D = 10^{-8}$ f/cm², leading to inversion layer response times of:

$$\tau_d = 2 \text{ sec}$$
$$\tau_{gD} = 5 \times 10^{-2} \text{ sec}$$
$$\tau_{gS} = 1 \text{ sec}$$

These response times of the inversion layer are orders of magnitude longer than the lifetime of the minority carriers. Since, in general, all three sources are acting simultaneously, the response time of the inversion layer will be:

$$\tau_I = (\tau_d^{-1} + \tau_{gS}^{-1} + \tau_{gD}^{-1})^{-1} \qquad \text{(2–76)}$$

or

$$\tau_I = (R_d^{-1} + R_{gS}^{-1} + R_{gD}^{-1})^{-1} C_D$$

If all sources are active in this particular system, the response time of the inversion layer is governed almost completely by generation and recombination in the depletion layer. This is a reasonable result since it is well known that the reverse-bias characteristics of a silicon p-n junction is dominated by junction generation and recombination.[45]

EXPERIMENTAL MEASUREMENTS OF THE INVERSION LAYER FREQUENCY RESPONSE. Experimental results,[46] shown in Fig. 2–18, for p-type units produced by thermal oxidation of silicon in steam indicate the actual frequency response is orders of magnitude higher than predicted on the

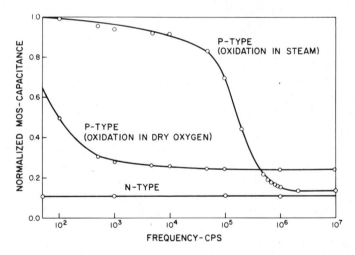

Figure 2–18. Frequency response of several MOS capacitors in the heavy inversion layer regime.

basis of the first-order model. For p-type units produced by thermal oxidation of silicon in dry oxygen, it is somewhat higher than predicted, while for all n-type units (both ambients) it is as low as 50 cps, the lower frequency limit of the measuring equipment.

There is an additional observation on some p-type units which cannot be explained by the first-order theory. A hysteresis was found[43, 46, 47] in the capacitance vs. applied voltage curve for p-type units when the gate voltage was varied from a positive to a negative value and then back again. This is shown in Fig. 2–19. This hysteresis effect was dependent on time and ambient, and was unstable.

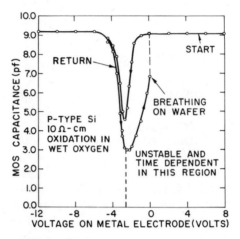

Figure 2–19. MOS capacitance characteristics showing inversion layer capacitance and hysteresis.

SECOND-ORDER MODEL. A second-order model, which can account for these "anomalies," has been proposed by Hofstein,[43] and discussed by Hofstein *et al.*[44,47,48] In oxide growth on p-type silicon with a wet oxygen ambient, the surface of the silicon inverts to n-type. This has been traced to the presence of positive charge in the oxide located near the oxide-silicon interface. A more accurate model for the MOS capacitor, taking this band bending into account, is shown in Fig. 2–20. The n-type inversion layer under the metal electrode, which is called the electrode inversion layer for convenience, is coupled to the *external* inversion layer extending out over the surface away from the metal electrode. When the electrode voltage is changed, minority carriers can move back and forth between the electrode inversion layer and the external inversion layer. The change in charge in the external layer is, in turn, capacitively coupled to the bulk. As a result, the electrode inversion layer is coupled to the bulk through a distributed RC network (see Fig. 2–20). To get a good physical grasp of the behavior of this system, we may approximate the distributed network by the simple RC lumped circuit, shown in Fig. 2–20.

If the effective coupling resistor, R_{Ee}, is small compared to the three other coupling resistors (R_d, R_{gD}, and R_{gS}) discussed earlier, the response time for the inversion layer will be determined by this coupling of the electrode inversion layer to the external inversion layer. The total input capacitance of the network (Fig. 2–20) at low frequencies is simply C_i. This is because the charge in the inversion layer can follow the applied signal so that only the oxide capacitance will be measured. At high

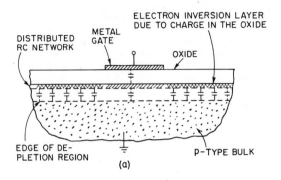

(a)

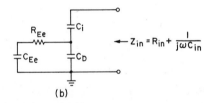

(b)

Figure 2–20. (a) Two-dimensional model for explaining the *anomalous* frequency response observed in some MOS capacitors; (b) approximate equivalent circuit.

frequencies, the charge in the inversion layer cannot follow the applied signal even with coupling through the external inversion layer, and so the series combination of oxide and depletion-layer capacitances are measured.

This second-order model can account for the two "anomalous" experimental observations just mentioned.

1. *Complementary type unit.* A thermally grown oxide does not invert the surface of an *n*-type substrate, but rather makes it even more *n* type. Hence there is no external inversion layer with which the *p*-type electrode inversion layer may exchange charge. The response of this inversion layer is determined by junction-generated currents. The observed frequency response of a unit of this type is also shown in Fig. 2–18. No inversion-layer capacitance was observed for measuring frequencies as low as 50 cps, the lower limit of the measuring equipment.

2. *Hysteresis.* A tangential electric field will cause charge to migrate on the surface of the oxide.[49] When the electrode voltage goes negative, negative charge appears on the external surface of the oxide along the periphery of the metal electrode. This is apparently due to the separation and migration of charged ions on the oxide surface. This negative charge tends to deplete electrons from the external *n*-type inversion layer. After the negative gate voltage is removed, this charge is neutralized by similar migration processes. Since surface migration may be a slow process, the electrons will be depleted from the ring-shaped area directly under this surface charge, essentially removing the inversion layer in this region. As long as this surface charge exists, the electrode inversion layer will not be coupled to the surrounding inversion layer, and the response time of the inversion layer will be determined by the bulk and surface-generated currents. In general, this response time will be much longer than that associated with inversion-to-inversion-layer coupling. This behavior is shown schematically in Fig. 2–21. The time dependence, or drift, of the lower curve in

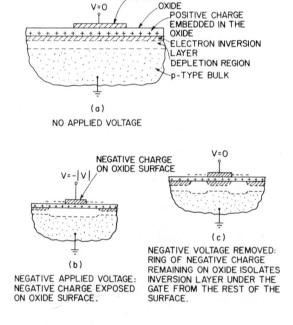

(a)

NO APPLIED VOLTAGE

(b)

NEGATIVE APPLIED VOLTAGE: NEGATIVE CHARGE EXPOSED ON OXIDE SURFACE.

(c)

NEGATIVE VOLTAGE REMOVED: RING OF NEGATIVE CHARGE REMAINING ON OXIDE ISOLATES INVERSION LAYER UNDER THE GATE FROM THE REST OF THE SURFACE.

Figure 2–21. Illustration of surface instability in an MOS capacitor (after Hofstein and Warfield[44]).

Fig. 2–19 at a fixed bias is a manifestation of the low surface mobility and long relaxation time of the charge on the surface of the oxide. The presence of water vapor in the ambient increases the surface mobility so that the lower curve relaxes to the upper one in a matter of seconds (rather than minutes) in a highly humid ambient.

EXPERIMENTAL CONFIRMATION OF SECOND-ORDER MODEL. The frequency response of a p-type MOS capacitor (oxidation in wet oxygen) has been investigated by Hofstein and Warfield.[44] Their results, shown in Fig. 2–22, are in very good agreement with the behavior predicted by this second-order model.

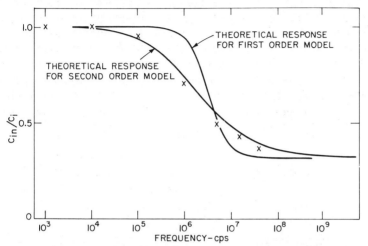

Figure 2–22. Normalized frequency response for MOS capacitor. The crosses are experimental points. The theoretical frequency response for the first-order model with a fixed shunt resistance, arbitrarily set to match the second-order curve at $f = 5.6$ mc/s, is shown to illustrate the relatively slow drop-off peculiar to the variable effective-coupling radius of the second-order model (after Hofstein and Warfield[44]).

Zaininger,[46] and Hofstein et al.[47] have investigated the effect of a guard ring surrounding the metal electrode. The results are reproduced in Fig. 2–23, where the input capacitance vs. input voltage is plotted for

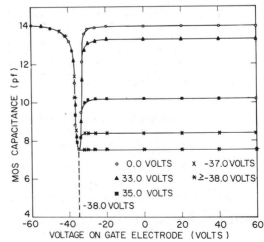

Figure 2–23. MOS capacitance characteristics as a function of the guard-ring potential.

several values of guard-ring potential. If the guard ring is biased negatively to deplete the surface inversion layer and increase the surface coupling resistance, the input capacitance drops sharply. This is due to the reduced frequency response of the gate inversion layer when $R_{Ee} \rightarrow \infty$.

In another experiment, Zaininger and Warfield[50] have measured the input capacitance vs. applied voltage characteristics of several p-type MOS capacitors in which the oxide was thermally grown in dry oxygen. The measurements, made at 1 kc/sec, gave a characteristic similar to n-type units. The measurements were repeated after successive exposures to hydrogen at increasingly elevated temperatures, a treatment which produces an inversion layer on the silicon surface surrounding the gate electrode. The results are reproduced in Fig. 2–24. It is seen that, as the external inversion layer forms, the frequency response of the gate inversion layer increases substantially.

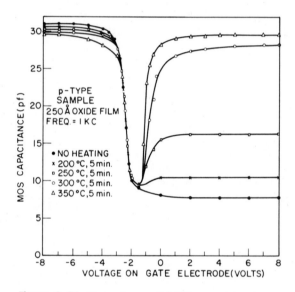

Figure 2-24. Dependence of MOS capacitor characteristics on temperature and duration of exposure to hydrogen. The oxide film was grown in dry oxygen.

2. Mobility in surface inversion layers

The mobility of a carrier in a solid is given by:

$$\mu_b = \frac{q\tau_b}{m^*} \tag{2-78}$$

where τ_b is the mean free time between collisions, and m^* is the effective mass. For *cold* carriers, i.e., carriers whose drift velocity is much less than their thermal velocity, τ_b is given by:

$$\tau_b \cong \frac{1}{v_T}[l_1^{-1} + l_2^{-1} + \cdots l_n^{-1} + \cdots]^{-1} \qquad (2\text{–}79)$$

where v_T is the average thermal velocity and the l's are mean free paths corresponding to different independent scattering mechanisms, e.g., thermal (electron-phonon) scattering, lattice defect scattering, scattering from impurity sites, etc. For carriers in single crystal bulk silicon, thermal scattering predominates at room temperature (300°K) for impurity doping densities less than $10^{14}/cm^3$. For doping levels above $10^{14}/cm^3$, impurity scattering becomes predominant.

In the case of a carrier in an inversion layer, an additional source of scattering is the semiconductor-insulator interface. If the surface scattering is specular (as from a potential barrier), the carrier momentum along the direction of conduction is unchanged and the surface does not affect the carrier mobility. However, if the particle is scattered in a random fashion, i.e., independent of its impinging direction, the surface can be considered a diffuse scatterer and the mobility is affected.

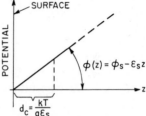

Figure 2–25. Linear potential-well for calculation of surface scattering effects.

Greene[51] has published an excellent survey paper covering computer solutions to the problem. Schrieffer[52] has considered the special case of the linear potential well, shown in Fig. 2–25, with the following assumptions:

1. An electron will hit the surface on the average $\bar{v}_T/2d_c$ times per second, where d_c is an effective channel depth given by the position at which the component of velocity normal to the surface goes to zero, i.e., $d_c q \mathscr{E}_s \equiv 1/2kT$.

2. The carrier loses all its drift velocity upon collision with the surface.

If the collisions with the surface are more frequent than the bulk scattering in the well, then:

$$\mu_{\text{eff}}/\mu_b = \frac{\tau_{\text{eff}}}{\tau_b} = \frac{\sqrt{kT m^*}}{q\tau_b \mathscr{E}_s} \qquad (2\text{–}80)$$

In the Schrieffer model of the surface well, it is assumed that the field in the surface space-charge region is constant and has the value of the surface field, $\mathscr{E}_s$. However, the field is not constant because of the space charge within the surface layer. One can correct for this field variation and its effect on the width of the well by using an effective well width,[43] given by the Debye length [Eq. (2–24)], λ_{n_s}, based on the electron density at the surface, n_s. The reason for this choice is that, physically, the Debye length is the distance over which the change in the potential energy of a charge is equal to its thermal energy.

For a nondegenerate inversion layer, it can be shown by using Eq. (2–32) that:

$$\lambda_{n_s} \cong \frac{kT}{q\mathcal{E}_s} = 2d_c \tag{2–81}$$

This indicates that the effective well width is just twice the width of the well in the Schrieffer approximation. Since the correction to the linear well approximation is relatively small for a nondegenerate inversion layer, Eq. (2–80) can be used as a description of the surface mobility in this case.

The preceding analysis may be readily extended to the case of a degenerate inversion layer by the substitution of the degenerate Debye length for the nondegenerate Debye length, and by the use of the Fermi velocity, v_F, instead of the Boltzmann velocity, v_T. When this is done, it may be shown[43] that the mobility varies approximately as $\mathcal{E}_s^{-3/5}$.

A plot of the mobility of the carriers in the surface layer is shown in Fig. 2–26 as a function of the electric field normal to the surface. As the

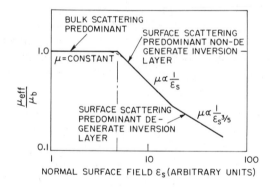

Figure 2–26. Normalized effective surface mobility as a function of surface field (after Hofstein[43]).

field increases, the layer goes from a depletion layer to a nondegenerate inversion layer, and finally to a degenerate inversion layer. The effect of diffuse surface scattering in a nondegenerate inversion layer on the characteristics of the transistor will be analyzed and compared with experiment in Section 5–2.

REFERENCES

1. I. Tamm, *Phys. Z. Sowjetunion* **1**, 733 (1932).

2. W. Shockley, *Phys. Rev.* **56**, 317 (1939).

3. W. G. Pollard, *Phys. Rev.* **56**, 324 (1939).

4. J. Bardeen, *Phys. Rev.* **71**, 717 (1947).

5. W. Shockley and G. L. Pearson, *Phys. Rev.* **74**, 232 (1948).

6. J. Bardeen and W. H. Brattain, *Phys. Rev.* **74**, 230 (1948).

✓ 7. C. G. B. Garrett and W. H. Brattain, *Phys. Rev.* **99**, 376 (1955).

8. R. H. Kingston, *J. Appl. Phys.* **27**, 101 (1956). This paper gives an extensive bibliography concerning experimental work up to 1955.

9. J. T. Law, "Semiconductor Surfaces," in *Semiconductors*, ed. N. B. Hannay (New York: Reinhold Publishing Corp., 1959) pp. 676–726.

10. T. B. Watkins, "The Electrical Properties of Semiconductor Surfaces," in *Progress in Semiconductors,* ed. A. F. Gibson (London: Heywood and Co., 1960), Vol. V, pp. 2–52.

11. J. Koutecky, *Phys. Stat. Sol.* **1**, 554 (1961).

12. G. Heiland, *Fortschr. d. Phys.* **9**, 393 (1961). This paper gives an exhaustive list of references up to 1961.

13. H. Flietner, *Phys. Stat. Sol.* **2**, 221 (1962).

14. A. R. Plummer, "The Semiconductor-Gas and Semiconductor-Metal System," in *The Electrochemistry of Semiconductors,* ed. P. J. Holmes (London: Academic Press, 1962) pp. 61–140.

✓ 15. A. Many, Y. Goldstein, and N. B. Grover, *Semiconductor Surfaces,* (Amsterdam: North-Holland Publishing Co., 1965).

16. J. L. Moll *IRE Wescon Convention Record*, Part 3, pp. 32–36 (1959).

17. F. Berz, *J. Elec. and Control* **6**, 97 (1959). Also, "Field-Effect at High Frequency" in *Solid State Physics in Electronics and Telecommunication* (London, Academic Bks., Ltd., 1960).

18. W. G. Pfann and C. G. B. Garrett, *Proc. IRE* **47**, 2011 (1959).

19. D. R. Frankl, *Solid State Electronics* **2**, 71 (1961).

20. J. A. Minahan, J. L. Sprague, and O. J. Wied, *J. Electrochem. Soc.* **109**, 94 (1962).

21. R. Lindner, *Bell Syst. Tech. J.* **41**, 803 (1962).

22. K. Lehovec, A. Slobodskoy, and J. Sprague, *IRE Trans. on Electron Devices* **8**, 420 (1961).

23. L. M. Terman, *Stanford Electronics Laboratory Report,* No. 1655–1 (1961), and *Solid State Electronics* **5**, 285 (1962).

24. K. Lehovec, A. Slobodskoy, and J. L. Sprague, *Phys. Stat. Sol.* **3**, 447 (1963).

25. K. Lehovec and A. Slobodskoy, *Solid State Electronics* **7**, 59 (1964).

26. K. H. Zaininger and G. Warfield, *IEEE Trans. on Electron Devices* **12**, 179 (1965).

27. H. K. Henisch, "Rectifying Semiconductor Contacts," Oxford: Clarendon Press, 1957.

28. J. R. McDonald, *Solid State Electronics* **5**, 11 (1962).

29. R. H Kingston and S. F. Neustadter, *J. Appl. Phys.* **26**, 718 (1955).

30. G. C. Dousmanis and R. C. Duncan, Jr., *J. Appl. Phys.* **29**, 1927 (1958).

31. H. Flietner, *Ann. Physik Leipzig* **3**, 396 (1959).

32. E. Groschwitz and R. Ebhardt, *Z. angew. Phys.* **11**, 9 (1959). E. Groschwitz, E. Hofmeister, and R. Ebhardt, *ibid.* **12**, 544 (1960).

33. D. R. Frankl, *J. Appl. Phys.* **31**, 1752 (1960).

34. C. E. Young, *J. Appl. Phys.* **32**, 329 (1961).

35. R. Seiwatz and M. Green, *J. Appl. Phys.* **29**, 1034 (1958).

36. F. P. Heiman and G. Warfield, *IEEE Trans. on Electron Devices* **12**, 167 (1965).

37. W. H. Brattain and J. Bardeen, *Bell System Tech. J.* **32**, 1 (1953).

38. L. R. Godefroy, in *Progress in Semiconductors* **1**, 197 (1956).

39. C. G. B. Garrett, *Phys. Rev.* **107**, 478 (1957).

40. A. E. Yunovich, *Sov. Phys., Techn. Phys.* **3**, 646 (1958).

41. A. E. Yunovich, *Sov. Phys., Solid State* **1**, 998 (1960).

42. F. Berz, *J. Phys. Chem. Solids* **23**, 1795 (1962).

43. S. R. Hofstein, Ph. D. thesis, Princeton University, Princeton, N.J., 1964.

44. S. R. Hofstein and G. Warfield, *Solid State Electronics* **8**, 321 (1965).

45. C. T. Sah, R. N. Noyce, and W. Shockley, *Proc. IRE* **45**, 1228 (1957).

46. K. H. Zaininger, Ph.D. thesis, Princeton University, Princeton, N.J., 1964.

47. S. R. Hofstein, K. H. Zaininger, and G. Warfield, *Proc. IEEE* **52**, 971 (1964).

48. S. R. Hofstein, K. H. Zaininger, and G. Warfield, Report at Solid State Device Research Conference, Boulder, Colorado, July, 1964.

49. M. M. Atalla, A. R. Bray, and R. Lindner, *Suppl. Proc. Inst. Elec. Engrs.* (London) Part B **106**, 1130 (1959).

50. K. H. Zaininger and G. Warfield, *Proc. IEEE* **52**, 972 (1964).

51. R. F. Greene, *J. Phys. Chem. Solids* **14**, 291 (1960).

52. J. R. Schrieffer, in *Semiconductor Surface Physics,* ed. R. H. Kingston, (Philadelphia, Pennsylvania: University of Pennsylvania Press, 1957) p. 55.

3

Conduction through Insulating Layers

Dietrich Meyerhofer

3-1 THE ROLE OF THE INSULATOR IN FIELD-EFFECT TRANSISTORS

In the insulated-gate field-effect transistor, the gate is separated from the conducting channel by a thin insulating layer. Its purpose is to act as a medium for transmitting the electric field, which controls the conduction between source and drain, without passing any current.

The gate insulator should have zero conductance and a very small capacitance to minimize dissipation and storage effects in the gate circuit. The first condition can be fulfilled with an ideal insulating material as long as the required fields are not too large. At fields on the order of 10^6 v/cm, various intrinsic conduction processes set in. The second condition has no ideal solution. On the one hand, a small capacitance is desirable, requiring a thick insulating layer and a low dielectric constant. On the other hand, a small control voltage is desirable, requiring a thin insulating layer and a large dielectric constant. In general, conduction through the insulator sets a lower limit to its thickness at its thinnest spot.

Real insulators may show conduction at considerably lower fields than those required for the intrinsic processes in the ideal insulator. This conduction may be linear or nonlinear. It may be uniquely defined, show hysteresis effects, or lead to permanent changes or destructive breakdown. The effects may be due to electronic or ionic conduction or to surface currents.

57

The purpose of this chapter is to provide a physical basis for understanding the high gate resistance and interpreting the various gate leakage, life, and stability phenomena. This requires first a presentation of the intrinsic electronic conduction processes. Impurities and defects are present in all real insulators and they directly affect the flow of electrons. To understand these processes, one must consider the band structure of the insulator and the electronic states of the impurities. Subsequently, ionic conduction, which is also caused by impurities, will be studied. These mechanisms will be found capable of changing the electronic processes in such a way as to modify operating parameters of the transistors temporarily or permanently.

3–2   ELECTRONIC CONDUCTION THROUGH INSULATING LAYERS

The number of free electrons in the conduction band of a large bandgap insulator in thermal equilibrium is negligible in most practical cases. Conduction can take place only after carriers have been introduced into the conduction band by some mechanism.† Some of those mechanisms are: injection of electrons from a contact over a barrier; tunneling through a barrier from a contact; tunneling from impurity states or from the valence band into the conduction band; and excitation of electrons from impurity states or valence band by radiation or hot electron impact. The carriers in the band move under applied fields in the conventional manner, describable by a mobility parameter. Because there are no intrinsic free carriers, conduction will be limited by space charge. The carriers may also be trapped at impurities, further limiting the conductivity.

This section first discusses the band structure model of the ideal insulator with contacts. Then, various electronic conduction processes will be considered individually.

1. The ideal insulator

The insulator used in field-effect devices consists of a very thin layer or sheet with comparatively large lateral dimensions. It is appropriate to approximate this physical structure by a one-dimensional model of a thin insulator sandwiched between a metal gate and the semiconductor body. Potential gradients, or current flow in a direction parallel to the plane of the insulating layer, are treated in Chapter 5 and will be neglected here. .

It is necessary to know the energy band structure for the discussion of electronic conduction, i.e., the distribution of states, which electrons can

---

†Most of the considerations in this section apply equally well to electrons in the conduction band and to holes in the valence band. The former case will generally be used to illustrate the discussion, but the equations apply to the latter case as well.

occupy, in energy and in space. A simple schematic energy band diagram of the one-dimensional model is shown in Fig. 3–1. The *vacuum level*, $\Phi(x)$, serves as a reference for the potential energy of the electrons. In an isolated homogeneous material it corresponds to the potential energy of an electron far removed from an uncharged region of this material.

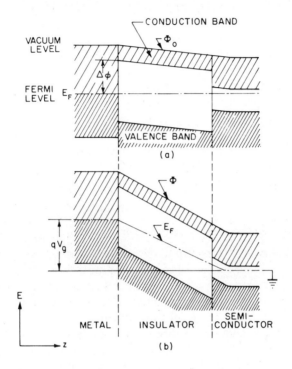

Figure 3–1. One-dimensional energy-band diagram of the field-effect transistor structure in a direction perpendicular to the insulating layer. The ordinate represents the electron energy. (a) Equilibrium; (b) under applied gate voltage V_g.

Here, the vacuum level does not have any absolute meaning, but represents the relative energy of electrons (at rest) located just outside the various regions of the material, at a sufficient distance so as not to be influenced by surface forces. The gradients in Φ are due to differences in work functions (contact potential differences) between the various materials. Even in the absence of an external voltage (Fig. 3–1a), a built-in field may exist in the insulator ($\mathcal{E}_{int} = \partial\Phi_0/\partial z$). If a voltage is applied to the insulator (Fig. 3–1b) the resulting field in the insulator is:

$$\mathcal{E} = \mathcal{E}_{int} + \mathcal{E}_{ext} = \frac{\partial\Phi_0}{\partial z} + \frac{\partial E_F}{\partial z} = \frac{\partial\Phi}{\partial z} \qquad (3\text{–}1)$$

The model of the semiconductor-insulator interface in Fig. 3–1 is that of the simplest situation where there is no surface charge. Other cases have been treated in Chapter 2. Furthermore, the voltage drop across the semiconductor ($\int \mathscr{E} \, dz$) is always less than E_G/q, the bandgap voltage, except under very special pulse conditions. Consequently it is generally much smaller than the applied voltage V_g. The field in the insulator is approximately:

$$\mathscr{E}_i = \frac{V_g}{d_i} \tag{3-2}$$

where d_i is the thickness of the insulator.

The band structure of the insulator is the same as that of a semi-conductor except that the valence and conduction bands are so far from the Fermi level that the number of free carriers in thermal equilibrium is negligible. The field across the insulator is shown constant in Fig. 3–1. This is the simplest possible situation which applies when no net charge density is present. More complex realistic situations will be discussed in later sections.

2. Conduction processes in the ideal insulator

INJECTION OVER A BARRIER (SCHOTTKY EMISSION). Consider the metal-insulator interface of Fig. 3–1. For a small barrier, $\Delta\phi$, or high temperatures, there will be some electrons in the metal with sufficient energies to pass over the barrier and flow into the insulator conduction band. In equilibrium, there will, of course, exist an equal number of electrons in the insulator flowing in the opposite direction. The latter are eliminated by a small applied field (Fig. 3–1b), and one may calculate the current flowing into the insulator when it is *not* limited by space charge. This injected current is referred to as *thermionic emission*.

The current per unit area flowing in the z-direction, j_z, is obtained by the integration of the charge flow over all the electrons in the metal, with sufficient momentum in the z-direction to overcome the barrier:

$$j_z = \frac{1}{(2\pi)^2} \frac{2qm(kT)^2}{h^3} \exp\left[-\frac{\Delta\phi}{kT}\right] \tag{3-3}$$

This is known as the *Richardson equation*, in the case of thermionic emission into vacuum.

Notice that the electron mass enters into these equations. The electrons in the metal and insulator are not completely free, as in vacuum, but are treated as quasi-free on the band-model approximation of a solid. The electron mass takes on an *effective* value, m^*, different from the free electron mass. In a parabolic band, the effective mass is a single, well-defined number. So long as the effective masses are the same in the two

NOTE

adjacent materials, the foregoing equations need not be modified except for replacing m by m^*. The alternate case will be considered in more detail in part 4 of this section.

The (thermionic) current given by the Richardson equation is negligibly small for the type of insulators and the range of temperatures considered in this book. However, the injection current may be increased by high fields, which modify the shape of the barrier and lower its height. This causes more thermionic carriers to flow over the barrier. This case is also well known from emission into vacuum and was first described by Schottky. To calculate this current, the model of the metal-insulator interface must first be modified to include the *image force*. An electron located in the insulator of dielectric constant $\kappa_i = \epsilon_i/\epsilon_o$ at a distance z from the metal interface experiences an attractive force:

$$q\mathscr{E}_{im} = \frac{q^2}{16\pi\epsilon_i z^2} \tag{3-4}$$

towards the metal. This reduces the potential energy of the electron by:

$$\phi_{im} = -\frac{q^2}{16\pi\epsilon_i z} \tag{3-5}$$

as shown in Fig. 3–2. Near $z = 0$, where the image potential would take on large negative values (dashed line), the simple concept no longer applies. The metal cannot be considered as a continuum, and the individual atoms and shielding electrons must be taken into account. The detailed considerations become complicated, but it is reasonable to make

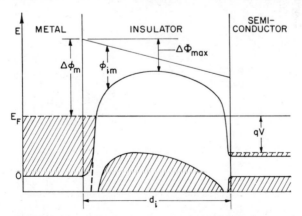

Figure 3–2. Band structure of the metal-insulator interface (Fig. 3–1) modified by the image force (potential ϕ_{im}). The applied electric field, $\mathscr{E}$, lowers the barrier height by an amount $\Delta\Phi_{max.} = (q^3\mathscr{E}/4\pi\epsilon_i)^{1/2}$

the approximation, shown in Fig. 3–2, that the conduction band of the insulator goes over smoothly into the conduction band of the metal.

A simple calculation, using Eq. (3–5), shows that the lowering of the barrier height by an applied field $\mathscr{E}$ is given by:

$$\Delta\phi_{max} = \sqrt{\frac{q^3\mathscr{E}}{4\pi\epsilon_i}} \tag{3-6}$$

Inserting Eq. (3–6) into Eq. (3–3) results in the *Schottky equation,* modified for emission into a solid, rather than into a vacuum:

$$j_z = \frac{1}{(2\pi)^2}\frac{2qm^*(kT)^2}{\hbar^3}\exp\left[-\frac{\Delta\phi-(q^3\mathscr{E}/4\pi\epsilon_i)^{1/2}}{kT}\right] \tag{3-7}$$

$$= 120\,\frac{m^*}{m}\,T^2 e^{-1.15\times10^4\Delta\phi/T}e^{13.8\sqrt{\mathscr{E}}/\sqrt{k_iT}}\ a/cm^2$$

In the latter formulation, T is to be taken in °K, $\Delta\phi$ in ev, and $\mathscr{E}$ in v/Å. The logarithm of the current is, therefore, proportional to $1/T$ and $\sqrt{\mathscr{E}}$.

Schottky emission into thin insulating layers was observed by Emtage and Tantraporn.[1] Similar experimental results of Pollack[2] on injection from lead into Al_2O_3 layers, 340 Å thick, are shown in Fig. 3–3. Both

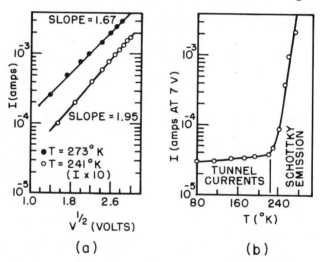

Figure 3–3. Experimental evidence for Schottky injection into a 340-Å-thick layer of Al_2O_3: (a) I vs. $V^{1/2}$; (b) I vs. T (After Pollack.[2])

the voltage and temperature dependence of the current are shown to demonstrate the applicability of Eq. (3–7). The data are consistent with a barrier height $\Delta\phi$ of 0.64 ev.

TUNNELING OR FIELD EMISSION. Tunneling is a quantum mechanical process without a classical analogue. Consider the simplest one-dimensional problem shown in Fig. 3-4. When the electron energy, E, is larger than the barrier height Φ_A, the electron may travel relatively freely over

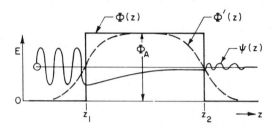

Figure 3-4. One-dimensional tunneling through a square potential barrier $\Phi(z)$ or through a smoothed-out barrier $\Phi'(z)$.

the barrier; for $E < \Phi_A$ there will be a finite probability of the electron tunneling through the barrier. The one-dimensional Schrödinger equation is:

$$-\frac{h^2}{2m}\frac{\partial^2 \psi}{\partial z^2} + \Phi(z)\psi = E\psi \qquad (3\text{-}8)$$

which may be solved exactly for the square potential barrier:

$$\psi = \psi_o e^{i(2mE/\hbar^2)^{1/2}z} \qquad \text{for } z < z_1$$
$$\text{or } z > z_2$$
$$\psi = \psi_o e^{-[2m(\Phi_A - E)/\hbar^2]^{1/2}z} \qquad \text{for } z_1 < z < z_2 \qquad (3\text{-}9)$$

The solutions must be matched at the boundaries. This demonstrates an exponentially decaying wave in the tunneling region. Since the expectation value of finding the electron at z is $|\psi(z)|^2$, the probability $P(E)$, that an electron incident on the barrier will pass through the barrier is:

$$P(E) = \frac{|\psi(z_2)|^2}{|\psi(z_1)|^2} = \exp\left\{-2[2m(\Phi_A - E)/h^2]^{1/2}(z_2 - z_1)\right\} \qquad (3\text{-}10)$$

Real barriers are never infinitely sharp, and a more realistic potential is one like $\Phi'(z)$ in Fig. 3-4. The solution of Eq. 3-8 becomes much more complicated, but if $\Phi'(z)$ varies smoothly enough (as is usually the case) the WKB approximation[3] may be applied. The result is:

$$P \cong \exp\left\{-\int_{z_1}^{z_2} [2m(\Phi'(z) - E)]^{1/2} dz\right\} \qquad (3\text{-}11)$$

The limits of integration, z_1 and z_2, are the points where $\Phi'(z) = E$, the so-called classical turning points. Equation (3–11) is very useful for calculating most practical tunneling problems using various analytical approximations or numerical integration.

For electron energies near the top of the barrier, the WKB formalism must be modified somewhat, as shown by Good and co-workers.[4]

An idea of the magnitude of the tunneling probability may be obtained if we calculate the transmission coefficient of a barrier 1 ev higher than the particle energy and 25 Å wide. Then the transmission probability is $P = 10^{-11}$. Because of the exponential dependence on thickness, barriers twice as wide as this have negligible transmission coefficients.

Tunneling may enter into the problem of conduction through insulating layers in a number of different ways. Some of these are depicted in Fig. 3–5. In the case of very thin insulating layers, electrons tunnel directly

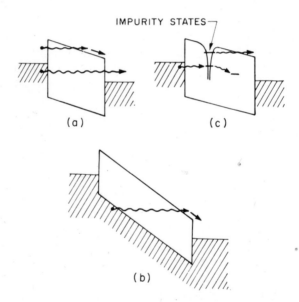

IMPURITY STATES

(a)   (c)

(b)

Figure 3–5. Various ways in which tunneling may contribute to conduction through thin insulating layers. (a) Tunneling from the contact; (b) band-to-band tunneling; (c) tunneling to and from impurity states.

from a metal through the forbidden energy gap into the conduction band of the semiconductor, or vice versa. The corresponding tunneling probability through thicker insulators is negligible, but the application of a large electric field narrows the barrier and permits electrons to tunnel into the insulator conduction band. These two processes are shown in Fig. 3–5a.

In very large fields it is also possible for electrons to tunnel from the valence band of the insulator into its conduction band (Zener tunneling[5] Fig. 3–5b). This process may be neglected in practice because of the large bandgap of typical insulators (5–12ev). The remaining tunneling processes (Fig. 3–5c) concern tunneling in and out of traps and will be discussed later.

One generally calculates the tunnel currents through thin insulating layers (Fig. 3–5a) by using the model of Fig. 3–2, which takes the image force into account. Because the valence band of the insulator is located sufficiently far below the conduction band (large bandgap), its presence may be neglected and the bottom of the conduction band, modified by the image force, may be treated as the potential $\Phi'(z)$ of the simple one-dimensional barrier (Fig. 3–4). The kinetic energy in the direction parallel to the interfaces must be conserved in this process.

Figure 3–2 shows that there is no longer any clear distinction between the two cases in Fig. 3–5a, one going over into the other as the parameters vary. Furthermore, it is clear that the tunneling transition takes place under conservation of **k** (a direct transition in semiconductor terminology), since the transition takes place entirely within the insulator, i.e., from the bottom of the conduction band at z_1 (cf. Fig. 3–4), to the bottom of the conduction band at z_2. The image force smooths out the barrier sufficiently so that the use of Eq. (3–11) is justified in this situation.

The *mass* in Eq. (3–11) is the effective mass of the conduction band of the insulator in this simplified model, since the tunneling takes place between z_1 and z_2, both of which lie within the insulator For the large bandgaps involved, m^*/m can generally be taken as one (little interaction between the bands). The dielectric constant which enters the image force is the optical value, because the electron spends only $\sim 10^{-13}$ sec in the insulator, which is not enough time for the lattice to polarize.

The tunnel current flowing through the insulator is now calculated by integrating over all electrons

$$j_z = q \int N(E) f(E) v_z P(E_z) \, d\mathbf{k} \tag{3–12}$$

The energy E is the kinetic energy of the electron in the cathode material, measured from the bottom of the conduction band.

There have been many attempts to evaluate Eq. (3–12). In some cases no consideration has been given to the image force, to the dielectric constant, or to the effective mass of the electron in the insulator, and the assumptions have not always been clearly stated and justified. The complete solution of the tunneling probability and the current integral cannot be obtained in analytical form (even when the image force is neglected), and most authors have calculated approximate forms of the integrals which may be valid within certain limits. Two of the most recent and complete calculations were made by Stratton[6] and by Simmons[7]. The former uses an expansion which would apply rigorously at low voltages if the image force could be taken into account exactly. The latter makes approximations which allow Eq. (3–12) to be solved analytically over the entire range of parameters, but which result in errors in

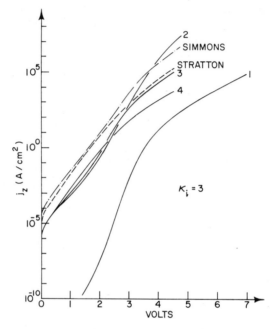

Figure 3–6. Calculated tunneling currents [Eqs. (3–11) and (3–12)] flowing through thin insulating layers (after Meyerhofer and Ochs[8]). Values of the barrier parameters are as follows:

1. $d_i = 40 \text{ Å}$ $\Delta\phi_1 = \Delta\phi_2 = 2ev$
2. $d_i = 25 \text{ Å}$ $\Delta\phi_1 = 1ev$ $\Delta\phi_2 = 3ev$
3. $d_i = 25 \text{ Å}$ $\Delta\phi_1 = 2ev$ $\Delta\phi_2 = 2ev$
4. $d_i = 25 \text{ Å}$ $\Delta\phi_1 = 3ev$ $\Delta\phi_2 = 1ev$

where $\Delta\phi_1$ is the barrier on the negative electrode and $\Delta\phi_2$ is the barrier on the positive electrode. For comparison, the curves calculated for the same parameter values as curve 3, by the approximation of Stratton[6] and Simmons,[7] are also shown.

current density varying from less than a factor of 2 in some regions to as high as a factor of 10^4 at medium and high currents, for barriers with small dielectric constants.

A different approach has been used by Meyerhofer and Ochs.[8] They calculated the integrals in the tunneling probability and the current density numerically with a final accuracy of $\pm 25\%$. Some typical curves are shown in Fig. 3–6. For comparison, corresponding characteristics calculated by the formulas of Stratton and Simmons are included.

These calculated tunneling currents may accurately represent real physical situations, as shown in Fig. 3–7, where measured current values

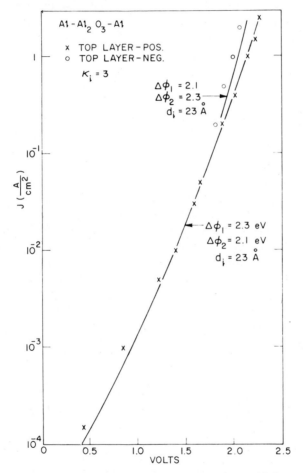

Figure 3–7. Experimental current-voltage characteristics for an Al–Al₂O₃–Al sandwich. The curves are calculated using the barrier parameters indicated (after Meyerhofer and Ochs.[8])

on Al–Al₂O₃–Al sandwiches are compared with calculated curves fitted to them.[8] A uniformly distributed current is assumed and confirmed by the good fit with the calculation. A slight asymmetry in the tunneling barrier is apparent. Similar experiments and curve-fitting have recently been performed by Pollack and Morris,[9] although a more complicated model and a nonuniform current distribution had to be assumed.

SPACE CHARGE LIMITED CURRENT. Carriers injected into the conduction band by Schottky emission or tunneling continue to flow toward the anode in the applied field. There is no compensating charge present, and the carriers give rise to space charge. This in turn changes the field distribution in the insulator. For an unlimited supply of electrons at the cathode end of the insulator ($z = 0$), the simple equation for one-carrier trap-free space-charge-limited current is obtained:

$$j = \frac{8}{9} \, \epsilon_i \mu \frac{V^2}{d_i^3} \tag{3–13}$$

This shows that very substantial currents can be drawn through insulating layers, if sufficient injected carriers are available. Smith and Rose[10] measured currents up to 20 a/cm² through insulating CdS crystals 2.5×10^{-3} cm thick, and demonstrated that they obey Eq. (3–13).

More complicated models of insulators will lead to other equations for space-charge-limited currents. In particular, the assumption of an unlimited supply of carriers at the cathode will generally not apply. At higher fields, the mobility no longer remains constant. Also, there are the important effects of traps on the current. This will be considered later in this section. Injection of two kinds of carriers will not be treated here since this phenomenon is mainly limited to semiconductors and is not generally observed in insulators.

Since space-charge-limited currents change the potential distribution, this will in turn affect the injection process. The field at the cathode is reduced compared to the uniform field. Geppert[11] calculated how much this decreases the tunnel current and found that the effect is negligible in most practical cases.

CONDUCTION IN HIGH ELECTRIC FIELDS. The electric fields applied to the insulating layer in the transistor are large compared to the fields usually encountered in electronic conduction. A gate voltage of 20 v applied to a typical insulator of 1000 Å thickness corresponds to an average field of 2×10^6 v/cm. This field is comparable to that in back-biased p-n junctions, and similar effects can be expected to occur in both cases.

Consider what happens to an electron in the conduction band of an insulator so long as it is not trapped. In small electric fields, it drifts in the field direction, gaining energy from the field and losing energy in collisions with impurities and acoustical phonons. Thermal equilibrium, and therefore the average energy of the electrons, is maintained. The mobility is constant, as was assumed in the calculation of space-charge-limited currents.

In larger fields, the energy loss by ionized impurity and acoustical phonon scattering is no longer fast enough to maintain the equilibrium. The electrons attain higher average energies (hot electrons) and new kinds of interactions take place, particularly optical phonon scattering, impact ionization, and pair production.

Electrons interact strongly with optical phonons, once they attain high enough energy. This reduces the mobility sharply at higher fields and causes the drift velocity to saturate. In contrast, the scattering by ionized impurities (Coulomb interaction) is reduced at higher energies and, at the same time, the trapping probability is decreased. This makes it more likely that the electrons will pass through a thin insulating layer without being trapped at all.

Hot electrons with sufficient energy can excite additional electrons into the conduction band, either from bound states of neutral impurity atoms (impact ionization) or from the valence band (pair production). These additional carriers also heat up and may, in turn, create further carriers leading to avalanche formation. These processes are identical to those observed in conventional semiconductors, particularly in *Zener* breakdown of *p-n* junctions. Multiplication will only take place in layers with thicknesses larger than the mean-free-path between ionizing collisions (~ 20 Å), since, otherwise, the electron leaves the crystal before colliding.

When the rate of creation of additional carriers exceeds the rate of recombination at some point in the material, the carrier concentration and, therefore, the conductivity increases at that point. This causes both an increase in the total conductance of the sample and a distortion of the electric field within it. Both effects allow more and more current to flow and destructive breakdown takes place. This is generally called *electronic or intrinsic breakdown*. There have been a number of attempts to calculate the intrinsic breakdown strength of an insulator (generally neglecting the injection problem) by balancing the energy gained by an electron from the field with the energy dissipation (cf., e.g., Whitehead,[12] Frantz[13]) but the experimental results are not yet sufficiently accurate to check the theories.

Typical measured values of dielectric breakdown strength obtained on the well-studied alkali halide crystals are $(0.5 - 1.0) \times 10^6$ v/cm.[14] Less is known about other materials. Von Hippel and Maurer[15] measured the breakdown strengths of both quartz crystals and thin layers of silica glass to be approximately 5×10^6 v/cm at room temperature. Grown layers of SiO_2 in field-effect transistors are less perfect and are therefore expected to exhibit smaller breakdown fields.

Electronic breakdown is caused by a field-produced increase in conductivity. A different type of breakdown, *thermal breakdown*, depends on the heating of material in high-current-density regions. The conductance increases with increasing temperature and breakdown takes place when the thermal conductivity is no longer sufficient to dissipate the heat produced. This process appears to be responsible for breakdown of very thin insulating layers. It may also lead to self-healing of a breakdown point if the temperature during the breakdown is sufficiently high to vaporize the metal contact in the region adjacent to the breakdown.

3. The insulator with traps

The insulator model discussed in Section 1 of this chapter is a very idealized one. It applies only for a perfect crystalline material without defects or impurities. Real insulators have large quantities of both kinds of imperfections. Their effects are twofold.

First, each imperfection introduces one or more localized energy states (as compared to the nonlocalized Bloch states which form the valence and conduction bands of the perfect material). In the case of insulators, these donor or acceptor states generally lie deep in the forbidden gap. States which are empty in equilibrium may trap free excess carriers, removing them from the conduction process.

Second, localized imperfections scatter free charge carriers, thereby reducing their mobility. This is particularly true if the states are electrically charged (ionized impurity scattering).

Consider the case of the space-charge-limited current that was calculated in the previous section. This is a steady-state process. Under the application of the electric field, electrons from a large reservoir flow into the insulator. If the density of electrons is smaller than that of the traps, most of the electrons will be trapped, leaving only a small number of thermally excited free carriers. The ratio of free-to-trapped charge, in the simplest situation, is:

$$\frac{n_c}{n_t} = \frac{N_c}{N_t} \exp\left[-\frac{\Delta E_t}{kT}\right] \tag{3-14}$$

where N_c is the density of states in the conduction band, N_t is the density of traps, and ΔE_t is the ionization energy of the traps, i.e., the energy separation of the trap level from the appropriate band edge. Consequently, the current flow will be reduced by this ratio from its trap-free value [Eq. (3-13)]. Since ΔE_t is usually many kT, the remaining current will be very small. As the voltage is increased and the number of carriers injected into the insulator becomes larger than the number of traps, the excess carriers remain free. It is therefore expected that the current through an insulator with traps will increase very strongly at a certain voltage, eventually approaching the value of the trap-free space-charge-limited case. Any remaining difference is caused by a reduction of the mobility due to the ionized traps.

There have been many observations of the effect of traps on space-charge-limited currents in insulators. One of the most ideal sets of data[16] is reproduced in Fig. 3–8. It was taken on ZnS crystals 5×10^{-3} cm thick.

Trapping may also have a strong effect on tunneling currents. Consider the process of injection into the conduction band by tunneling (Fig. 3–5a). Again, this is a steady-state situation, and the traps may be considered in quasi-thermal equilibrium with the conduction band. The carriers are only trapped between the point of injection and the anode. The resulting space charge reduces the field near the cathode, causing the barrier for tunneling to become thicker and reducing the injection. This effect is just the opposite of that caused by electron multiplication at high fields and, consequently, tends to increase the measured dielectric breakdown strength.

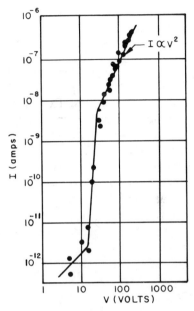

Figure 3–8. Space-charge-limited current in a 5×10^{-3} cm-thick ZnS crystal. It shows the effect of trap filling and the applicability of Eq. (3–14) at high currents (after Ruppel[16]).

Geppert[11] has calculated the changes caused by trapping in detail, and one set of his curves is shown in Fig. 3–9. A large effect is seen for this thin junction of 100 Å width. Some experimental evidence for this effect has been found by Meyerhofer and Ochs[8] in a study of current flow through thin films of BeO.

It was seen in the previous section that, for hot electrons, the trapping cross section is reduced. The equilibrium number of free carriers [Eq. (3–14)] is increased, and the effects of traps are reduced at the high fields.

The filling or emptying of a trap has been considered to take place as a vertical transition to or from the conduction band by thermal activation. The process may also take place by emission and absorption of radiation. The latter causes increased conductivity (photoconductivity). This will be particularly important at high fields, where the added photocarriers hasten the onset of dielectric breakdown. The high fields also increase the ionization rate by lowering the barrier surrounding the trap (Schottky emission).

Traps may also communicate horizontally by tunneling, either with the contacts, with the insulator conduction band (field ionization), or with other impurities (Fig. 3–5c). All these processes increase the current flowing in the insulator over its equilibrium value. Calculation of the transition probabilities is complicated by the three-dimensional nature of the impurity state (cf., e.g., Franz[13]).

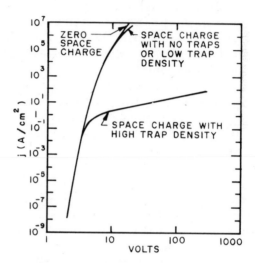

Figure 3-9. Calculated tunneling current through an insulating layer with the parameter values $d_i = 100$ Å, $\Delta\phi = 1$ev, $\kappa_i = 9$. The effect of 10^{20} traps cm³, at a depth, such that $n_c/n_t = 10^{-7}$, is shown (after Geppert[11]).

Mead[17] has measured current-voltage characteristics of Ta_2O_5 layers from 50 to 5000 Å thick and suggested that the observed currents are due to thermal or field ionization from traps. Substantial currents flowed even at fields lower than 10^6 v/cm.

The processes by which electrons enter and leave trap states all tend to have long time constants. Thermal equilibrium then exists only under d–c conditions. Under a–c conditions, different phenomena make themselves felt, depending on the frequency of operation. For example, hysteresis effects have been observed in capacitance measurements as functions of gate voltage (see Chapter 2) and have been described by a very simple model of tunneling from one of the contacts into impurity energy states.

4. Refinements of the model

The discussion of electronic conduction in insulators (Fig. 3–1) has been based on band theory. Insulator, semiconductor, and metal are presumed to have parabolic conduction bands with well-defined (and equal) effective electron masses. The transition from one material to another is one-dimensional and abrupt (except for the image force potential). The entire voltage drop is assumed to occur across the insulator.

In this section the validity of some of the features of this model will be investigated and others refined. In particular, we will discuss the applicability of the band model treating the case of differing effective masses and investigating the effect of electric fields on the metal contact. The corresponding problem of the electric field in the semiconductor has already been discussed in Chapter 2.

The very thin insulator may consist of as few as ten atomic layers. The *band structure model* is derived from the Bloch scheme and requires infinite extent, or at least periodic boundary conditions. Certainly this is not true of a layer ten interatomic distances thick, particularly since the outermost atoms interact with the atoms of the adjacent material and do not experience the same forces as the interior atoms. Furthermore, there is generally some interdiffusion between the insulator and the adjacent metal or semiconductor, particularly in the case of grown oxide layers, such as Al_2O_3 or SiO_2. In the latter case, there is no well-defined boundary and only the central region of the insulator is undisturbed.

Many of the insulating layers may be amorphous (see Chapter 4), i.e., without a periodic lattice, so that the band-structure calculations appear to be inapplicable. However, any system has a certain amount of short-range order that does not show up in X-ray experiments and the band theory may still be approximately applicable.

The conduction between two materials with parabolic bands but *with different effective masses* will now be discussed. This case has generally been neglected in the literature on tunneling and emission into vacuum. The previous calculations may, however, be extended easily by including a varying effective mass.

Consider first the case of thermionic or Schottky emission (Fig. 3–2). An electron with high enough energy can pass from one material, with the smaller electron affinity, to the other (thermionic emission). If the effective mass is different in the two materials, then some of the electrons will not satisfy energy and momentum conservation conditions and will be reflected at the boundary. Under these conditions it can be shown that the thermionic current is still given by the Richardson equation [Eq. (3–3)], but using the effective mass of the material *into which the electrons are flowing*. It is independent of the effective mass of the emitting material. The same is, of course, true for Schottky emission [Eq. (3–7)].

Similar considerations must be applied to tunneling calculations. The situation is more complex in this case, because the tunneling probability itself also depends on m^*. Furthermore, the virtual states in the forbidden gap of the insulator may also have a varying effective mass. The effects can be included in the tunneling calculations as was shown by Franz[13] and

Stratton.[6] At present, the insulator band structure is not well enough known to allow comparison of these calculations with experiment.

Another problem to be taken into consideration is the effect of an electric field on a *metal*. In the previous calculation the external field $\mathscr{E}_z$ was assumed to change abruptly at the metal-insulator interface as is shown in Fig. 3–1 (the image force only changes the internal field and need not be included in the present considerations). A more accurate picture of the band structure in the vicinity of the interface is shown in Fig. 3–10. The bands in the metal bend to accommodate the charge required by the metal-insulator capacitor.

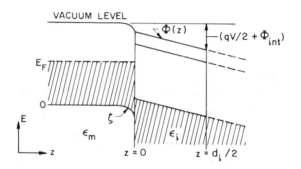

Figure 3–10. Detailed model of the band energies in the immediate vicinity of a metal-insulator interface (cf. Fig. 3–1). The image potential is not shown.

The *capacitance* of the symmetric structure of an insulator of thickness, d_i, with two metal contacts may be calculated as follows: The space charge in the *metal* in the case of a parabolic conduction band is given by:

$$\rho = qn_o\left[\left(\frac{\zeta + E_F}{E_F}\right) - 1\right] \tag{3-15}$$

where n_o is the density of electrons in equilibrium and $\zeta(z)$ is the amount of band bending. Integration of Poisson's equation $(\rho/\epsilon = d\mathscr{E}/dz)$ gives:

$$\mathscr{E}_m = \sqrt{\frac{2e^2n_o}{\epsilon_m}}\left[\frac{2}{5}E_F\left(1 + \frac{\zeta}{E_F}\right)^{5/2} - \frac{2}{5}E_F - \zeta\right]^{1/2} \approx \frac{\zeta}{d_m} \tag{3-16}$$

where d_m is the thickness of the space-charge region in the metal.

$$d_m = \sqrt{\frac{2}{3}\frac{\epsilon_m E_F}{q^2 n_o}} \tag{3-17}$$

The last approximation in Eq. (3-16) is always valid, since $\zeta < E_F$. For a typical metal $n_o = 10^{22}$ cm^{-3}, $E_F = 10$ev, and the dielectric constant $\kappa_m = 1$, since the value in the *absence* of conduction electrons must be taken. Then $d_m = 0.8$Å.

At the metal-insulator interface there is now no charge, so:

$$\epsilon_m \mathscr{E}_m(z = 0) = \epsilon_i \mathscr{E}_i(z = 0) \tag{3-18}$$

Inserting this relation into Eq. (3-16), we integrate the electric field over half the symmetrical structure and set it equal to $(V/2 - \Phi_{int}/q)$ [cf. Eq. (3-1)]. Then the capacitance per unit area becomes:

$$C = \frac{\partial Q}{\partial V} = \frac{1}{d_i/\epsilon_i + 2d_m/\epsilon_m} \tag{3-19}$$

This shows that the capacitance due to the insulator (ϵ_i/d_i) is in series with capacitances of the two metal contacts (ϵ_m/d_m). The latter quantity can have an important effect on thin insulating layers $(d_i < 50$Å$)$, reducing the measured capacitance. It determines the maximum possible capacitance of such a structure:

$$C_{max} = \frac{\epsilon_m}{2d_m} = 5.6 \,\mu\text{f/cm}^2 \tag{3-20}$$

if the previously given value of d_m is inserted.

3-3 DEFECTS IN INSULATORS

Many kinds of defects exist in insulators and they can all influence the conduction properties in one way or another. In some cases this influence is direct, by the movement of charged defects; in other cases, it is indirect, by a change in the electronic conductivity.

Consider first the *intrinsic defects*. All common insulators have two kinds of intrinsic defects: A Frenkel defect consists of a vacancy and an interstitial atom of the *same* kind, a Schottky defect of two vacancies of *different* ions, to preserve charge neutrality. For thermodynamic reasons, these defects are present even in perfectly pure materials with ideal crystal structures. This is analogous to the fact that there are always some electrons above the Fermi level at any finite temperature. The number of these defects is determined by the temperature, by the vapor pressure of the constituents of the insulator at that temperature, and by the number and distribution of impurities and other kinds of defects. These defects and their relationship to impurities are responsible for ionic conduction which will be discussed in the following section.

Impurities are also a kind of defect. They may act as donors or acceptors. In contrast to the semiconductor case, impurity energy levels lie very deep (> 0.1 ev) in insulators and carriers are not excited from them by thermal energy. Excitation may, however, be caused by photon absorption or impact ionization. Due to the inverse process the impurities may act as traps, which have already been discussed in Chapter 2. They also reduce the mobility of the carriers, particularly if they are charged.

Other kinds of structural defects are stacking faults, dislocations, grain boundaries, and other combinations of the simple defects. They may or may not act as traps or scattering centers. In some cases they increase the breakdown strength of the pure material. A more complicated situation is the amorphous insulator, such as will generally be used for the gate insulator. Defects are then no longer clearly defined (Chapter 4).

One type of defect, which may be present in any kind of insulating layer, is a void or conglomeration of vacancies. They may adversely affect the properties of the layer in various ways. If the voids reach the surface they may be filled up with metal atoms during deposition of the gate. They may increase the surface area, thereby increasing the problems due to absorbed ions. Finally, they reduce the breakdown strength of the layer because of their reduced dielectric constant.

3–4. IONIC CONDUCTION

1. Mechanism

The forces holding an insulator together are generally ionic in character, in contrast to the forces in metals and semiconductors. This means that the building blocks of an insulator are ions with closed shells of electrons, which are tightly bound. The binding force is the Coulomb attraction of the ions. The tightly bound electrons cannot partake in conduction; in other words, the Fermi level lies in the middle of a large energy gap. This is a very simplified picture, and materials with combined ionic and covalent binding also may be insulators, such as some of the II–VI and III–V compounds.

At all temperatures above absolute zero, the thermodynamic equilibrium lattice is not a perfect lattice but, rather, a structure containing a certain number of vacancies and other imperfections. Furthermore, there is a certain probability that these imperfections, and therefore the lattice ions, may move. This is the process of diffusion. When an electric field is applied to the insulator, diffusion of the electrically charged ions will take place preferentially along the field lines, causing current to flow. Diffusion takes place by "hopping" of ions from one vacancy (or interstitial position) to another and depends exponentially on temperature:

$$D = D_o e^{-\Delta E/kT} \qquad (3-21)$$

The Einstein equation relates diffusion and low-field conductivity:

$$\sigma = \frac{q^2 N}{kT} D = \frac{q^2 N}{kT} D_o e^{-\Delta E/kT} \tag{3–22}$$

Here ΔE is the activation energy (the height of the potential barrier over which the ion must pass in moving from one lattice position to the next) and N is the number of mobile charge carriers (vacancies or interstitial ions). An experimental demonstration of this behavior is shown in Fig. 3–11.[18] The purest KCl follows Eq. (3–22) over most of the temperature range with $\Delta E = 2.0$ ev. This is the intrinsic ionic conductivity of the material.

Figure 3–11 shows that doping the KCl by replacing monovalent potassium with divalent barium increases the conductivity in the low-temperature range (extrinsic conductivity). The reason for this is that for every Ba atom introduced, an additional potassium vacancy must also be formed to preserve charge neutrality. The number of vacancies, N [Eq. (3–22)] can become much larger than the intrinsic concentration.

Even if the extrinsic conductivity is taken into account, the low-field ionic conduction will generally be too small to have any effect. However, the situation is analogous to the case of electronic conduction out of impurity states

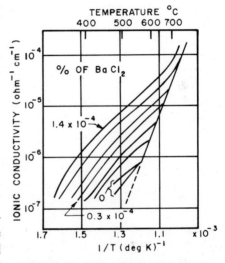

Figure 3–11. Ionic conductivity of pure and doped KCl. The percentage of BaCl$_2$ in the sample is indicated (after Kelting and Witt[18]).

(Fig. 3–5c), since in both cases the carrier is located in a Coulomb type of three-dimensional well. A large applied field causes field emission, and, in the present case, field emission of the ion out of its well. The conductivity is no longer constant, but strongly field-dependent. Because the activation energy for diffusion is of the same order of magnitude as the ionization energies for electrons, these processes are expected to become important at comparable field strengths (10^6 v/cm).

Generally, the d-c ionic conductivity decreases during the time the field is applied, because ions cannot be injected or extracted from the material (exceptions will be discussed in the following section). After an initial current flow, negative and positive space charge starts to build up near the two electrodes. This causes a distortion of the potential distribution, as shown in Fig. 3–12a. When the external field is removed

(Fig. 3–12b), large internal fields remain which cause some, but not all, of the ions to flow back toward their equilibrium positions (Fig. 3–12c). This shows that for slowly varying high fields, large hysteresis effects will appear.

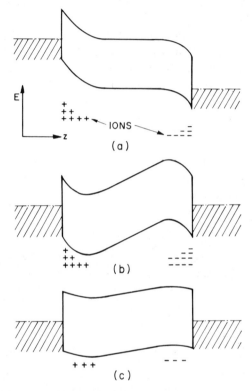

Figure 3–12. Schematic field-distribution in an insulator (a) at the point where ionic conduction has saturated, (b) after removal of the field, and (c) after final equilibrium has been reached.

2. Formation of an insulating layer; oxidation and anodization

The thin insulating layers required for the insulated-gate field-effect transistor can be formed in two different ways. In the first case, the insulator is deposited onto the semiconductor, either from a gas by chemical reaction, from a solution, from a melt, or by evaporation in a vacuum (cf. Chapter 9). If the constituents of the insulator are different from those of the semiconductor, there is little interaction between the two, except for formation of surface states. The theory of the ionic conduction discussed in the previous section should, then, adequately describe conduction in that material.

The second way of forming an insulating layer is by growth from the semiconductor itself, either by oxidizing the semiconductor or by anodizing it. The nature of these processes in the growth of SiO_2 is the subject of Chapter 4. The present discussion merely outlines their relationship to conduction through the insulator. *Anodization* is the introduction of an ion (generally oxygen) into the semiconductor from an electrolytic solution under an applied electric field, thereby forming a compound. The insulating layer grows by field-aided diffusion (ionic conduction) of oxygen ions, semiconductor ions, or both through the already-formed compound. Because of the ionic nature of anodization, large fields are required [$(5-25) \times 10^6$ v/cm]. Typically, one volt applied will cause the oxide to grow 4–20 Å.

Electric fields applied subsequently during device operation are not expected to affect the oxide by ionic conduction so long as they remain below the anodizing values. In actual practice it is found, however, that even fields lower than the anodizing field may cause breakdown of the completed insulating layer because of imperfections. In the electrolytic bath, such breakdown is prevented by a self-healing process.

Oxidation is a restricted form of anodization in the low temperature limit: The electrolyte is an oxygen-containing gas and no external field is applied. The electric field is an internal one caused by difference in chemical potentials between the phases. If the oxide layer is continuous and without pores, the field decreases as the layer grows, and eventually drops below the value required for ionic conduction. This limiting thickness value is observed at low temperatures.

As the temperature is raised the diffusion becomes rapid enough so that the gradient of the ion concentration causes continued growth of the oxide layer beyond the low temperature limiting value (thermal oxidation). Such layers may differ considerably from ones produced by anodization because of the different driving forces in the two cases.

3. Interaction of electronic and ionic conductivity

Ionic conductivity is too small to cause any observable currents, so long as one stays below the anodization field. Nevertheless, the ions migrate when a d-c field is applied for sufficiently long periods of time. This causes a build-up of space charges, as shown in Fig. 3–12, and increases the field at the electrodes. These fields may reach sufficiently high values to cause Schottky emission or tunneling, and free carriers are injected into the conduction band of the insulator. For small fields this will produce only a small current flow. The gate resistance is reduced somewhat. In practical operation, fields may be sufficiently large to cause dielectric breakdown when a sizeable number of injected carriers is present.

As the ionic charges accumulate near the insulator interfaces (Fig. 3–12a), they affect the surface conductance of the semiconductor. They act just like the electronic surface charges that were discussed in Chapter 2. They bend the bands in the semiconductor and may anchor them at a fixed energy level. In this way, ionic conductance can modify both the channel conductance and the transconductance of the field-effect transistor. The difference between electronic and ionic surface charges is that the latter respond only to very low frequencies.

Ionic conductivity also has a very different long-term effect. The SiO_2 layer may be grown by an anodic process (Chapter 4). If the gate voltage has the same sign as the anodizing voltage, ionic conduction will cause the insulator to grow if oxygen is available at the surface (e.g., by diffusion through the gate contact). The reverse process will take place at high enough fields without such a restriction. It can lead to the formation of gas pockets under the gate electrode. There may also be other electrolytic phenomena taking place, e.g., an electrochemical reaction between the gate metal and the insulating layer.

It is obvious that a change in insulator thickness will cause not only a change in electronic processes, particularly the breakdown voltage, but will also affect the capacitance of the gate, thus changing the operating conditions of the transistor.

This discussion shows that it is the combination of electronic and ionic conduction that has the most important influence on the operation of the insulator. Ionic current flow is small and takes place very gradually; but its effects are large on the electronic properties that are related to the gate performance of the transistors.

3–5 SURFACE CONDUCTION

So far, conduction through the bulk of the insulator has been discussed. From a device point of view, conduction along the surface of the insulator is just as important and may well be the dominating process.

Some of the surface conduction phenomena are similar to the bulk conduction phenomena. For example, there are dangling bonds at the surface in the covalent description which cause electronic states in the forbidden gap (Tamm states). Electrons may conduct through these states by tunneling (hopping). Ionic conduction takes place more readily because two rather than four bonds (for a tetrahedral crystal structure) need to be broken when an ion leaves its position. These effects are, however, usually negligible in the actual device, because the field along the surface is smaller than that across the bulk.

The loose bonds on the surface encourage adsorption of impurities and may strongly influence the conduction properties. These effects have been studied extensively in the case of semiconductor surfaces,[19] but similar detailed investigations have not yet been made in the case of insulator surfaces. It is obvious that the adsorbed ions will move in the electric field and produce a considerably higher conductivity than the insulator ions because they are less tightly bound. Consequently, the adsorbed ions may have sufficient conductivity to modify the operation of the device, even in the low fields that exist along the surface in a good design.

Adsorbed surface atoms may also produce direct electronic conductivity if they introduce a sufficient number of electronic states in the forbidden gap to allow impurity conduction by hopping. This is a tunneling process and it behaves similarly to other tunneling currents. However, no such effects have yet been observed on semiconductor surfaces, and they can also be expected to be small in the case of insulator surfaces.

REFERENCES

1. P. R. Emtage and W. Tantraporn, *Phys. Rev. Letters* **8**, 267 (1962).

2. S. R. Pollack, *J. Appl. Phys.* **34**, 877 (1963).

3. W: A. Harrison, *Phys. Rev.* **123**, 85 (1961).

4. S. C. Miller, Jr. and R. H. Good, Jr., *Phys. Rev.* **91**, 174 (1953); E. L. Murphy and R. H. Good, Jr., *Phys. Rev.* **102**, 1464 (1956).

5. C. Zener, *Proc. Roy. Soc.* (London) **A145**, 523 (1934).

6. R. Stratton, *J. Phys.Chem. Solids* **23**, 1177 (1962).

7. J. G. Simmons, *J. Appl. Phys.* **34**, 1793, 2581 (1963).

8. D. Meyerhofer and S. A. Ochs, *J. Appl. Phys.* **34**, 2535 (1963).

9. S. R. Pollack and C. E. Morris, *J. Appl. Phys.* **35**, 1503 (1964).

10. R. W. Smith and A. Rose, *Phys. Rev.* **97**, 1531 (1955).

11. D. V. Geppert, *J. Appl. Phys.* **33**, 2993 (1962).

12. S. Whitehead, *Dielectric Breakdown of Solids* (Oxford: Clarendon Press, 1953) Chap. 2.

13. W. Franz, *Handbuch der Physik* ed. S. Flügge (Berlin: Springer-Verlag, 1956); Vol. XVII, p. 155.

14. R. S. Alger and A. von Hippel, *Phys. Rev.* **76**, 127 (1949).

15. A. von Hippel and R. J. Maurer, *Phys. Rev.* **59**, 820 (1941).

16. W. Ruppel, *Helv. Phys. Acta* **31**, 311 (1958).

17. C. A. Mead, *Phys. Rev.* **128**, 2088 (1962).

18. H. Kelting and H. Witt, *Z. Physik* **126**, 697 (1949).

19. cf. "Semiconductor Surfaces" *Proceedings of the 2nd Conference,* ed. J. N. Zemel (New York: Pergamon Press, 1960).

4

Growth and Properties of Thin SiO$_2$ Films

Akos G. Revesz

4–1 INTRODUCTION

The gate electrode of the MOS field-effect devices is isolated from the conducting material by an insulating film. Direct electronic interactions take place between electronically active centers (traps) in this film and the conducting material, and there is a high electric field across the insulator (leading to possible ionic displacements). Consequently, the requirements on this film are much more stringent than those concerning the passivating SiO$_2$ films on various silicon devices (e.g., planar transistors). The problem is to establish a well-defined structure which fulfills the following basic requirements:

1. Proper insulation to withstand the maximum applied field;

2. Surface states characterized by a definite surface potential (i.e., a definite density of states per cm^2 and distribution per energy range) and having a proper distribution of response times;

3. Stability, i.e., prevention of any change in the nature and distribution of the surface states by migration of the active centers.

There are many possible compounds and methods of preparation of these compounds which might fulfill these conditions. However, the discussion will be restricted to SiO$_2$ films produced on Si surfaces by thermal oxidation. Evaporated films are discussed in Chapter 9.

Relating the behavior of these films to well-understood basic principles is hampered by the fact that the SiO$_2$ films are noncrystalline. The knowledge of imperfections, which play a very important role in all aspects of the insulating film, is much less for noncrystalline than for crystalline solids. These films are thin, of the order of one wavelength of the visible light, and their properties deviate considerably from bulk properties.

Since the structure of SiO$_2$ films including imperfections is predominantly determined by the method of preparation, these methods will be described after a brief outline of oxidation theories. The bulk properties of noncrystalline SiO$_2$ will be discussed from the standpoint of imperfections. Finally, the interface behavior of silicon-oxide-electrode systems will be described, with emphasis on the role of the oxide film.

4–2   THE GROWTH OF SiO$_2$ ON SILICON

1. Outline of oxidation theories

The growth of SiO$_2$ by oxidation of Si follows the reaction:

$$Si_{(s)} + O_{2(g)} \rightarrow SiO_{2(s)} - \Delta G_T^o \tag{4-1}$$

The standard Gibbs free energy (free enthalpy), ΔG_T^o, of this reaction is very large and decreases with increasing temperature. This means that the oxidation of silicon is very probable from the standpoint of thermodynamics even at very low pressures of oxygen. The calculated equilibrium pressures of oxygen, using the data of Kubaschewski and Evans[1] are, for instance, 10^{-37} and 10^{-21} atm for temperatures of 900°K and 1500°K, respectively.

Chemical reactions generally need a definite activation energy for their start. Since oxidation is basically the formation of a new phase, it is a nonequilibrium process and a so-called "driving force" (e.g., oxygen pressure higher than the equilibrium pressure) is needed for the growth. Depending on how the activation energy and the "driving force" are supplied, various methods can be distinguished, the two most important being thermal and anodic oxidation.

Because the molar volume of noncrystalline SiO$_2$ is about 2.2 times larger than that of silicon, oxidation of silicon results in a protective oxide film.[2] The important factor in determining the growth of the film is the manner in which the reacting species is supplied to the interface where the growth occurs. The concentration gradient of the migrating species, the electric field in the film (due to adsorption of ions, space-charge regions, and applied voltage), the imperfections in the film, and the interactions between these factors determine the kinetics of the process and the atomic structure of the oxide film. Some of the possible rate-determining steps, the corresponding rate equations, and the approximate thickness range in the case of thermal oxidation are shown in Table 4-1.

Table 4-1 Rate-Determining Processes in Thermal Oxidations

Rate determining process	Describing equation	Range of thickness
Chemisorption	$d_i = K_1 \log (at + t_0)$	a few monolayers
Electron tunneling	$d_i = K_2 \log (bt + t_0)$	$d_i < \sim 50$ Å
Ion transfer in electric field	$\dfrac{1}{d_i} = A - K_3 \log t$	$d_i < \sim 80$ Å
	$d_i^2 = K_4 t$ $d_i^3 = K_5 t$	$d_i < 1000$ Å
Surface reaction	$d_i = K_6 t$	$d_i < \lambda_i$
Diffusion (Wagner)	$d_i^2 = K_7 t$	$d_i > \lambda_i$

d_i = thickness of the film; K = rate constant; λ_i = Debye length in SiO_2 under the specific conditions; t = time; a and b are constants.

2. Thermal oxidation

Oxygen and/or water vapor ambients are used for the thermal oxidation of silicon. Both the gaseous atmosphere and the silicon may contain impurities which influence the growth kinetics. Preoxidation surface preparation is of utmost importance to achieve good, reproducible results.

THERMAL OXIDATION IN PURE OXYGEN. The first step of the oxidation is the adsorption of oxygen on the surface. The adsorption may be physical or chemical, depending on the binding energy which is less than 10 or in the range of 100 kcal/mole, respectively. Brennan et al.[3] measured the heat of adsorption of oxygen on evaporated silicon films while the surface coverage, θ, was increasing from zero to one. The maximum measured heat of adsorption was 230 kcal/mole. This value corresponds quite well to the heat of formation of SiO_2 at 25°C, which is approximately 210 kcal/mole. This indicates that the bonding in the surface layer is probably very similar to that in the bulk oxide. They also found that the coverage was one atom of oxygen per surface silicon atom. The heat of adsorption after the formation of one monolayer was found by Law[4] to be 5.8 and 9.4 kcal/mole for $\theta = 1$ and 2, respectively, in the temperature range of 0–50°C. These values of activation energy are characteristic of a physical adsorption. The rate of adsorption and sticking probabilities as a function of temperature and oxygen pressure found by various workers are not in complete agreement. Wolsky[5] described the room temperature oxidation of an ion-bombarded and annealed (100) silicon surface by the following equation:

$$N_t = 3.85 \times 10^{14} + 0.915 \times 10^{14} \log_{10} t \qquad (4\text{–}2)$$

for $p_{O_2} = 3$ Torr and $1 < t < 1000$ min, where N_t is the surface density of oxygen atoms adsorbed in t minutes of exposure to oxygen. No evidence of pressure dependence was found. Law[4], on the other hand, found that the rate of adsorption (for $1 < \theta < 2$) depends on the pressure of oxygen according to the equation:

$$\frac{dN}{dt} = a p_{O_2}^{1/2} \exp(-bN) \qquad (4\text{–}3)$$

for $10^{-4} < p_{O_2} < 4 \times 10^{-2}$ Torr and $t < 100$ min, where a and b are constants. Integration of Eq. (4–3) gives:

$$N_t = \frac{1}{b} \ln \left\{ a p_{O_2}^{1/2} \, bt + \exp[bN_o] \right\} \qquad (4\text{–}4)$$

The square-root dependence on the pressure indicates that oxygen is present on the surface as atoms. To explain Eq. (4–3), it was stipulated that the activation energy for the process increases linearly with the coverage, i.e.:

$$E = 5.76 \times 10^3 + 3.65 \times 10^{12} [N_t - N_o] \text{ cal/mole} \qquad (4\text{–}5)$$

The final conclusion was that a rapid chemisorption up to a monolayer of oxygen atoms is followed by a slow logarithmic process. This process is related to a rearrangement of the surface structure as was shown later by Lander and Morrison,[6] who investigated silicon surfaces by low energy electron diffraction. Schlier and Farnsworth[7] reported that the rate of adsorption was proportional to the pressure for $p_{O_2} < 10^{-6}$ Torr, and depended on the preceding treatment of the crystal. The initial sticking probabilities of oxygen on silicon at room temperature have been measured and earlier data tabulated by Hagstrum.[8] The values vary from 0.1 to 0.18, depending on the method of measurement, orientation of the crystal, and preceding treatment. The sticking probability decreases three orders of magnitude in going from one to five layers of oxygen on the surface as was shown by Law and François.[9]

After adsorption, the oxidation begins. The results obtained by various workers are summarized in Table 4-2. It is evident that both the experimental conditions and the results vary, and the correlation between them is not good. Nevertheless, it is useful as a starting point in practical applications to summarize the results in a concise form. The growth of the oxide film in oxygen at 1 atm. pressure can be described with a reasonable approximation by the equations:

$$d_i^2 \cong 2 \times 10^9 t \exp\left(-\frac{1.3}{kT}\right) \qquad 1300°K < T < 1500°K \qquad (4\text{-}6)$$

and

$$d_i^2 \cong 3 \times 10^{11} t \exp\left(-\frac{1.7}{kT}\right) \qquad 1000°K < T < 1300°K \qquad (4\text{-}7)$$

where d_i is in Ångstroms and t is in minutes. For low temperatures and/or small thickness, this approximation is less accurate because of the temperature dependence of the activation mechanism and the deviations from a parabolic growth law.

An important fact should be mentioned. Several workers showed either by radioactive methods [14, 21, 22] or by marker experiments[16] that the diffusing species during oxidation is oxygen. Jorgensen[16] proved by imposing an electric current through the oxide film by porous electrodes that the oxygen is in an ionic form and its migration is accompanied by an appreciable flow of electrons and/or holes. It is not clear whether the oxygen diffuses by a vacancy and/or interstitial mechanism.

THERMAL OXIDATION IN THE PRESENCE OF WATER VAPOR. Because the growth rates in an oxygen ambient are rather low, water vapor is often introduced to speed up the process. The adsorption of water on silicon was investigated by Law and François[9] by a flash desorption technique. The amount of desorbed water corresponds to a surface density of 2×10^{12} to 8×10^{12} molecules/cm^2 at 300°K for the pressure range of 2×10^{-7} to 6×10^{-6} Torr of water vapor. The amount of desorbed hydrogen was about ten times larger than that of water. This effect was probably caused by the decomposition of water on the surface due to the formation of Si–O bonds.

The adsorption of water results immediately in the formation of oxide. The results of investigations concerning the growth of the oxide film in the presence of water vapor are summarized in Table 4-3. These results are even less consistent than those for oxidation in pure oxygen.

Table 4–2 Thermal Oxidation of Silicon in Oxygen

Ref.	p_{O_2}, Torr	Temperature, °C	Rate equation	Thickness of SiO$_2$, Å	Time of oxidation, hours	Notes
10	200	950	$d_i^2 = Kt$	~5000		$b = 0.4\ \text{min}^{-1}$
		1160				
		950–1160	$d_i = a \log (1 + bt)$			
11	5×10^{-2}	727–1027	$d_i^2 = Kt + d_o$	100–1000	$\leqslant 2$	$d_{i\ \text{initial}}^2 > d_i^2 = Kt + d_o$
12	760	1200–1360	$d_i^2 = Kt + d_o$	~10^4	$\leqslant 25$	
13	few–760	700–1100	$d_i^2 = Kt$			
14	62	844	$d_i^2 = Kt$	15–60		a_1, a_2, a_3, a_4 are constants
			$d_i = a_1 t + a_2$	60–100		
			$d_i^2 = a_3 d_i + a_4 t$	100–200		

						oxidation under electric field
15	100–800	750–1360	$d_i^2 = Kt$			
16	760†	850	$d_i^2 = Kt$	200–670	≤ 120	
17	760	1000–1200	$d_i^2 = Kt$	≈ 10⁴		$K_{1000°} = 1.48 \times 10^4$ Å²/min $K_{1200°} = 7.64 \times 10^4$ Å²/min
18	760	1000–1300	$d_i^2 = Kt$	1000–4000		
19	760	1200	$d_i^2 = Kt$	< 3600	< 3.3	$K_{1200°} = 7.6 \times 10^4$ Å²/min
20	760	700–1200	$d_i^2 = Kt$	4000		$K_{900°} = 7.6 \times 10^3$ Å²/min $K_{1000°} = 12.3 \times 10^3$ Å²/min $K_{1200°} = 66 \times 10^3$ Å²/min

d_i = thickness of SiO$_2$ film; K = parabolic rate constant = $K_o \exp\left(-\dfrac{Q}{kT}\right)$; a and b = nonparabolic rate constants; p = pressure; t = time, d_o = integration constant.
†Probable value, not specified exactly.

However, comparing the oxidation in oxygen to that in the presence of water vapor, we make the following qualitative observations:

1. The growth rate is generally higher in the presence of water vapor than in oxygen alone;

2. The activation energy, in some cases, is less in the presence of water vapor;

3. The range of surface reaction or other nondiffusive rate controlling mechanisms extends to higher thickness values (depending on the temperature and the pressure of water vapor) in the presence of water vapor;

4. One of the consequences of the shift mentioned earlier is that the influence of the crystallographic orientation of the silicon substrate is more marked in the presence of water vapor.

In connection with high-pressure steam oxidation, the following facts should be noted: The growth rate becomes nonlinear at relatively high pressures and long oxidation times (probably due to the "solubility" of SiO_2 in steam). Above a certain pressure, etching of silicon occurs instead of oxide growth. The pre-exponential part of the rate constant, K_o', is inversely proportional to the absolute temperature.

To condense the data of Table 4-3 into a usefully concise form, it is found that the growth of the oxide film in steam at 1 atm. pressure is approximately given by:

$$d_i^2 \cong 1.5 \times 10^9 t \exp\left(-\frac{0.87}{kT}\right) \qquad 1300°K < T < 1500°K \qquad \text{(4-8)}$$

where d_i is in Ångstroms and t is in minutes. In view of the less consistent results in this case, the accuracy of this approximation is not as good as that given before for oxidation in dry oxygen.

INFLUENCE OF IMPURITIES ON THERMAL OXIDATION. The growth of an oxide film is a transport process and depends very much on the presence of imperfections in the oxide. It is convenient to treat this problem in two ways, depending upon whether the impurities are in the bulk silicon or introduced from the ambient during oxidation. This division is arbitrary because of the possible interactions between the two kinds of impurities.

A redistribution of the electrically active bulk impurities may take place during the oxidation in the silicon close to the Si-SiO₂ interface as shown by Atalla and Tannenbaum.[28] This redistribution may lead to an accumulation or a depletion region, depending on the distribution coefficient of the impurity at the interface, on its diffusion coefficients in the silicon and in the oxide, and on the rate and time of oxidation. If two types of impurities are present in the silicon and their distribution coefficients or diffusion coefficients in the silicon differ, a $p-n$ junction can be formed close to the Si-SiO_2 interface by thermal oxidation. If the concentration of impurities in silicon is high enough, they may influence the rate of oxidation. According to reference (15), this limit is about $5 \times 10^{18}/cm^3$. The influence of impurities may be related to a change in the reaction rate at the Si-SiO_2 interface or to a different diffusion coefficient of the oxidizing species through the oxide if the impurities penetrate the oxide. Indeed, Ligenza[24] reported that a concentration of 10^{21} phosphorus atoms/cm^3 at the surface of silicon increased the linear growth rate by a factor of 5.7 for steam oxidation at 650°C and 120 atm. On the other hand, Yeh[29] has shown that a concentration of 2×10^{21} phosphorus atoms/cm^3 at the surface resulted in a great increase of the parabolic growth rate compared to that for a concentration of 5×10^{18} boron atoms/cm^3 for steam oxidation at 970°C and 1 atm. The phosphorus was rejected by the oxide causing an accumulation, while boron was probably dissolved in the oxide, leading to a depletion in the silicon near the surface.

Turning now to the problem of impurities that originate in the oxidizing ambient, the first question is related to the oxygen itself. Since oxygen is the migrating species during oxidation and the growth occurs at the Si-SiO_2 interface, the possibility of dissolution of oxygen in silicon has to be considered. The solubility of oxygen in silicon at 1000°C is about 2×10^{17} atoms/cm^3.[30] During the cooling period after the oxidation or during further processing at a temperature 300 to 500°C, the oxygen in silicon may lead to the formation of donor levels at 0.09 and 0.13 ev from the conduction band. It may also react with other impurities, and even precipitation of SiO_2 may occur. These complex reactions have been treated by several workers.[31] From the standpoint of the defect structure of the oxide, water vapor in the oxidizing ambient is also an impurity. Nitrogen is a common component of the oxidizing ambients and the possibility of the formation of silicon nitride[12] cannot be excluded. The free energy of the formation of one mole SiO_2 is greater by a factor of 2 than that of the formation of one mole Si_3N_4 at 1300°K. The factor is about 6.2 if the calculation is based on one gram of silicon instead of one mole of the product.[1] However, these two reactions cannot be directly compared from the standpoint of kinetics because of insufficient information. If oxygen is replaced in the SiO_2, nitrogen could also decrease or increase the oxidation rate, depending upon whether oxygen diffuses in the oxide through interstitial or through vacancy sites.[2d] Because of the uncertainties involved in both the kinetics of nitridization and the mechanism of oxygen diffusion, it is advisable to avoid the use of nitrogen.

Technologically, the presence of doping elements (e.g., boron, gallium, phosphorus, arsenic) or compounds of these elements in the oxidizing ambient is very important in processes using complete or partial masking by the oxide film. The doping agents also affect the oxidation process itself. As a matter of fact, the oxide growth and the diffusion of the doping

Table 4–3 Thermal Oxidation of Silicon in the Presence of Water Vapor

Ref.	p_{H_2O}, Torr or atm	Other components of ambient	Temperature °C	Rate equation	Thickness of SiO_2, Å	Time of oxidation, hours	Notes
23	15 Torr	air, ~ 1 atm	28	$d_i = a_1 + a_2 \log(t+t_0)$	12–30	< 280	$a_1 = -9.74$Å $a_2 = 6.86$Å $t_0 = 1500$ sec
14	1–16 Torr	?	< 1000	$d_i^2 = Kt$			
24	25–400 atm		500–850	$d_i = K't$		0.5–8.0	$K' = 25.7$ Å/min for $T = 650°C$ and $p = 50$ atm
25	40–150 atm		500–800	$d_i = K't$	1500–10,000		
17	0.8 atm†	O_2, ~ 0.2 atm	1000–1200	$d_i^2 = Kt$‡	~ 3200–17,400		$K_{1000°} = 38.5 \times 10^4$ Å²/min $K_{1200°} = 117.5 \times 10^4$ Å²/min
	1 atm						$\dot{K}_{1000°} = 54.5 \times 10^4$ Å²/min $K_{1200°} = 159 \times 10^4$ Å²/min
26	~ 20 Torr§	air§, ~ 1 atm	300–560	no oxidation		≤ 4	
			560–950	$d_i = Kt + d$	~ 10–1200		$K_{950°} \cong 9.6 \times 10^3$ Å²/min
			950–1000	$d_i^2 = Kt + d_o$	~ 300–200		$K_{1000°} \cong 2.0 \times 10^4$ Å²/min

27	1 atm		1000	$d_i = K' t^{1.2} d_o'$	400–2000	< 0.3	
				$d_i^2 = Kt + d_o$	~3000–10,000	~0.33–3.3	
19	O₂, ~1 atm	~28 Torr†	1200	$d_i^2 = Kt$	< 4200	<~3.3	$K_{1200°} = 12.2 \times 10^4$ Å²/min
	O₂ ~0.13 atm	~0.57 atm‡			2500–5000	<~0.4	$K_{1200°} = 87.0 \times 10^4$ Å²/min
	A, ~1 atm	~28 Torr†			< 4000	<~5.4	$K_{1200°} = 5.8 \times 10^4$ Å²/min
	A, ~0.13 atm‡	~0.57 atm‡			< 5000	<0.8	$K_{1200°} = 121 \times 10^4$ Å²/min
	1 atm				< 5000	<0.8	$K_{1200°} = 130 \times 10^4$ Å²/min
18	1 atm		1000–1300	$d_i^2 = Kt$	3000–20,000	0.2–4.0	
20	1 atm		700–1200	$d_i^2 = Kt$	400		$K_{800°} = 27 \times 10^3$ Å²/min $K_{1000°} = 327 \times 10^3$ Å²/min $K_{1200°} = 1600 \times 10^3$ Å²/min

Legend: d_i, K, p, t, and d_o as for Table 4–2; K' = linear rate constant.

†Assuming that the carrier gas bubbling through the water is saturated, i.e., the partial pressure of water vapor in the gas mixture is equal to the equilibrium vapor pressure at the temperature of the water bath.

‡Below 1000°C the equation becomes parabolic-linear.

§Assumed values.

elements through the oxide, and eventually into the silicon, are very intimately related processes. Further details are given by Thurston and Ki Dong Kang[15] who also give many references related to this problem.

The oxidation is generally performed in a resistance-heater furnace using a fused silica tube. A negative temperature gradient exists between the tube and the specimen, and impurities originating in the tube may be deposited on the specimen. At high temperatures, water vapor may also diffuse through the tube or the "water" of the tube may diffuse out and change the oxidizing ambient.

4–3 THE STRUCTURE OF SiO₂

Silicon dioxide has three basic crystallographic forms which are stable in the following temperature ranges:

$$\xrightarrow[\text{Quartz}]{} 870°C \xleftrightarrow[\text{Tridymite}]{} 1470°C \xleftrightarrow[\text{Cristobalite}]{} 1710°C(\text{m.p.})$$

The transitions between the three basic forms are very sluggish because $Si-O-Si$ bonds must be broken (reconstructive transformations). Therefore, these forms can exist quite easily in thermodynamically metastable conditions. Each form has a low- and high-temperature modification, (α and β, respectively). The transition ranges are:

$\alpha-\beta$ quartz: 573°C
$\alpha-\beta$ tridymite: 120–160°C
$\alpha-\beta$ cristobalite: 200–275°C

These transitions are relatively easy because there is no change in the first coordination (displacive transformations). The fact that the $\alpha-\beta$ transitions are generally characterized by a temperature range instead of a well-defined temperature is primarily due to impurities. There is even doubt concerning the existence of tridymite as a pure SiO_2 modification without incorporated impurities.[32] Silicon dioxide may also exist in a noncrystalline (amorphous) form as fused silica, which is obtained by slow cooling of molten quartz.

The SiO_2 films formed by the methods described earlier are generally noncrystalline. Exceptions are the films mentioned in reference (10) for oxidation times exceeding 100 minutes, or the films heated at 1200°C for about 16 hours resulting in α-cristobalite and quartz. The oxidation described in reference (12) also resulted in cristobalite, probably due to the high temperature and long oxidation time.

By comparing transmission and reflection electron-diffracting diagrams of specimens prepared and oxidized by various methods, Revesz[33] concluded that the oxide film forms in the noncrystalline state but surface imperfections may act as crystallization centers during a later stage of the growth. The product of the devitrification was generally α-cristobalite, and sometimes β-cristobalite or quartz (but never tridymite). It was revealed only by reflection, never by transmission diffraction. Lander and Morrison[6] also did not find crystalline SiO$_2$ by low-energy electron diffraction in the first stages of oxidation. It is of interest to note that devitrification of fused silica results in β-cristobalite, which nucleates at surface impurities; its growth rate is enhanced by at least an order of magnitude by the presence of water vapor and/or oxygen in the gas phase.[34] It is evident that localized crystallization (devitrification) of an otherwise homogeneous noncrystalline SiO$_2$ film on Si should be avoided because of the possibility of the formation of various discontinuities.

The defect structure of the SiO$_2$ films is of utmost importance from the standpoint of almost all properties of MOS devices. The usual concepts of imperfections as applied to crystals are not completely applicable to these films because of their noncrystalline nature. Therefore, the structure of noncrystalline solids will be discussed before a description of imperfections and their role in these solids is given.

1. Structure of noncrystalline solids

Whether solidification of a liquid or condensation of a vapor phase will result in a crystalline or noncrystalline form is a matter of competition between nucleation and crystallization. By a proper choice of the forming conditions, such as the quenching temperature for condensation from vapor[35] or the overvoltage for electrolytic deposition,[2e] almost any material can be obtained in the noncrystalline state. Characteristic of this state is the lack of long-range order in the structure. From this point of view, a solid in this state is similar to a liquid. If the noncrystalline state has been reached by the supercooling of a liquid so that it solidifies without crystallization, the solid is in the vitreous state (glass). Such a solid differs from a liquid in the sense that its relaxation time (the time required for the structure to adjust itself to new conditions) is much longer. Noncrystalline solids may also be considered as aggregates of very small crystallites whose dimensions are of the order of the lattice constant. Because studies on noncrystalline solids were, until very recently, almost completely restricted to glasses, the concepts and results of studies on glass will be applied to the noncrystalline SiO$_2$ films.

2. Structure of vitreous SiO$_2$

As a first approximation, the generally accepted structure of fused silica is a continuous three-dimensional network of silicon and oxygen atoms (ions). This is Zachariasen's random network model of glasses.[36]

In the ideal case, each silicon atom is surrounded tetrahedrally by four oxygen atoms, and these tetrahedrons are joined together at their corners by oxygen bridges. The Si−O distances (short-range order) are very closely the same as in the crystalline forms of SiO$_2$ ($\sim$ 1.6Å), but the long-range order is almost completely missing. The network is very loose (only 43% of the total space is occupied[37]), and it is looser than any crystalline form of SiO$_2$ as shown by the density values: 2.65, 2.26, 2.30, and $\sim$ 2.20 for quartz, tridymite, cristobalite, and fused silica, respectively. The over-all structure resembles the cristobalite to some extent as shown by density and X-ray investigations; and, as already mentioned, crystallization generally results in cristobalite. The energy content of vitreous silica is greater than that of cristobalite, but the difference is very small (about 1%). This fact is characteristic of the vitreous state in general, as pointed out by Zachariasen. It was recently shown by electron microscopy[36] and by the temperature behavior of various optical properties,[38] that there are domains in the network which resemble the structures of the different crystalline forms of SiO$_2$. These domains are smaller than about 10^{-5} cm and are not revealed by X-ray diffraction. Others [see reference (36)] conclude from X-ray diffraction analysis that there is a tendency to form rings with six silicon atoms, and the necessary broken oxygen bridges are due to fast cooling from high temperature and/or to the incorporation of impurities, especially OH$^-$ ions. For the purpose at hand, the simple random network theory will be sufficient.

3. Defect structure of vitreous SiO$_2$

Although vitreous SiO$_2$ could be considered as a crystal full of defects, the ideal network, as defined previously, will be considered here as a defect-free material; any deviation from the ideal condition will be called *defect*. Furthermore, SiO$_2$ will be treated as an ionic compound although the Si−O bond is considered to have about 50% ionic and 50% covalent character. Both assumptions are based on various optical and mechanical properties of SiO$_2$ compared to those of ionic crystals.[39] The concept of defect as applied to the Si−O network is very similar to that used in the field of ionic crystals. Due to the random and rather loose nature of the network, the variety and possible combinations of imperfections in vitreous SiO$_2$ exceed those in ionic crystals. Following Stevels and Kats,[40] the most important imperfections in vitreous SiO$_2$ are as follows:

1. A silicon vacancy is not very probable because of the very high energy of the Si−O bonds; but a similar defect may exist under certain conditions. This defect is a reduced form of silicon.

2. Silicon may be replaced by *network-forming* (e.g., B^{3+}, P^{5+}, As^{5+}) or *intermediate* (e.g., Al^{3+}, Ti^{4+}, Be^{2+}) ions. The oxides of the network-formers can form glasses alone, whereas the intermediate ions can replace the network-formers in an existing network and/or become interstitials.

3. Bridging oxygen vacancy.

4. Individual nonbridging oxygen vacancy.

5. Nonbridging oxygen interstitial which is still associated with the network.

6. Individual interstitial oxygen (not part of the network).

7. Replacement of oxygen by another anion.

8. Interstitial cations, network-modifiers, or intermediates (e.g., Na, K, Ba, Al).

9. Silicon itself may occupy an interstitial position if the stronger network-former phosphorus replaces it. This structure is analogous to that of SiP_2O_7 where the Si^{4+} ion is surrounded by six oxygen ions, and the P^{5+} ion by four oxygen ions, i.e., the Si^{4+} is in the position of a network-modifier.

10. Interstitial anion other than oxygen.

Most of these defects are shown in Fig. 4–1. Reactions between the various impurities can, of course, occur; hence, a great variety of combinations is possible.

4–4 PROPERTIES OF SiO_2 FILMS

Properties of solids and phenomena related to them can be classified on the basis of various criteria, e.g., sensitivity to imperfections, the level of occurrence (macroscopic, atomic, or electronic), the nature of interactions (weak or strong), or the extent of interactions (close neighbors or many atoms). The same criteria can be applied to noncrystalline solids, but the distinction between various classes may become less sharp. The loose structure of noncrystalline SiO_2 and the great variety of imperfections make the distinction between macroscopic and atomic phenomena, or between imperfection-sensitive and insensitive properties often very difficult. Additional difficulty is caused by the ability of a noncrystalline solid to adjust its structure during the measurement. The time of the measurement should be smaller than the relaxation time characteristic of the phenomenon under investigation. Because the SiO_2 films are thin, interface effects may have great influence on the measurements and on the inferred properties. This is especially true for electrical measurements where electrode effects may completely mask the "bulk" properties because of the large Debye-length of SiO_2.

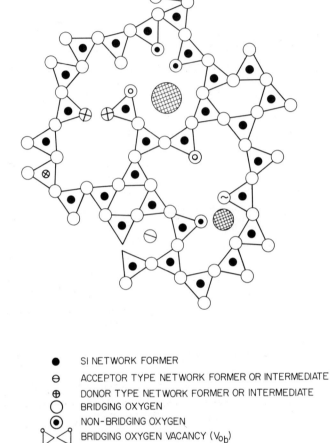

●	SI NETWORK FORMER
⊖	ACCEPTOR TYPE NETWORK FORMER OR INTERMEDIATE
⊕	DONOR TYPE NETWORK FORMER OR INTERMEDIATE
○	BRIDGING OXYGEN
⊙	NON-BRIDGING OXYGEN
▷◁	BRIDGING OXYGEN VACANCY (V_{ob})
◎	INDIVIDUAL NON-BRIDGING OXYGEN VACANCY (V_{oni})
~	NON-BRIDGING OXYGEN INTERSTITIAL (ASSOCIATED WITH THE NETWORK) ($O_{i,a}$)
⊖	INDIVIDUAL INTERSTITIAL OXYGEN (NOT ASSOCIATED WITH THE NETWORK) (O_i)
⊗	UNIVALENT ANION (EQ. OH⁻) IN THE POSITION OF NON-BRIDGING OXYGEN
◉	INTERSTITIAL CATION (NETWORK MODIFIER OR INTERMEDIATE), e.g., Na^+
◉	INTERSTITIAL CATION (NETWORK MODIFIER OR INTERMEDIATE), e.g., Ba^{++}

Figure 4–1. Schematic two-dimensional representation of a noncrystalline SiO₂ network containing various defects.

In this section, the morphology and gross structure of SiO$_2$ films and related properties (density and index of refraction) will be discussed first. A résumé of transport properties (diffusion and electrical conductance) and typical relaxation phenomena will be given, emphasizing the role of the coherence of the Si−O network. After a short description of close neighbor interactions and point defect effects (e.g., optical absorption due to imperfections, magnetic resonance), the interface phenomena will be treated. This division is arbitrary to a great extent, and the various groups unavoidably overlap.

1. Gross structure of SiO$_2$ and some related properties

Besides the general structural aspects of SiO$_2$, there are properties which are related to the morphology and/or the over-all structure of the SiO$_2$ films but not to the exact nature of deviations from the "ideal" Si–O network and their origin. Ing et al.[41] inferred from gas permeability measurements on 2–4 μ thick SiO$_2$ films, produced by thermal oxidation in steam, that the oxide film contained microchannels because even the most compact films had permeation constants one or two orders of magnitude higher than those of fused SiO$_2$. It was concluded from electron microscope investigations that the size of these channels is less than 50 Å. If crystallization occurred, resulting in crystallites having dimensions of 4–40 μ, then the permeation rates increased further by several orders of magnitude. The authors stressed the importance of the preoxidation surface preparation, rather than the method of oxidation, in order to minimize the crystallization. The existence of flaws in thermally grown SiO$_2$, and the relatively pore-free nature of the oxide film grown in nonaqueous electrolyte was indicated by Haas[42], who improved the insulation resistance of thermally grown SiO$_2$ films (as measured in a Si−SiO$_2$-electrolyte system) by a factor of 100 by applying anodic bias in 0.04 N KNO$_3$−NMA† electrolyte. Since the bias voltage was so low that no further growth occurred, the improvement was explained by the plugging of the flaws in the SiO$_2$ film during the anodic process. Claussen and Flower[19] reported holes even in films grown by anodic oxidation in nonaqueous electrolytes but attributed them to insufficient cleanliness.

Other properties related to the gross structure (morphology) of the SiO$_2$ films include density, index of refraction, and dielectric strength. Both the density and refractive index can be used to define an index of compactness to characterize the reproducibility of the cleaning and oxidizing processes by the standard deviation of the distribution of the measured values; they can also be used to gain some information on the

---

†N-methyl-acetamide.

information on the homogeneity of the film. The *index of compactness*, δ, is defined as follows:

$$\delta_d = \frac{d}{d_o} \tag{4-9}$$

or

$$\delta_n = \frac{(n^2 - 1)/(n^2 + 2)}{(n_o^2 - 1)/(n_o^2 + 2)} \tag{4-10}$$

where d_o and n_o are the density and refractive index, respectively, of the reference material; d and n are the density and index of refraction, respectively, of the material examined. Since some of the published values for d and n are higher than those of fused SiO$_2$ ($d = 2.20$, $n = 1.460$ for λ = 5461 Å), α-cristobalite can be chosen as a reference material ($d_o = 2.30$, $n_o = 1.486$) because of its great structural and thermodynamical similarity to fused SiO$_2$.[27] From the reported values of density and index of refraction[17,19,27,43,44] the following conclusions can be drawn. In the case of thermal oxidation, the highest values were reported[43] for oxide films grown in steam at 50 to 100 atm pressure and 650°C. These values are $d = 2.32$ and $n = 1.475$ ($\delta_d = 1.009$ and $\delta_n = 0.980$). The lowest density,[17] $d = 2.05$, and refractive index,[27] $n = 1.445$, were found for films grown in atmospheric steam at 1200°C and 900–1000°C, respectively. The corresponding values of the index of compactness are $\delta_d = 0.892$ and $\delta_n = 0.927$. For films grown in pure oxygen, density values vary from 2.23[43] to 2.27[17] and the refractive indices from 1.450[43] to 1.458,[20] corresponding to $0.970 \leqslant \delta_d \leqslant 0.986$ and $0.935 \leqslant \delta_n \leqslant 0.950$. For oxide films produced in a mixed ambient of water vapor and some other gas ($p_{\text{H}_2\text{O}} < 1$ atm), both the d- and n-values are between those for atmospheric steam and pure oxygen.

In those cases where both the density and the index of refraction have been determined, a comparison of the δ_d and δ_n values indicated relative differences of 3.50%, 2.96%, and 1.03% for thermal oxidation in oxygen, in high pressure steam, and for anodic oxidation in an aqueous electrolyte, respectively, δ_d being always higher than δ_n. The first two values, combined with the observation that the corresponding density and refractive index data were much closer to those of α-cristobalite than to the respective values characteristic for the anodic oxide, indicate some changes in the polarizability of the oxides. These changes are probably due to slight differences in the structure of the Si−O networks. On the other hand, it was shown[27] that, although the OH ion content of SiO$_2$ films grown in atmospheric steam at 900°C and 1000°C is quite high (about 2×10^{-2} moles per mole of SiO$_2$), it alone cannot be responsible for the measured low refractive index (1.445) if the role of OH ions in this SiO$_2$ film is the same as in fused silica.[45] The influence of water vapor on the formation of macromolecular voids and defects during the oxide growth was indicated by the large scatter in the density and breakdown voltage, especially when cleanliness conditions were not sufficiently controlled and condensation of water on the specimens was not prevented.[17]

Breakdown properties show the same trend as density and index of refraction. According to Deal,[17] the breakdown fields of thermally grown oxides varied from 4.9×10^6 to 5.5×10^6 v/cm as the density increased from 2.05 to 2.23. Dubrovskii et al.[46] measured breakdown fields from 5.0 to 16.6×10^6 v/cm for films grown by anodic oxidation in water. Both the polarity of the field and the conductivity type of the silicon influenced the measured values. The dielectric strength of SiO$_2$ films produced by anodic oxidation varied from 2×10^7 to 5.2×10^6 v/cm as the film thickness changed from 600 to 2300 Å.[44] Other investigations showed that some properties are functions of the distance from the Si$-$SiO$_2$ interface. Edagawa et al.[18] reported that, in SiO$_2$ films grown thermally in steam, the number of Si$-$O bonds increases within a range of 2000 Å from the Si$-$SiO$_2$ interface. According to Ishikawa et al.[47] the SiO$_2$ film grown anodically in an aqueous electrolyte has an $n-i-p$ structure inferred from the high-temperature-rectification behavior of the Si$-$SiO$_2-$MnO$_2$ system. However, other workers[19,22] did not find any variation of the structure across the oxide film, and it is clear that more work is needed to understand the defect structure of these films.

2. Transport and relaxation phenomena

Transport phenomena, especially diffusion and electrical conduction, are very important from the standpoint of growth, dielectric properties, transient behavior, and stability of the SiO$_2$ films. They also provide information on the defect structure of the oxide. The growth process is responsible to a large extent for the nature and distribution of imperfections. Since both transport and relaxation phenomena generally involve movement of atoms, there is a close relationship between them.

The diffusing species can be classified as a molecule, an ion which is not part of the Si$-$O network (e.g., Na$^+$), or an ion or atom which is in an exchange process with the network (e.g., O$_i$, V$_O$). In some cases, this distinction is not clear. The loose nature of the network can be increased by application of tensile force or by the method of preparation, leading to increased diffusion. Thus, there is a gradual transition to the diffusion due to gross imperfections. It is also possible that two or more mechanisms are involved in the same experiment (see the following). Diffusion in glasses has recently been reviewed by Stevels[36] and Doremus.[48]

The rate of diffusion in fused silica is generally much higher than in crystalline solids. The introduction of network modifiers causes a decrease of the diffusion rates of gases through SiO$_2$ by filling up the interstices. In simple sodium silicate glasses, the diffusivity of the sodium ion increases with the concentration of these ions, i.e., with decreasing coherence of the Si$-$O network (increasing number of broken Si$-$O$-$Si bridges). This is the opposite of the behavior of gases. For more complex glasses, both types of diffusivity decrease with increasing concentrations of the nonsilicon components. A crude scale of decreasing diffusivity is: fused silica, borosilicates, alkali-lime silicates, and alumina-lime silicate. These effects are utilized to improve the stability of silicon devices by depositing alumina-silica or boro-alumina-silica films either on thermally oxidized or unoxidized surfaces.[49] In the following, the discussion will be confined mainly to oxygen, water, and hydrogen because of their importance in the growth and behavior of grown SiO$_2$ films. The data, however, were obtained on fused SiO$_2$.

Norton[50] calculated the diffusion coefficient of oxygen in silica from gas permeation measurements. In the temperature range 900°C to 1100°C, he found that the activation energy is about 1.2 ev, and $D_{950°} = 4.2 \times 10^{-9}$ cm^2/sec. The rate of permeation was found to be linearly proportional to the oxygen pressure, and it was concluded that the mechanism is a molecular flow. Haul and Dümbgen[51] used an isotope-exchange process to study the self-diffusion of oxygen, and they deduced that for 900°C to 1200°C, $D = 4.3 \times 10^{-6} \exp(-2.4/kT)$ cm^2/sec. They also found that the diffusion coefficient increases linearly with the pressure. It was concluded after a comparison of the self-diffusion and Norton's molecular diffusion coefficients, that the concentration of oxygen, as molecules dispersed in the interstices of the Si$-$O network, is about 10^{-6} moles per mole SiO$_2$ at 1000°C. This value corresponds well with Norton's solubility (2.3×10^{-6} moles O$_2$ per mole SiO$_2$). The activation energy of self-diffusion is higher than that of molecular flow because the former includes the energy of the exchange process between the molecular and network oxygen. The latter is only characteristic for the molecular flow. According to Sucov,[52] the mechanism of the self-diffusion of oxygen is the breaking of a single Si$-$O bond and the subsequent interstitial motion of an oxygen ion. The diffusion coefficient for the temperature range 925°C to 1225°C is given as:

$$D = 1.51 \times 10^{-2} \exp\left(-\frac{3.1}{kT}\right) \frac{\text{cm}^2}{\text{sec}} \tag{4-11}$$

Because the pre-exponential factor is very sensitive to composition while the activation energy is not, it was concluded that the concentration of single Si$-$O bonds (broken Si$-$O$-$Si bridges) may show great differences; but the mechanism is essentially the same.

It is evident from the various growth processes that water vapor plays an important role. Studies on fused SiO$_2$ show that the diffusion of both hydrogen and water are related to the introduction and removal of hydroxyl. Recently, Lee[53] has reviewed the field. The first important point he makes is the distinction between *permanent* and *metastable* hydroxyl. The former develops by the attachment of hydrogen ions to nonbridging oxygen ions during the preparation process; the latter is incorporated by subsequent reaction with hydrogen or water vapor. This incorporation process leads to configurations of varying stability, depending upon the means of introduction and/or the localized network structure due to the presence of imperfections. The permanent hydroxyl cannot be removed by vacuum degassing at 1000°C. Metastable hydroxyl can be added above 500°C and fully or partially removed. Besides the two types of hydroxyls, both hydrogen and water can be accommodated as molecules in the interstices of the Si−O network. The solubility, S, and diffusivity, D, of molecular hydrogen in silica are given as:

$$S = 9.4 \times 10^{18} \exp\left(\frac{0.06}{kT}\right) \frac{\text{molecules}}{\text{cm}^3} \tag{4–12}$$

$$D \doteq 5.65 \times 10^{-4} \exp\left(-\frac{0.45}{kT}\right) \frac{\text{cm}^2}{\text{sec}} \tag{4–13}$$

The solubility and diffusivity behavior of hydroxyl ions produced by the reaction between silica and hydrogen is complicated by the conversion of metastable hydroxyl to hydrogen gas and by the fact that below 980°C the metastable hydroxyl can only partially be removed by degassing. The quantities of hydroxyl introduced by water vapor are much higher than those due to hydrogen. The diffusion of "water" is not fully understood. Both hydroxyl and water molecules are possible diffusing species. It is important to note that the reactions between SiO$_2$ and H$_2$ or H$_2$O are not the same despite the hydroxyl as a common reaction product. In the presence of impurities, such as aluminum, the reaction product is different.

The electrical conductivity of solids, either ionic or electronic, is related to their defect structure. If this relationship is well-defined, the conductivity can be connected to other imperfection-sensitive properties by simple equations. If the ionic conductivity is due to one species only, it is related to the diffusivity by the modified Einstein relation:

$$\frac{\mu}{D} = \frac{1}{f} \times \frac{zq}{kT} \tag{4–14}$$

where μ is the mobility, zq is the effective charge, D is diffusion coefficient of the moving species, and f is a correlation factor.[2c]

The mobility is related to the conductivity by the equation:

$$\sigma = czq\mu \qquad\qquad (4\text{-}15)$$

where c is the carrier concentration. These relationships are fulfilled for sodium, silver, etc., ions in glasses. For vitreous silica, the situation is more complicated because the nature of the conducting species is not clear. According to Cohen,[54] electrons are the current carriers. Wenden[55] attributed the conductance in quartz to the diffusion of oxygen ions, and Owen and Douglas[56] stipulated that the conductance is due to minute traces of sodium ions. The latter hypothesis was corroborated by Sucov[52] who found that the activation energy of oxygen self-diffusion (3.1 ev) was much larger than that of sodium diffusion.(1.3 ev) and Wenden's value (1.6 ev). Since oxygen ion transport during the thermal growth of SiO_2 has been established,[16] conductivity in this high-purity SiO_2 may be partially due to oxygen ions. The ionic transport number was found to be only 0.40, so electronic current cannot be excluded. It is of interest to note that thermal growth of SiO_2 is generally characterized by an activation energy 1.0 to 2.0 ev,[15] which is appreciably lower than Sucov's value for oxygen self-diffusion. Thus the relationships between diffusion, growth, and electrical conductance are far from being understood.

Because the ionic conductivity increases exponentially with the electric field if the relationship $aq\mathscr{E}/kT \ll 1$ is not satisfied[57] (a = jump distance, q = charge of ions, $\mathscr{E}$ = field), the influence of the field on the conductivity must be considered.

The behavior of silica during d-c measurements generally does not correspond to that of an ideal dielectric. Various anomalies, such as continued discharge currents after the capacitor has been short-circuited, have been observed. This behavior is similar to that of an electrochemical cell. Sutton[58] considered the silica as an electrolyte and analyzed its behavior on the basis of electrode polarization for one mobile carrier. Charge dissociation and recombination, ionic diffusion and conduction, and the concentration of mobile and immobile charges were considered. It was concluded that the mobile ion is always positive and that current, space charge, and dielectric absorption could be explained by the flow of alkali ions alone. Lindmayer[59] considered the anomalous charging and discharging behavior of insulators on the basis of trapping of electronic current carriers. According to this theory, the trapping levels are distributed uniformly in the bandgap. The trap density depends on the method of preparation of the SiO_2 film.

The d-c and a-c behavior of $Si - SiO_2 - Me$ system, where the metal, Me, may be Al, Ti, Au, or Pt, has been recently investigated by Yamin and Worthing.[60] The oxide was thermally grown and its thickness was 6000 Å. Charge storage and rectification effects were observed in the temperature range of 150°C to 400°C. When the silicon was negative relative to the metal, the system showed forward conductance. The changeover point between forward and reverse conductance was at zero volts for aluminum or titanium, whereas it was at -1.5 v (voltage of silicon relative to metal) for gold or platinum contacts. The effects were explained tentatively by electrochemical reactions at the interfaces. Comparing these results with the growth experiment under electric field indicates that the moving species could only be oxygen vacancies and/or gold ions from the gold electrode. The thermal growth of SiO$_2$ in an oxygen ambient is generally pressure-dependent, while the oxygen vacancy mechanism would result in pressure-independent rate; so there is a discrepancy which is difficult to resolve at present. The rectification effects observed in the $Si-SiO_2-MnO_2-Pt$ system at temperatures 700°C to 1100°C are very similar to the phenomena described earlier. However, they were explained on the basis of electronic conduction and the $p-i-n$ structure of the oxide.[47] At present, it is difficult to assess the merits of these theories. The forward characteristics of a $Si-SiO_2-Al$ rectifying system, where the SiO$_2$ is thermally grown and its thickness is 180 Å, has been described by Forlani and Minnaja[61] by diffusion of electrons through the oxide after tunneling through the interfacial potential barrier.

The electrical properties of glass in an alternating field depend not only on the mobile ions (or electrons) but also on other relatively immobile ions, or on dipoles, which are part of the network.[62] The loss spectrum results from migration, deformation, and vibration losses. Migration losses are related to ionic movements, both large-distance (d-c conductance) and small-distance (ionic relaxation). Deformation losses are due to small displacements of atoms or ions and are connected with acoustic losses since both are caused by bending of $Si-O-Si$ bonds.[39] The vibration loss is a resonance phenomenon arising from the vibration of the ions and atoms about their equilibrium positions. Depending on temperature and frequency, one of these mechanisms is generally predominant. At room temperature, the major contributor is ionic relaxation at $\sim 10^2$ cps and vibration at $\sim 10^{12}$ cps, while the total loss is minimum at $\sim 10^7$ cps.

Concerning the influence of impurities on the d-c and a-c behavior of fused silica, it is of interest that OH ions alone do not influence the d-c conductivity, but they increase the dielectric constant and decrease the loss angle in the temperature range of 300°C to 700°C and for frequencies lower than 5 kc/s. If the concentration of the OH ions is large, the dielectric behavior reveals a quartz-like transition at about 575°C. In the presence of aluminum, the distribution of OH ions in fused SiO$_2$ changes under the action of an electric field of 1.5×10^3 v/cm at 1050°C; this results in an increasing accumulation toward the anode[63] and indicates a protonic diffusion. The complex behavior of OH ions in fused SiO_2 is not fully understood.

3. Electronic and magnetic effects

Investigations with X ray do not give as detailed information on the structure of noncrystalline solids as they do on that of crystalline solids because of the lack of long-range order in the former. Therefore, other methods are important from the standpoint of providing more information on the structure of these solids. The methods of main interest are optical spectroscopy in the infrared and ultraviolet, and nuclear magnetic and electron paramagnetic resonance. All these methods can be used to obtain information both on the "pure" and "defect" structure of solids.

The predominant feature of the infrared spectrum of fused silica is the strong absorption at 1100 cm⁻¹ (~ 9.1 μ) associated with Si – O – Si bond stretching. The position of this absorption peak is about the same in the crystalline modifications of SiO_2, indicating the same short-range order in various silica. The absorption band at 800 cm⁻¹ (12.5 μ) is much weaker in vitreous than in crystalline silicas, and it is structure-sensitive. For details see, for example, Simon's review paper.[64] The fundamental absorption edge of quartz determined by UV spectroscopy is at 8.5 ev (1450 Å), and in fused SiO_2 the transmission region extends to ~ 8.1 ev (1380 Å).[65] Bray and Silver[66] investigated boron oxide and borosilicate glasses by utilizing the nuclear electric quadrupole perturbations of nuclear-magnetic resonance arising from the ¹¹B isotope. One of their results, which may be important from the standpoint of SiO_2 as used in MOS devices, is that the B – O and Si – O networks in borosilicate glasses are largely independent, i.e., the boron retains its threefold coordination characteristic of boron oxide glass.

Infrared spectroscopy has contributed to the understanding of "water" in fused silica.[53,64] An important conclusion was that hydroxyls are present as unassociated OH groups, rather than water molecules, giving rise to a strong absorption band at 3660 cm⁻¹ (2.73 μ) and to its weaker overtone at 7300 cm⁻¹ (1.37 μ). These bands were also observed in SiO_2 films grown thermally in steam atmosphere.[27,33] Ultraviolet spectra furnished information on defects produced in fused silica by various radiations and/or by introducing impurities. Neutron irradiation produces absorption bands at 6200–4500, 2070–2180, 1730, and 1630 Å, which are designated as A, C, D, and E bands, respectively.[67] It is believed that the A band is related to aluminum impurities, the C band is due to electrons trapped at oxygen ion vacancies, and the E band is caused by trapping of holes at interstitial oxygen ions. The interaction of hydrogen with fused silica results in the formation of trivalent silicon ions which form color centers having an absorption peak at 2425 Å.[68]

The relation between the concentration of OH⁻ ions in fused SiO₂ and color centers introduced by γ-ray irradiation has been studied by UV, IR, and ESR techniques as a function of the original and introduced OH⁻ ion content.[69] It was established that the generation of the so-called E′ centers (intrinsic paramagnetic states) associated with an absorption band at 2120 Å is inversely related to the concentration of the OH⁻ and other impurity ions which occupy a site in the SiO₂ somewhat similar to that of the OH⁻ ion.

4. Interface phenomena

Flietner[70] reviewed the properties of "real" (as compared to "clean") semiconductor surfaces. Although his paper dealt mostly with germanium, some points are important from the standpoint of the Si − SiO₂ interface. The density of the slow states decreases with increasing thickness of the oxide film, and for an oxide of ∼ 0.4 μ the relaxation time of the surface is practically infinite (stabilization). It was assumed that the electronic transition process, due to thermionic emission of electrons, becomes independent of the thickness of the potential barrier. The fast states can be influenced by post-oxidation chemical treatment of the oxide film. Humidity is important in this respect because it accelerates the oxidation of an unstable surface and increases the density of fast states. From the standpoint of the density of fast states, the perfection of the oxide and the presence of water are important. The relaxation spectra of the fast states can also be influenced by oxidation, impurities, etc.

The first detailed study on the influence of oxide films on the surface properties of silicon was performed by Atalla et al.[71] They found that thermal oxidation of floating zone silicon resulted in acceptor and donor fast states; the density of the former was 10¹¹ and that of the latter, 10¹⁰ cm⁻². Oxidation of pulled silicon was less reproducible from the standpoint of surface states and, generally, donor surface states were predominant. It was observed that impurities on the surface before oxidation or introduced during oxidation markedly influenced the interface behavior of the system. The surface potential determines not only the bending of the bands in the semiconductor but also the surface recombination velocity of the nonequilibrium carriers. This effect was utilized by Harten[72] to investigate an Si(p) − Si(n) − SiO₂-electrolyte system by measuring the photovoltage of the p-n junction as a function of the surface potential. It was found that the oxide film (produced by anodic oxidation in non-aqueous electrolyte) increased the density of the recombination centers but did not change their nature.   Measurement of surface conductivity as a function of surface potential showed that, with increasing oxide thickness, the influence of the surface potential decreased. If the thickness exceeded that corresponding to a 50-v forming voltage, the surface states screened the semiconductor. It has also been observed in MOS capacitors that similar oxide films introduce a very high density of surface states.[73] This may be due to the incorporation of the organic solvent (NMA) into the oxide as indicated by Harrick.[74] However, stabilization was observed for an oxide film grown anodically in pure water.[46] Millea *et al.*[75] observed a continuous drift in the surface conductance of thermally oxidized silicon for several minutes following a change in the d-c bias voltage on the field electrode. The effect increased with oxide thickness and was the same whether the oxide was produced thermally in oxygen, in high-pressure steam, or anodically. These phenomena were attributed to conduction through surface states. It is possible that they are due to charge-storage effects. Concerning the depth of the active region of the SiO₂ film, according to Edagawa *et al.*[18] the *n*-type inversion layer produced by steam oxidation of *p*-type silicon begins to disappear if the oxide thickness approaches 2000 Å. This was revealed by successive etching and measurement of the photoresponse of an oxidized *p-n⁺* junction. Recall that this thickness is equivalent to that in which the number of the Si−O bonds rapidly increases. However, Hurd and Wrotenbery[76] concluded from the interfacial capacity as a function of the polarization of silicon electrodes that the states responsible for the interfacial capacitance are located at the juncture between the silicon and the oxide, rather than within the oxide itself.

Further data emphasizing the role of the defect structure of the oxide and the interfaces for MOS performance have recently appeared.[77,78,79]

REFERENCES

1. O. Kubaschewski and E. L. Evans, *Metallurgical Thermochemistry,* (New York: Pergamon Press, 1958), p. 342.

2. (a) K. Hauffe, in *Kinetics of High Temperature Processes,* W. D. Kingery, ed., (John Wiley & Sons, Inc., New York, 1959), p. 282.
   (b) T. B. Grimley, in *Chemistry of the Solid State,* ed., W. E. Garner (New York: Academic Press, 1955), p. 336.
   (c) F. A. Kröger, *Chemistry of Imperfect Crystals,* (New York: Interscience, 1964).
   (d) O. Kubaschewski and B. E. Hopkins, *Oxidation of Metals and Alloys,* (London: Butterworth & Co., Ltd., 1962).
   (e) D. A. Vermilyea, in *Advances in Electrochemistry and Electrochemical Engineering,* eds., P. Delahay and C. W. Tobias (New York: Interscience, 1963), p. 211.
   (f) L. Young, *Anodic Oxide Films,* (New York: Academic Press, 1961).

3. D. Brennan, D. O. Hayward, and B. M. Trapnell, *J. Phys. Chem. Solids,* **14,** 117 (1960).

4. J. T. Law, *J. Phys. Chem. Solids* **4**, 91 (1958).

5. S.P. Wolsky, *J. Phys. Chem. Solids* **8**, 114 (1959).

6. J. J. Lander and J. Morrison, *Annals New York Acad. Sci.* **101**, Art. 3, 605 (1963).

7. R. E. Schlier and H. E. Farnsworth, *J. Chem. Phys.* **30**, 917 (1959).

8. H. D. Hagstrum, *J. Appl. Phys.* **32**, 1020 (1961).

9. J. T. Law and E. E. François, *J. Phys. Chem.* **60**, 353 (1956).

10. M. B. Brodsky and D. Cubicciotti, *J. Am. Chem. Soc.* **73**, 3497 (1951).

11. J. T. Law, *J. Phys. Chem.* **61**, 1200 (1957).

12. W. Evans and S. K. Chatterji, *J. Phys. Chem.* **62**, 1064 (1958).

13. J. R. Ligenza and W. G. Spitzer, *J. Phys. Chem. Solids* **14**, 131 (1960).

14. M. M. Atalla, in *Properties of Elemental and Compound Semiconductors*, (Metallurgical Society Conferences, 1960), Vol. V. p. 163.

15. M. O. Thurston and Ki Dong Kang, U.S. Govt. Rep. AD294657, (1962).

16. P. J. Jorgensen, *J. Chem. Phys.* **37**, 874 (1962).

17. B. E. Deal, *J. Electrochem. Soc.* **110**, 527 (1963).

18. H. Edagawa, Y. Morita, S. Maekawa, and Y. Inuishi, *Jap. J. Appl. Phys.* **2**, 765 (1963).

19. B. H. Claussen and M. Flower, *J. Electrochem. Soc.* **110**, 983 (1963).

20. C. R. Fuller and F. J. Strieter, The Electrochemical Society Meeting, Toronto, May 1964; Abstract No. 74.

21. Kahng and Tsai, as quoted by M. O. Thurston and Ki Dong Kang, op. cit., p. 64.

22. N. Karube, K. Yamamoto and M. Kamiyama, *Jap. J. Appl. Phys.* **2**, 11 (1963).

23. R. J. Archer, *J. Electrochem. Soc.* **104**, 619 (1957).

24. J. R. Ligenza, *J. Electrochem. Soc.* **109**, 73 (1962).

25. J. R. Ligenza, *J. Phys. Chem.* **65**, 2011 (1961).

26. J. Sládková, *Czech. J. Phys.* **13**, 452 (1963).

27. A. G. Revesz and K. H. Zaininger, International Colloquium on the Optics of Solid Thin Films, Marseille, Sept. 1963. *J. de Physique* **25**, 66 (1964).

28. M. M. Atalla and E. Tannenbaum, *Bell Syst. Tech. J.* **39**, 933 (1960).

29. T. H. Yeh, *J. Appl. Phys.* **33**, 2849 (1962).

30. F. A. Trumbore, *Bell Syst. Tech. J.* **39**, 205 (1960).

31. (a) C. S. Fuller and R. A. Logan, *J. Appl. Phys.* **28**, 1427 (1957).
    (b) C. S. Fuller and F. H. Doleiden, *J. Appl. Phys.* **29**, 1264 (1958).
    (c) W. Kaiser, H. L. Frisch and H. Reiss, *Phys. Rev.* **112**, 1546 (1958).

32. e.g. R. Cyprès, *Bull. Soc. Franç. Céramique*, No. 55, p. 71 (1962).

33. A. G. Revesz, in U.S. Govt. Rep. AD436802 (1964).

34. N. G. Ainslie, C. R. Morelock, and D. Turnbull, in *Symposium on Nucleation and Crystallization in Glasses and Melts,* ed., M. K. Reser (The American Ceramic Society, 1962), p. 109.

35. R. Hilsch, in *Non-Crystalline Solids,* ed., V. D. Fréchette (New York: John Wiley & Sons, Inc., 1960), p. 348.

36. e.g. J. M. Stevels, in *Encyclopaedia of Physics,* ed., S. Flügge (Berlin: Springer Verlag, 1962), Vol. XIII. p. 510.

37. E. D. Lacy, in *The Vitreous State,* (Sheffield, England: Glass Delegacy of University of Sheffield, 1955).

38. A. Winter, *Bull. Soc. Franç. Céramique,* No. 55, p. 17 (1962).

39. O. L. Anderson and G. J. Dienes, in *Non-Crystalline Solids,* ed., V. D. Fréchette (New York: John Wiley & Sons, Inc., 1960), p. 449.

40. J. M. Stevels and A. Kats, *Philips Res. Rep.* **11**, 103 (1956).

41. S. W. Ing, R. E. Morrison, and J. E. Sandor, *J. Electrochem. Soc.* **109**, 221 (1962).

42. W. Haas, *J. Electrochem. Soc.* **109**, 1192 (1962).

43. R. J. Archer, *J. Opt. Soc. Am.* **52**, 970 (1962).

44. E. F. Duffek, E. A. Benjamini, and C. Mylroie, The Electrochemical Society Meeting, Toronto, May 1964; Abstract No. 77.

45. G. Hetherington and K. H. Jack, *Phys. Chem. Glass.* **3**, 129 (1962).

46. L. A. Dubrovskii, V. G. Melnik, and L. L. Odynets, Russian *J. Phys. Chem.* **36**, 1183 (1962).

47. Y. Ishikawa, Y. Sasaki, Y. Seki, and S. Inowaki, *J. Appl. Phys.* **34**, 867 (1963).

48. R. H. Doremus, in *Modern Aspects of the Vitreous State,* ed., J. D. Mackenzie (London: Butterworth & Co., Ltd., 1962), Vol. II. p. 1.

49. (a) D. R. Peterson, H. B. Bell, and A. L. Epstein, Electrochemical Society Meeting, Toronto, May 1964, Abstract No. 79.
    (b) D. L. Tolliver, H. C. Evitts, and A. L. Epstein, *ibid.,* Abstract No. 80.

50. F. J. Norton, *Nature* **191**, 701 (1961).

51. R. Haul and G. Dümbgen, *Z. Elektrochem.* **66**, 636 (1962).

52. E. W. Sucov, *J. Am. Cer. Soc.* **46**, 14 (1963).

53. R. W. Lee, *Phys. Chem. Glass.* **5**, 35 (1964).

54. J. Cohen, *J. Appl. Phys.* **28**, 795 (1957).

55. H. F. Wenden, *Am. Mineralogist* **42**, 859 (1957).

56. A. E. Owen and R. W. Douglas, *J. Soc. Glass Techn.* **43**, 159 (1959).

57. e.g. A. J. Dekker, *Solid State Physics,* (Englewood Cliffs, N. J.: Prentice-Hall, Inc., 1957), p. 177.

58. P. M. Sutton, *J. Am. Cer. Soc.* **47**, 188, 219 (1964).

59. J. Lindmayer, Electrochemical Society Meeting, Toronto, May, 1964, Abstract No. 12.

60. M. Yamin and F. L. Worthing, *ibid,* Abstract No. 75.

61. F. Forlani and N. Minnaja, *Phys. Status Sol.* **5**, 407 (1964).

62. e.g. A. E. Owen, in *Progress in Ceramic Science,* ed., J. E. Burke (New York: The Macmillan Company, 1963), Vol. III. p. 197.

63. V. Garino Canina and M. Priqueler, *Phys. Chem. Glass.* **3**, 43 (1962).

64. I. Simon, in the *Modern Aspects of the Vitreous State,* ed., J. D. Mackenzie, (London: Butterworth & Co., Ltd., 1960). Vol. I., p. 120.

65. E. W. J. Mitchell and E. G. S. Paige, *Phil. Mag.* **1**, (Ser. 8.), 1085 (1956).

66. P. J. Bray and A. H. Silver, in *Modern Aspects of the Vitreous State,* ed., J. D. Mackenzie (London: Butterworth & Co., Ltd., 1960), Vol. I., p. 92.

67. e.g. J. H. Schulman, *Color Centers in Solids,* (New York: The Macmillan Company, 1962).

68. T. Bell, G. Hetherington and K. H. Jack, *Phys. Chem. Glasses,* **3**, 141 (1962).

69. R. A. Weeks and E. Lell, *J. Appl. Phys.* **35**, 1932 (1964).

70. H. Flietner, *Phys. Status Sol.* **2**, 221 (1962).

71. M. M. Atalla, E. Tannenbaum, and E. J. Scheibner, *Bell Syst. Tech. J.* **38**, 749 (1959).

72. H. U. Harten, *Z. Naturforsch.,* **16a**, 459 (1961).

73. A. G. Revesz and K. H. Zaininger, unpublished work.

74. N. J. Harrick, *Annals New York Acad. Sci.* **101**, Art. 3., 928 (1963).

75. M. F. Millea, T. C. Hall, and J. O. Kopplin, *J. Phys. Chem. Solids,* **23**, 611 (1962).

76. R. M. Hurd and P. T. Wrotenbery, *Annals New York Acad. Sci.* **101**, Art. 3., p. 876 (1963).

77. *IBM J. Res. Dev.* **8**, No. 4, Sept. 1964.

78. *Trans. Met. Soc. AIME* **233**, No. 3, March 1965.

79. *IEEE Trans. Electr. Dev.* **ED–12**, No. 3, March 1965.

5

Field-Effect Transistor Theory

Steven R. Hofstein

5-1 FUNDAMENTAL CHARACTERISTICS OF THE INSULATED-GATE FIELD-EFFECT TRANSISTOR

1. Basic Concepts of field-effect transistors

Two forms of the insulated-gate field-effect transistor are illustrated in Figs. 5–1 and 5–2. For convenience the figures and the description refer to n-type units (n-type channel; n-type source and drain contacts). One may readily extend the discussion to p-type units (complementary type) by exchanging n for p and reversing the polarity of the voltages. For an elementary description of their mode of operation, see the introductory section, Terminology, at the front of the book.

In the device of Fig. 5–1, a bias voltage applied to the metal gate generates a depletion region in a bar of homogeneously doped n-type semiconductor. The depth of the depletion region increases as the negative gate voltage increases, and it reduces the effective cross section for conduction of current from drain to source (electrons from source to drain). This principle is analogous to the one used in the junction-gate field-effect transistor described by Shockley[19] and which is treated in Section 5–3.

In the device of Fig. 5–2, most of the current from drain to source travels in a thin conducting surface layer which is generated at the surface of a lightly doped n-type or p-type semiconductor. The conducting layer is the result of the application of a field perpendicular to the surface through charge located either on the gate electrode or built into the oxide insulator. This charge induces an equal charge of opposite polarity in the semiconductor close to the surface. The charge in the semiconductor is

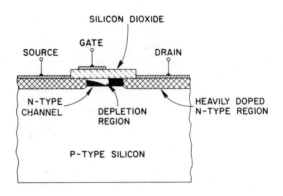

Figure 5-1. Depletion-type MOS transistor with a doped channel.

free to move, resulting in increased conductivity. To reduce the conduction through the bulk which cannot be modulated, the channel is best made in the form of an inversion layer. In this case the channel is n-type on a p-type substrate.

In the device of Fig. 5-1, the doped region is thin enough to be completely pinched off by a negative voltage on the gate. In the device of Fig. 5-2, the conducting channel has no intentional doping and the thickness of the conducting channel is determined only by the built-in charge. This insures that pinch-off can be accomplished by the application of a similar amount of charge of the opposite polarity on the control electrode. A combination of the two forms is possible. The second form is usually preferred for insulated-gate units, while a modification of the first form is usually preferred for junction-gate units.

If the source and drain electrodes of Fig. 5-1 are connected together and a reverse bias is applied between the gate and the source-drain terminals, the maximum depth of penetration of the depletion region is limited by the formation of an inversion layer of holes at the semiconductor-insulator interface. Further increase in gate voltage is taken up by an increase in the charge in the inversion layer rather than by an increase in the depth of the depletion region. If a voltage is now applied between the source and drain, it can be shown[1] that the inversion layer of holes will be modified by the presence of the drift field. In general, the drift field will remove the holes faster than they can be supplied by thermal generation, and the inversion layer will be destroyed.

This contrasts with the structure of Fig. 5–2 in which the n-type inversion layer is supplied with electrons from the highly doped source contact.

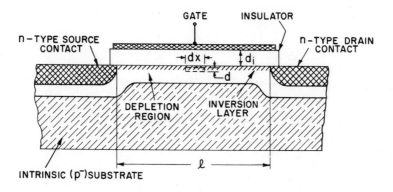

Figure 5–2. MOS transistor utilizing a surface inversion layer channel.

For this case, the supply of electrons is considered unlimited in the sense that quasi-thermal equilibrium statistics may be applied to compute the charge distribution in the inversion layer (see Section 5–2).

2. Statement of assumptions

To derive the important device characteristics, such as current-voltage characteristics, transconductance, and frequency response one must know the drift mobility of the charge carriers in the channel region. This mobility depends on the applied drift field between source and drain. For low fields, $< 10^3$ v/cm in n-type silicon and $< 5 \times 10^3$ v/cm in p-type silicon, the mobility is constant and the carrier velocity is directly proportional to the field. For moderate fields, 10^3–10^4 v/cm in n-type silicon and 5×10^3–5×10^4 (extrapolated value) v/cm in p-type silicon, the mobility is approximately proportional to the inverse square root of the applied field, and the carrier velocity is proportional to the square root of the field. For very high fields in some materials (e.g., 3×10^3 v/cm in n-type germanium), the carrier velocity becomes nearly constant, so that the mobility becomes inversely proportional to the applied field. These three regions will be treated in turn.

The assumptions on which the analysis is based are:

1. Uniformly doped p-type substrate with n-type contacts.

The complementary case may be readily extrapolated.

    2. Zero surface doping (zero pinch-off voltage).

From Section 5–2 it can be shown that the effect of a shallow surface doping is simply a shift in the effective applied gate voltage. Hence, the case of nonzero pinch-off voltage may be corrected for in the final equations by a simple shift in the effective applied gate voltage. This is accomplished by the substitution of $(V_g - V_p)$ for V_g.

    3. The surface Debye length of the inversion layer, and the effective channel depth, are small compared to the gate insulator thickness. (See Chapter 2.) The validity of this assumption depends on the substrate doping level and/ or the magnitude of the applied gate field.

The Debye length that governs the spatial distribution of the mobile charge in the inversion layer is either that based on the mobile charge itself, or that of the lattice charge, whichever length is smaller. Typical gate fields for these devices range from 0.01 $\mathscr{E}_b$ to $\mathscr{E}_b$, where $\mathscr{E}_b$ is the breakdown field for the gate insulator (e.g., 5×10^6 v/cm for a good insulator). For these fields, typical values of the Debye length are 10 Å to 100 Å.

    The simplifying value of this assumption lies in the fact that the total channel mobile charge may be treated as a sheet charge, and the voltage drop in the semiconductor may be neglected compared to the drop in the insulator.

    4. The substrate will be considered so lightly doped that its gating action on the channel may be neglected. The effect of substrate doping will be considered in Section 5–2.

3. Constant mobility and linear carrier velocity gradual channel approximation

This case, which is valid for low electric fields ($< 10^3$ v/cm in n-type silicon and $< 5 \times 10^3$ v/cm in p-type silicon) in the channel region, is characterized by the fact that the carrier mobility is constant and the carrier velocity is directly proportional to the applied field.

    The gradual channel approximation refers to the condition that the rate-of-change of the electric field parallel to the current flow (i.e. the drift field) is much less than the rate-of-change of the electric field normal to the current flow (i.e. the gate field), or $d\mathscr{E}_x/dx \ll d\mathscr{E}_z/dz$. Then the one-dimensional Poisson's equation and Gauss' law may be used to find the channel mobile charge per unit area as:

$$\sigma(x) \approx - C_i[V_g - V(x)] \qquad (5\text{–}1)$$

where C_i is the capacitance per unit area across the insulator. The assumption is made that the gradual channel approximation holds for $V(x) \leq V_g$. It will be seen shortly that this is not strictly true, but it is sufficiently accurate for a first-order analysis.

The drain current, I_d, per unit channel width is:[1, 2]

$$I_d = \frac{\mu_o C_i}{2l} [V_g^2 - (V_g - V_d)^2] \qquad (V_d < V_g) \qquad \text{(5–2)}$$

As V_d approaches some value, $V_{d\text{-}c}$, the drift field at the drain becomes large enough so that the gradual channel approximation fails. In other words, as the rate-of-change of the drift field exceeds the rate-of-change of the gate field in some part of the channel, the charge density in that part of the channel begins to be controlled by the drift field. This is simply the condition for space-charge-limited current flow, where the applied electric field (in this case, the drift field) determines *both* the drift velocity *and* the space-charge density.

If we set:

$$\left. \frac{d\mathscr{E}_x}{dx} \right|_{x=l} = \left. \frac{d\mathscr{E}_z}{dz} \right|_{x=l} \qquad \text{(5–3)}$$

and approximate:

$$\frac{d\mathscr{E}_z}{dz} \approx \frac{\mathscr{E}_z}{\lambda} = \frac{q\,\mathscr{E}_z^2}{kT} \qquad \text{(5–4)}$$

where λ is the Debye length in the channel, we can show that the critical drain voltage, $V_{d\text{-}c}$, at which the space-charge region is just generated is given by:[3]

$$V_{d\text{-}c} \approx V_g \left[1 - \left(\frac{\epsilon_s d_i d}{\epsilon_i} \right)^{1/2} l^{-1} \right] \qquad \text{(5–5)}$$

where d is the effective channel depth at the drain. It is immediately apparent that $V_{d\text{-}c}$ is less than V_g by the amount $V_g/l \times (\epsilon_s d_i d/\epsilon_i)^{1/2}$. In most devices it can be shown that the error introduced when we set $V_d = V_g$ for saturation is small enough to be safely neglected. For example, in a typical structure $l = 10\mu$, $d \approx 1000$ Å, $d_i \approx 1000$ Å, and $\epsilon_i/\epsilon_s = 1/3$. Then $V_{d\text{-}c} \approx 0.9\,V_g$; and the error is less than 10%.

As the drain voltage exceeds $V_{d\text{-}c}$, the excess drain voltage generates a space-charge region extending from the drain into the channel a distance l_d. Using the convention of Wright,[2] we will refer to this region as the *drain region*. The *source region* of the channel is defined as that portion of the channel in which the gradual channel approximation applies. It extends from the source at $x = 0$ to the edge of the drain region at $x = l_s$. The total channel length, l, is simply (see Fig. 5–3):

$$l = l_s + l_d \qquad (5–6)$$

Saturation of drain current for $V_d > V_g$ is basically a geometry-dependent effect. The possibility of saturation of carrier velocity is considered

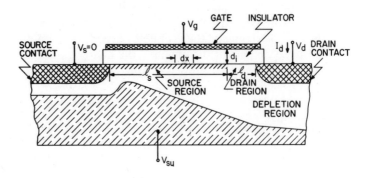

Figure 5–3. Model for calculation of transistor behavior with drain voltage applied.

separately in Section 5–1.5. The current in the source region of the channel per unit width is, to a good approximation:

$$I_{d\,\text{source region}} = \frac{\mu_o C_i}{2l_s}[V_g^2 - (V_g - V_{d\text{-}c})^2] \approx \frac{\mu_o C_i}{2l_s} V_g^2 \qquad (5–7)$$

where, by continuity requirements:

$$I_{d\,\text{drain region}} = I_{d\,\text{source region}} = I_d \qquad (5–8)$$

An exact analytic solution for l_s and l_d as a function of the drain and gate voltage is difficult because of the complex nature of the two-dimensional field pattern within the drain region.

In general, the length of the drain region is much smaller than the length of the source region, and to a first approximation $l_s \approx l$. From Eq. (5–7), this leads immediately to the *saturated* current per unit channel width of:

$$I_{ds} \approx \frac{\mu_o C_i V_g^2}{2l} \qquad (V_d > V_g) \qquad (5–9)$$

where the additional subscript s is used to denote *saturation*.

The deviations from this first-order approximation are important because they determine the finite drain resistance in saturation and, hence, the voltage gain of the transistor. Further consideration of these effects appears in Section 5–2.

The transconductance, g_m, per unit channel width is:

$$g_m = \frac{\mu_o C_i V_g}{l} \qquad (V_d > V_g) \qquad (5\text{–}10)$$

These are the equations of a *square-law* device. It is worth reiterating that this square-law dependence is a direct result of the original assumption of a channel much shallower than the insulator thickness. The qualitative aspects of the characteristic curves are illustrated in Fig. 5–4.

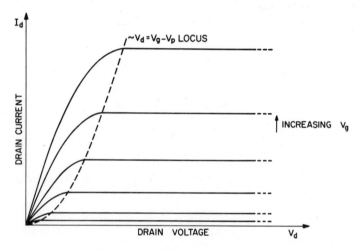

Figure 5–4. Qualitative illustration of MOS transistor characteristic curves, drain current vs. drain voltage (with gate voltage as a parameter).

The gain-bandwidth product of this device is:

$$\frac{g_m}{C_{in}} = \tau_{gb}^{-1} = \frac{\mu_o V_g}{l^2} \qquad (5\text{–}11)$$

C_{in} is the input capacitance per unit channel width, where:

$$C_{in} = C_i l \qquad (5\text{–}12)$$

and where the effect of stray capacitance and resistance have been neglected. The transit time, τ_T, of a carrier in the channel as it moves from source to drain is:

$$\tau_T = \int_0^l \frac{dx}{\mu_o \mathscr{E}_x(x)} = \frac{4l^2}{3\mu_o V_g} \qquad (V_d > V_g)$$

Then:
$$\tau_{gb} \approx \tau_T \tag{5–14}$$

Thus, the gain-bandwidth product may be related to the physics of this device in a relatively simple form. This relation is true only if the capacitance in the gain-bandwidth calculation is the active input capacitance, i.e., that part of the input capacitance which controls charge in the active channel region.

The l^2 dependence of τ_T in the preceding analysis results, in part, from the assumption of constant carrier mobility. A typical value for the channel length is $l \approx 10\mu$, for which a carrier velocity of 1×10^7 cm/sec leads to a transit time of $\tau_T \approx 10^{-10}$ sec and a gain-bandwidth product on the order of $\mathrm{GB} = (2\pi\tau_T)^{-1} \approx 10^9$ cps.

4. Inverse square-root mobility; square-root carrier velocity

This case is valid for moderate fields in the channel, i.e., 10^3–10^4 v/cm in n-type silicon and 5×10^3–5×10^4 v/cm (extrapolated value) in p-type silicon. The mobility-dependence on the electric field will be deduced and applied to the derivation of the device characteristics.

In MOS devices the magnitude of the diffuse scattering from the insulator-semiconductor interface varies widely from unit to unit. It may be so small that it is masked by other effects, such as the parasitic source and drain resistances. This effect will not be included in the following calculations, but it will be discussed semiquantitatively in Section 5–2 in order to estimate some of the second-order phenomena observed in particular units.

The mobility of an electron in a solid, for the first-order model, is given by the ratio of average drift velocity to the applied electric field:

$$\mu \equiv \frac{\bar{v}_d}{\mathscr{E}} = \frac{q\tau_{mfp}}{m^*} = \frac{q\lambda_{mfp}}{m^*v_s} \tag{5–15}$$

where: τ_{mfp} = mean-free-time between collisions;
m^* = effective mass of carrier;
λ_{mfp} = mean-free-path of carrier between collisions; and
v_s = average speed of carrier between collisions.

For no applied electric field, $\bar{v}_s = \bar{v}_k$, where $\bar{v}_k$ = average thermal speed of the carriers. For a Boltzmann and Fermi gas, respectively:

$$\bar{v}_{kB} \approx \left(\frac{3kT}{m^*}\right)^{1/2} \tag{5–16}$$

$$\bar{v}_{kF} \approx \left(\frac{2E_F}{m^*}\right)^{1/2} \tag{5–17}$$

The approximation of constant mobility comes from the assumption that, for sufficiently small drift fields, the average carrier speed between collisions is constant at $\bar{v}_k$. As the drift field is increased, the perturbation on $\bar{v}_s$ becomes significant, and field-dependent mobility is observed.

Shockley[5] has shown that for interaction with acoustic mode phonons, where energy transfer from the carrier to the phonon may be quite inefficient, the average speed of the carrier between collisions may exceed the thermal speed for drift velocities substantially smaller than v_k. This may be demonstrated by the following argument: If the phonon is treated as a particle of mass, M, then the fraction of energy transferred to the phonon by a scattered hole or electron is:

$$\frac{\delta E_c}{E_c} \approx \frac{m^*}{M} \tag{5-18}$$

where E_c is the excess over thermal energy, and where $m^* \ll M$. The energy gained by the carrier between collisions is (approximately):

$$\delta E_c = |\mathcal{E}| q \lambda_{mfp} \tag{5-19}$$

where $\mathcal{E}$ is the applied drift field. For steady state, this energy gain must equal the energy transfer. Then, from Eqs. (5–18) and (5–19):

$$E_c \frac{m^*}{M} = |\mathcal{E}| q \lambda_{mfp} \tag{5-20}$$

We define: $\mathcal{E}_c$ = drift field for which the excess energy of the carrier is just $\frac{3}{2}kT$ (hence total carrier energy = $3kT$). Then:

$$\mathcal{E}_c = \frac{3kT}{2} \times \frac{m^*}{M} \times \frac{1}{q\lambda_{mfp}} \tag{5-21}$$

For $\mathcal{E} \gg \mathcal{E}_c$:

$$\bar{v}_s = \left(\frac{2E_c}{m^*}\right)^{1/2} \tag{5-22}$$

and

$$\mu - \frac{q\lambda_{mfp}}{m^*}\left(\frac{3kT}{m^*} \times \frac{\mathcal{E}}{\mathcal{E}_c}\right)^{1/2} - \mu_o\left(\frac{\mathcal{E}}{\mathcal{E}_c}\right)^{-1/2} \tag{5-23}$$

This is a region of *square-root* mobility. The drift velocity for $\mathcal{E} = \mathcal{E}_c$ is simply:

$$\bar{v}_d = \mu_o \mathcal{E}_c \tag{5-24}$$

It can be shown that $v_d = c$ = velocity of sound in the material (acoustic mode) and:

$$\mathcal{E}_c = \frac{c}{\mu_0} \tag{5–25}$$

In many materials, interaction with optical mode phonons is dominant. For these phonons, the energy transfer process for electron scattering is quite efficient. If the electron loses all of its excess energy each time it is scattered, we can show that:

$$v_d \approx v_k \tag{5–26}$$

and

$$\mathcal{E}_c \approx \frac{v_k}{\mu_0} \tag{5–27}$$

Experimental curves for mobility in silicon and germanium have been obtained by Ryder,[6] and by Prior.[7] These curves are reproduced in Figs. 5–5 and 5–6.

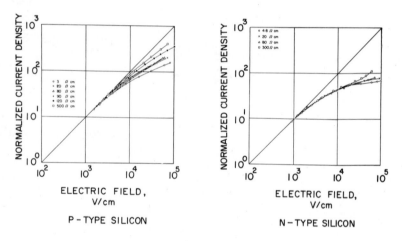

P – TYPE SILICON   N – TYPE SILICON

Figure 5–5. Variation of current density with applied electric field in silicon (after Prior).

LINEAR CURRENT RANGE $(V_d < V_g)$. It will be assumed that the channel drift field is such that:

$$\mathcal{E}(x) > \mathcal{E}_c \qquad (0 \leqslant x \leqslant l)$$

The mobility of the carriers at any point x in the channel is then:

$$\mu(x) = \mu_0 \left(\frac{\mathcal{E}_c}{\mathcal{E}(x)} \right)^{1/2} \tag{5–28}$$

If this expression for mobility is used in the equation for drain current and the integration carried through, the characteristic device equation is:

$$I_d = \frac{\mu_o C_i \mathscr{E}_c^{1/2}}{l^{1/2}} \left[\frac{V_g^3}{3} - \frac{(V_g - V_d)^3}{3} \right]^{1/2} \tag{5-29}$$

provided $\mathscr{E}(x) > \mathscr{E}_c$ for all x, and $V_d < V_g$.

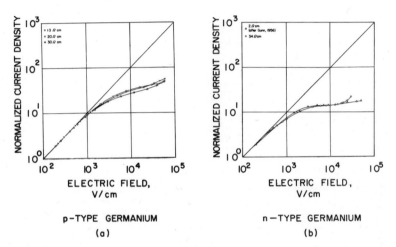

Figure 5-6. Variation of current density with applied electric field in germanium (after Prior).

SATURATED CURRENT RANGE $(V_d > V_g)$. The saturation drain current per unit channel width due to drain pinch-off, which occurs for $V_d > V_g$ is:

$$I_{ds} = \frac{\mu_o C_i \mathscr{E}_c}{\sqrt{3} l^{1/2}} V_g^{3/2} \qquad \mathscr{E}(x) > \mathscr{E}_c \tag{5-30}$$

The transconductance per unit channel width under these conditions is:

$$g_m = \frac{\mu_o C_i \mathscr{E}_c^{1/2}}{l^{1/2}} \times \frac{\sqrt{3}}{2} V_g^{1/2} \tag{5-31}$$

The active input capacitance per unit channel width of the device is $C_{in} = C_i l$. Hence, the gain-bandwidth time constant, τ_{gb}, is:

$$\tau_{gb} = \left(\frac{g_m}{C_{in}} \right)^{-1} = \frac{2}{\sqrt{3}} \times \frac{l^{3/2}}{\mu_o \mathscr{E}_c^{1/2}} V_g^{-1/2} \tag{5-32}$$

The transit time, τ_T, of a carrier from the source to drain, using Eq. (5-28), is given by:

$$\tau_T = \int_0^l \frac{dx}{\mu \mathscr{E}(x)} = \int_0^l \frac{dx}{\mu_o \mathscr{E}_c^{1/2} \mathscr{E}(x)^{1/2}} \tag{5-33}$$

From Eqs. (5–28) and (5–29) the channel field, $\mathcal{E}(x)$, is:

$$[\mathcal{E}(x)]^{1/2} = \frac{I_d l}{\mu_o C_i \mathcal{E}_c^{1/2}}\left[V_g^3 - \frac{3I_d^2 x}{\mu_o^2 C_i^2 \mathcal{E}_c}\right]^{-1/3} \tag{5–34}$$

This leads, after integration of Eq. (5–33) and some algebraic manipulation, to:

$$\tau_T = \frac{1}{\mu_o \mathcal{E}^{1/2}} \times \frac{\mu_o^3 C_i^3 \mathcal{E}_c^{3/2}}{4I_d^3}\left[V_g^4 - (V_g - V_d)^4\right] \quad (V_d < V_g) \tag{5–35}$$

and in saturation where $I_d = I_{ds}$, and $V_d > V_g$:

$$\tau_T = \frac{3\sqrt{3}}{4} \times \frac{l^{3/2}}{\mu_o \mathcal{E}_c^{1/2} V_g^{1/2}} \approx \tau_{gb} \tag{5–36}$$

It is important to compare the transconductance under conditions of square-root mobility with that under conditions of constant mobility. To facilitate this comparison, it is convenient to rewrite Eq. (5–31) in terms of $\mathcal{E}(0)$, the drift field at the source. From Eqs. (5–34) and (5–30):

$$\mathcal{E}(0) = \frac{V_g}{3l} \tag{5–37}$$

Substitution into Eq. (5–31) gives the transconductance per unit channel width under conditions of square-root mobility:

$$g_{ms} = \tfrac{3}{2}\mu_o C_i[\mathcal{E}_c\ \mathcal{E}(0)]^{1/2} \tag{5–38}$$

From Eqs. (5–10), (5–37), and (5–38) the transconductance per unit channel width for the condition of constant mobility is:

$$g_{mc} = \left(\frac{4V_g}{3l\mathcal{E}_c}\right)^{1/2} g_{ms} \tag{5–39}$$

For the case of square-root mobility, the field everywhere in the channel, including $\mathcal{E}(0)$, must be greater than $\mathcal{E}_c$. Hence, $g_{mc} > g_{ms}$. The transition from the constant mobility regime to square-root mobility regime (in saturation) occurs at a gate voltage, V_{gc}, on the order of:

$$V_{gc} = \tfrac{3}{4}l\mathcal{E}_c \tag{5–40}$$

A plot of normalized transconductance vs. normalized gate voltage using Eqs. (5–10), (5–31), and (5–40) appears in Fig. 5–7.

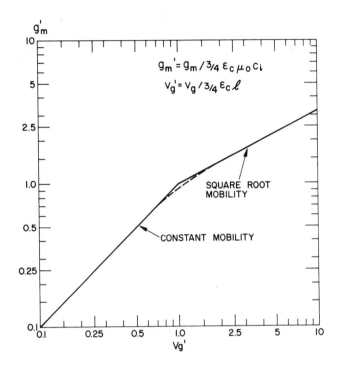

Figure 5-7. Normalized transconductance vs. normalized gate voltage.

5. Inverse linear mobility; constant carrier velocity

In many materials there are additional mechanisms which limit the drift velocity. If there is a scattering mechanism such that the scattering cross section shows a sharp rise above a particular energy, E_o, then the lifetime of a carrier with energy above E_o becomes extremely short. The result is that the drift velocity saturates at a value corresponding to E_o. Further increases in the applied drift field merely act to decrease the average scattering mean-free-time so that drift velocity increases only slightly.

Ryder[6] has shown experimentally the existence of the $\mathscr{E}^{1/2}$ mobility dependence in silicon and germanium, as well as the existence of a saturated drift velocity in germanium for electrons. It should be noted that the onset of saturated velocity may occur before or after the onset of the $\mathscr{E}^{-1/2}$ region in a particular material or, as in the case of silicon, may not occur at all.[7]

Consider the simple case of a transistor in which all carriers are moving at saturated velocity. The channel current per unit channel width is:

$$I_d = v_l \sigma(x) \tag{5–41}$$

where v_l is the saturated velocity. From the requirements of current continuity, the mobile channel charge per unit area must be constant over the length of the channel, with a magnitude of:

$$\sigma(x) = \frac{I_d}{v_l} = \text{constant} \tag{5–42}$$

Since the channel potential, $V(x)$, is not constant over the length, it is apparent that the expression for the channel charge derived from the one-dimensional Poisson's equation, Eq. (5–1), is no longer valid. It is necessary to consider the two-dimensional Poisson's equation in order to obtain a self-consistent analysis for the saturated velocity case.

Unfortunately, it is impossible to obtain a general analytic solution to the two-dimensional Poisson's equation. For purposes of this analysis, a perturbation technique may be used to obtain a good insight into the actual physical picture. The solution must be checked to determine the range over which it applies without violating the original approximations, and extensions to the physical model must be developed if needed.

In the following model, the channel will be divided into two regions with the boundary between them at $x = x_l$. Region I, extending from the source to x_l, is defined as that region in which the carriers have not reached saturated drift velocity. In region II, extending from x_l to the drain, the carriers have reached their saturated velocity. The behavior in region I of the channel is described by the gradual-channel case treated in Sections 5–1.3 and 5–1.4, with V_l substituted for V_d, and x_l substituted for l_s, where V_l is the voltage at the point $x = x_l$. At this point, the behavior in region II may be analyzed, and the joining solution for regions I and II may be derived to predict the over-all behavior of the device.

For the gradual-channel case where:

$$\frac{d\,\mathscr{E}_x}{dx} < \frac{d\,\mathscr{E}_z}{dz} \approx \frac{\mathscr{E}_z}{\lambda} \tag{5–43}$$

the inversion layer charge distribution is approximately described by the one-dimensional analysis of Section 2–5.

Let the gate voltage be held constant and consider what happens when the drain voltage is increased from zero to V_d. The channel voltage at a point x in the channel rises to some value $V(x)$. The resulting change in the gate electric field (in the insulator) at x is then:

$$\Delta\,\mathscr{E}_z(x) = \frac{V(x)}{d_i} \tag{5–44}$$

Referring to Fig. 5-1, we may draw a "pillbox" of length dx and depth λ around the channel charge. The top of the pillbox is just inside the semiconductor surface. From Gauss's law:

$$\mathcal{E}_{zs}dx + \left[\frac{d\mathcal{E}_x(x)}{dx}dx\right]\lambda = \frac{\sigma(x)}{\epsilon_s}dx \qquad (5\text{-}45)$$

This may be put in the form:

$$\frac{d^2V}{dx^2} = k^2[V(x) - V_g] \qquad (5\text{-}46)$$

where:

$$k^2 \equiv \frac{\epsilon_i}{\epsilon_s \lambda d_i} \qquad (5\text{-}47)$$

and with the boundary condition:

$$\sigma(x) = \sigma(x_c) = \frac{\epsilon_i}{d_i}\left[V_g - V(x_l)\right] \qquad (x > x_l) \qquad (5\text{-}48)$$

The solution for Eq. (5-48) using the boundary conditions that, at $x = x_l$,

$\mathcal{E}(x_l) = \mathcal{E}_l$ and $V(x_l) = V_l$ is:

$$V(x) = V_l + \frac{\mathcal{E}_l}{k}\sinh k(x - x_l) \qquad (x > x_l) \qquad (5\text{-}49)$$

Hence, it can be seen that k^{-1} is a length constant associated with the region of saturated velocity.

It will be useful to pause at this point and examine the physical consequences of the results obtained so far.

Assume that the material possesses a saturated carrier drift velocity, $\bar{v}_l$, at a drift field, $\mathcal{E}_l$, where $\mathcal{E}_l$ is the channel drift field at the point $x = x_l$. Let the gate voltage be held at some Value V_g, and consider what happens as a drain voltage is slowly increased above zero. As the drain voltage rises, current flows from source to drain, according to the simple first-order gradual-channel analyses of Sections 5-1.3 and 5-1.4. The drain region of the channel is formed when $d\mathcal{E}_x/dx > d\mathcal{E}_z/dz$ at the drain. However, if the field at the drain reaches $\mathcal{E}_l$ before $d\mathcal{E}_x/dx > d\mathcal{E}_z/dz$, a region of saturated velocity appears. The length of this region is on the order of $l_l \approx k^{-1}$.

For typical parameters (e.g., $d_i = 1000 \text{ Å}$, $\lambda = 100\text{–}200 \text{ Å}$, $l = \mu$, $\epsilon_i / \epsilon_s = 1/3$):

$$l_l \approx 1000 \text{ Å} \ll l$$

This region affects the drain current in much the same fashion as the conventional drain region. That is, the drain current shows a sharp tendency towards saturation. As the drain voltage continues to rise, the point will be reached where:

$$\frac{d\mathcal{E}_x}{dx}\bigg|_{x=l} = \frac{d\mathcal{E}_z}{dz}\bigg|_{x=l}$$

and the drain region of the channel will be formed, in which the mobile charge density is determined by the drift field, and the drift velocity is fixed at $\bar{v}_l$.

If the situation exists where $\mathcal{E}_l$ is so large that the drain voltage must almost equal the gate voltage before the drain drift field exceeds $\mathcal{E}_l$, then the effects of velocity saturation become intermingled with the formation of the drain region and it becomes a moot point to argue which of the two is "causing" saturation of the drain current.

The behavior of the transconductance versus gate voltage in the regime of saturated drain current will be considered for the case where the onset of a region of saturated velocity occurs substantially before channel pinch-off at the drain and before the generation of the space-charge-limited drain region.[8] V_l is substantially less than V_g. This permits ready differentiation between the effects of velocity saturation and formation of the drain region. For this case, region I of the channel will be the conventional source region and $x_l = l_s$.

The transition from constant mobility to saturated velocity is considered abrupt; so the effect of square-root mobility in region I of the channel may be neglected. This will simplify the mathematics while retaining the fundamental characteristics of the physical behavior.

The electric field at the drain is:

$$\mathcal{E}_l = \frac{I_d}{\mu_o \sigma(X)} = \frac{1}{2l}\frac{V_g^2 - (V_g - V_d)^2}{V_g - V_d} \quad [\mathcal{E}(l) < \mathcal{E}_l] \tag{5–50}$$

Setting $\mathcal{E}(l) = \mathcal{E}_l$ yields the drain voltage at which region II just forms at the drain:

$$V_{dl} = V_g + \mathcal{E}_l l - (\mathcal{E}_l^2 l^2 + V_g^2)^{1/2} \tag{5–51}$$

The current per unit channel width in the source region of the channel is

$$I_d = \frac{\mu_o C_i}{2(l - l_l)}\left[V_g^2 - (V_g - V_{dl})^2 \right] \approx \frac{\mu_o C_i}{2l}\left[V_g^2 - (V_g - V_{dl})^2 \right] \tag{5–52}$$

since $l \gg l_l$. Substituting Eq. (5–51) into (5–52) yields the characteristic equation for the device:

$$I_d = \frac{\mu_o C_i}{l} (\mathscr{E}_l l)^2 \left\{ \left[1 + \left(\frac{V_g}{\mathscr{E}_l l} \right)^2 \right]^{1/2} - 1 \right\}$$
(5–53)

Differentiating yields the transconductance per unit channel width:

$$g_m = \mu_o C_i \mathscr{E}_l V_g'(1 + V_g'^2)^{1/2}$$
(5–54)

where:

$$V_g' \equiv V_g / \mathscr{E}_l l$$
(5–55)

From Eq. (5–54) it can be seen that the transconductance saturates for gate voltage $V_g' \gg 1$. The physical reason is that, for large V_g', the channel field becomes more uniform since voltage variations along the channel are small compared to V_g. The channel field is then given approximately by V_d/l, and it is independent of V_g. The channel current per unit channel width is then:

$$I_d = C_i v_l V_g \qquad (V_g \gg \mathscr{E}_l l)$$
(5–56)

and the transconductance per unit channel width is:

$$g_m = C_i v_l = \mu_o C_i \mathscr{E}_l \qquad (V_g \gg \mathscr{E}_l l)$$
(5–57)

A plot of normalized transconductance vs. normalized gate voltage is shown in Fig. 5–8.

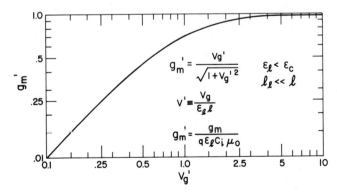

Figure 5–8. Normalized transconductance vs. normalized gate voltage for the case of limited carrier velocity, $v_l = \mu_o \mathscr{E}_l$.

The effect of saturation of carrier velocity causing current saturation (i.e., current saturation before channel pinch-off at the drain occurs) has been experimentally observed for germanium junction-type field-effect transistors.[8] In silicon junction-gate and MOS transistors, saturation of current occurs for a value of drain voltage so close to that corresponding to pinch-off at the drain, that the effect of mobility variation with field within the drain region is no longer dominant.

6. Modulation of the carrier mobility

As the applied gate field is increased, carrier concentration in the inversion layer increases and the Debye length associated with the surface charge decreases. This was discussed in Section 5–1.2. If the surface of the semiconductor is a diffuse scatterer, the effective sheet mobility of the inversion layer will be reduced because of the increased number of carriers which "see" the surface. Schrieffer[4] has proposed a model and shown that, to a first approximation, the surface mobility varies inversely with the applied gate field. The effect of this variation of mobility on device characteristics is discussed in Section 5–2.

5–2 FUNDAMENTAL PHYSICAL LIMITATIONS OF THE MOS TRANSISTOR

1. Maximum Drain Voltage

Voltage breakdown at the drain will be analyzed and found to consist of a *soft* channel breakdown superimposed on a *hard* direct breakdown from drain to substrate. This latter breakdown will be shown to be influenced by the potential on the gate and to be relatively independent of substrate doping.

CHANNEL DRIFT-FIELD BREAKDOWN. To obtain maximum drift velocity, minimum transit time, and hence, maximum gain-bandwidth product, it is desirable to have as large a channel drift field as possible. As the channel field is increased, however, there is an increase in the hole-electron pair generation due to impact ionization by hot carriers (avalanche breakdown). This generation is greatest in the region of maximum field, i.e., the space-charge region near the drain. The case of an *n*-type channel will be considered; the discussion may be readily extended to the complementary case of a *p*-type channel.

The electrons generated in the region near the drain are rapidly swept to the drain by the channel drift field. However, the holes are swept into the channel towards the source electrode by the drift field and into the substrate by the applied gate and drain fields. The total generation rate in the channel is proportional to the magnitude of the drift field and the channel current. This dependence on the channel field is reflected in a decrease in the saturation drain resistance. This resistance also decreases for increasing gate voltage due to the increase in channel current. This effect is shown in Fig. 5–9, which shows a family of drain characteristics with

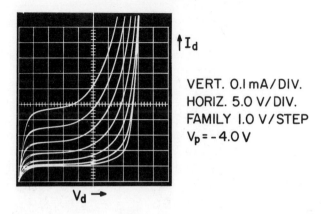

Figure 5–9. Characteristic curves of an n-type transistor illustrating channel breakdown, $V_g > V_p$.

gate voltage as a parameter. The soft channel breakdown caused by carrier generation is greatest for maximum gate voltage and becomes almost negligible at channel pinch-off. The final sharp drain-current rise represents direct breakdown to the substrate and is discussed in the next section.

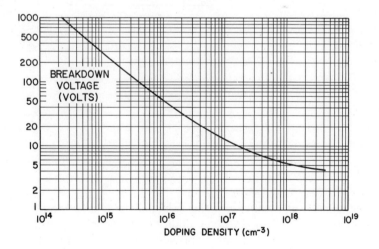

Figure 5–10. Breakdown voltage for $p^+\!-n$ or $n^+\!-p$ junctions in silicon as a function of doping on the low-doped side of the junction.

DRAIN DIODE BREAKDOWN. The usual approximation is that the breakdown voltage of the drain-to-substrate diode is simply that of an n^+-p diode. For example, the breakdown voltage from a heavily doped n-type region to a 10 ohm-cm p-type substrate is approximately 270 v for a junction in which surface effects may be neglected and whose field distribution approximates the plane-parallel one-dimensional case. This last condition is readily met by deep diffused or alloyed junctions. Figure 5–10 gives the voltage breakdown for silicon *step* junctions as a function of doping density.

The diodes used in planar devices are often diffused to depths of less than 0.1 μ. This structure may possess high fields along the periphery of the junction. Figure 5–11 illustrates the qualitative aspects of the field distribution for both the deep and shallow diffused junctions. Field crowding occurs when the diffusion depth is less than the width of the depletion region.

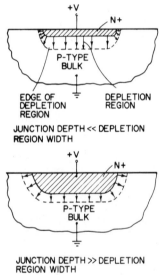

Figure 5–11. Qualitative picture of field distribution in deep and shallow diffused junctions, indicating crowding at periphery of the shallow diffused junction.

If, as a first approximation, the field distribution at the edge of the planar junction is assumed to be cylindrical, Poisson's equation may be solved for the electric field, and the breakdown voltage may be computed. Hilibrand[9] has computed the breakdown voltage based on the model of Fig. 5–12 for silicon with a multiplication factor $\alpha = 1.95 \times 10^{-24} \mathscr{E}^5$ for holes and electrons.[10] The results are shown in Fig. 5–13.

The concentration of the electric field at the periphery of the junction results in surface region avalanche breakdown at a voltage lower than

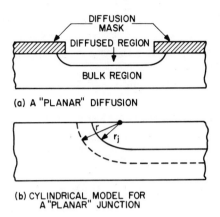

(a) A "PLANAR" DIFFUSION

(b) CYLINDRICAL MODEL FOR A "PLANAR" JUNCTION

Figure 5-12. The geometry of a planar junction.

that required for breakdown of the bulk portion of the diode. Breakdown voltages on the order of 60 to 80 v are observed in planar diodes fabricated with an n^+ diffusion depth on the order of 2000 Å in a 10 ohm-cm p-type (10^{15}/cm^3 doping level) substrate. This is significantly lower than the 270 v measured for deep-diffused and alloyed junctions.

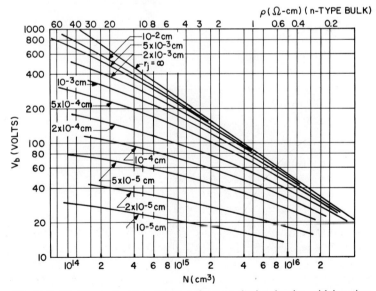

Figure 5-13. Theoretical breakdown voltage vs. doping density, with junction radius as a parameter. The plane parallel case corresponds to $r_j = \infty$.

GATE MODULATION OF DRAIN BREAKDOWN. A further reduction of the breakdown voltage has been observed[1] when an insulated metal electrode (such as a transistor gate) overlaps the diode junction. The breakdown voltage of the drain to substrate for the unit whose characteristics are displayed in Fig. 5–9 is on the order of 40 v. Removal of the gate electrode by chemical etching restores the breakdown to 70 v.

The reduced breakdown voltage results from the increased field in the surface portion of the junction depletion region produced by the presence of the conducting metal gate. This effect is illustrated in Fig. 5–14. The breakdown is due to the collective action of both the drain-to-substrate·

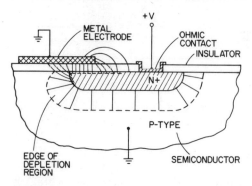

Figure 5–14. Qualitative picture of field distortion in a planar *p-n* junction due to the overlying metal electrode.

and drain-to-gate field, with the substrate acting as the collector of the carriers produced either by impact ionization or field emission. According to this concept, the drain voltage for breakdown should vary with the gate voltage. This is, in fact, observed as shown in Fig. 5–15.

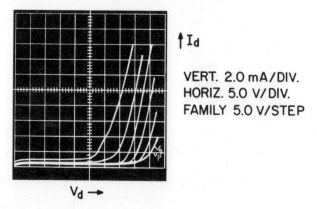

↑ I_d

VERT. 2.0 mA/DIV.
HORIZ. 5.0 V/DIV.
FAMILY 5.0 V/STEP

V_d →

Figure 5–15. Drain voltage required for breakdown as a function of gate voltage, $V_g < V_p$.

Since the substrate in the MOS structure is lightly doped and acts only as a collector, the drain breakdown voltage should have only a weak dependence on the resistivity of the substrate. This also has been confirmed experimentally. Variation of substrate resistivity from 5 ohm-cm to 20 ohm-cm produces no noticeable change in the drain breakdown voltage which remains at approximately 35–40 v.

Operation in the breakdown region by controlling the breakdown voltage with the gate provides an active device with some attractive features. Whether sufficiently close control of the parameters in this mode will be possible in practice is uncertain. Consideration of the device potential of this phenomenon has been made by Hofstein,[3] Nathanson, Szedon, and Jordan,[17] and Hofstein and Warfield.[11]

"PUNCH-THROUGH" BREAKDOWN. Another source of voltage breakdown at the drain is punch-through to the source. The drain depletion region extends across the channel region until it reaches the source and draws space-charge-limited current. This is analogous to punch-through breakdown in the bipolar transistor. This breakdown is less significant in the MOS transistor than in the bipolar transistor for the following reasons:

1. The gate electrode acts as an electrostatic shield. The voltage on the drain required to move the depletion region across to the source is higher than that required to move it the same distance into the substrate. The distortion is indicated in Fig. 5–14.

2. The space-charge-limited currents that are drawn after punch-through is achieved are less than in the bipolar transistor because the source-drain electrodes are not parallel and facing each other, as are the collector and emitter in the bipolar transistor.

2. Theory of the drain saturation resistance and voltage gain limitations

In this section the low-frequency drain saturation resistance will be examined. A theory based on a capacitive coupling from the drain to the source region of the channel through the substrate-channel depletion region will be proposed to explain the experimental observations. The modulation of the length of the drain region (space-charge region) of the channel as a contributor to the drain saturation resistance also will be considered. It will be shown that the application of substrate reverse bias causes the drain saturation resistance to increase or decrease, depending on whether the drain region modulation or capacitive feedback mechanism, respectively, is dominant. Experimentally, it is found that the resistance decreases with increasing substrate reverse bias.

In the first section of this chapter, the drain current was shown to saturate to first order as V_d exceeded $V_{d\text{-}c} \approx V_g$. To predict the voltage gain of the transistor in the saturation regime, it is necessary to consider two major second-order effects: 1. modulation of the drain-region length with drain voltage, and 2. feedback capacitance from the drain to the source region of the channel.

To semiquantitatively examine the effect of the modulation of the drain-region length on current saturation, a one-dimensional analysis[2] yields a drain region length of:

$$l_d \approx \left(\frac{\epsilon_s}{\epsilon_i} l d_i d_a\right)^{1/3} \left(\frac{V_d - V_g}{V_g}\right)^{2/3} \tag{5-58}$$

where d_a is the effective channel depth in the drain region. It is difficult to determine d_a since the mobile charge distribution and channel depth are no longer controlled by the gate field as in the source region. A rough estimate may be obtained if we set d_a equal to the drain contact depth. The cube-root dependence of l_d on d_a allows for an order-of-magnitude uncertainty in d_a to be reduced to a factor-of-two uncertainty in l_d. The drain current is then:

$$I_{ds} = \frac{\mu_o C_i}{2l_s} V_g^2 = \frac{\mu_o C_i}{2[l - l_d]} V_g^2 \quad (V_d > V_g) \tag{5-59}$$

From Eqs. (5–58) and (5–59), it can be readily shown that:

$$r_{ds}^{-1} = g_{ds} \approx g_m \frac{(1/\alpha)[V_g/(V_d - V_g)]}{1 + (1/\alpha)[V_g/(V_d - V_g)]^{-1/3}} \tag{5-60}$$

where:

$$\alpha \equiv \left(12\frac{l^2}{d_d d_i} \times \frac{\epsilon_i}{\epsilon_s}\right)^{1/3} \tag{5-61}$$

and the voltage gain is:

$$A = \frac{g_m}{g_{ds}} \approx \frac{1 + (1/\alpha)[(V_d - V_g)/V_g]^{1/3}}{(1/\alpha)[V_g/(V_d - V_g)]^{1/3}} \tag{5-62}$$

For large gain, $(1/\alpha)[(V_d - V_g)/V_g] \ll 1$ and:

$$A \approx \alpha(V_d/V_g - 1)^{1/3} \tag{5-63}$$

This theory indicates a voltage gain on the order of:

$$A \approx \left(12\frac{l^2}{d_d d_i} \times \frac{\epsilon_i}{\epsilon_s}\right)^{1/3}$$

(5–64)

which increases with increasing drain voltage. For the typical parameters $l = 10\,\mu$, $d_i \approx 0.1\,\mu$, $d_d \approx 0.1\,\mu$, $\epsilon_i/\epsilon_s \approx \frac{1}{3}$, $A \approx 10$. The validity of this one-dimensional approximation will be evaluated immediately following consideration of the second effect: feedback capacitance from the drain to the channel source region. The channel length-to-depth ratio for transistors of the type under discussion may range typically from 10 to 100. However, penetration of the drain field into the channel region is a function of the effective spacing between the metal gate and the *substrate gate*. This spacing includes the doped channel plus the space-charge region between the channel and substrate. For a lightly doped substrate, this spacing may become as large as, or even exceed, the channel length when the drain voltage rises into the saturation region. Hence, penetration of the drain field into the channel region may be significant, and a new model must be postulated. This model is shown in Fig. 5–16. The basic assumption is that for a lightly doped substrate, where

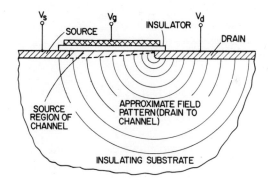

Figure 5–16. Model for analysis of the saturation drain resistance.

the substrate depletion-region depth is of the same order as the channel length, the penetration and coupling of the drain field to the channel source region may be significant. This mechanism will be analyzed by the use of Laplace's equation as a first approximation. Experimental results show that this assumption is a very good approximation to the actual physical behavior. The drain electrode now acts both as a collector of channel carriers and as an inefficient gate.

In the model of Fig. 5–16, a change in drain voltage, ΔV_d, causes a change in the average channel sheet charge of $\Delta Q = C_{dc}\Delta V_d/l$ per unit area, where:[1]

$$C_{dc} = \text{effective drain-to-channel coupling capacitance} \approx \epsilon_s \quad (5\text{–}65)$$

This change in charge sees an average field from source to drain of V_g/l with an effective channel mobility of μ_{eff}. The change in the drain current per unit channel width is:

$$\Delta I_{ds} = \left(\frac{C_{dc}\Delta V_d}{l}\right)\left(\frac{V_g}{l}\right)\mu_{\text{eff}} \quad (5\text{–}66)$$

The saturation drain resistance for a channel of unit width becomes:

$$r_{ds} = \frac{l^2}{C_{dc}\mu_{\text{eff}}}(V_g)^{-1} \quad (5\text{–}67)$$

For the special case of a square-law device, it was found in Section 5–1 that:

$$g_m = \frac{C_i\mu_{\text{eff}}}{l}V_g \quad (5\text{–}68)$$

and the voltage amplification factor becomes:

$$A = g_m r_{ds} = \frac{C_{gc}}{C_{dc}} \quad (5\text{–}69)$$

where:

$$C_{gc} = \text{gate-to-channel capacitance} = C_i l, \text{ and } \frac{C_{gc}}{C_{dc}} \approx \frac{\epsilon_i}{\epsilon_s}\times\frac{l}{d_i} \quad (5\text{–}70)$$

Therefore, the transistor voltage amplification factor depends only on the geometry. This result is analogous to that for the vacuum-tube triode. At this point, the two mechanisms affecting the saturation drain resistance may be compared.

Modulation of the drain region length gives a saturation drain resistance that is inversely proportional to the effective channel depth. If the substrate gate of the transistor is reverse-biased to increase the channel-to-gate electric field, crowd the carriers closer to the surface, and reduce the channel depth, the drain saturation resistance will increase. If the capacitive feedback mechanism is dominant, increasing the reverse bias on the substrate increases the substrate depletion region depth, decreases the shielding effect on the channel, and increases the drain-channel coupling capacitance with a corresponding decrease in the drain saturation resistance.

The experimental curves of Fig. 5–17 show that the application of reverse bias on the substrate causes a substantial *reduction* of the drain

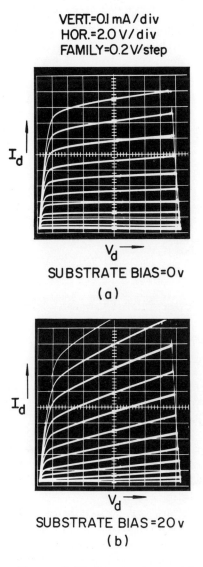

VERT.=0.1 mA / div
HOR.=2.0 V / div
FAMILY=0.2 V/step

SUBSTRATE BIAS=0 v

(a)

SUBSTRATE BIAS =20 v

(b)

Figure 5–17. Output characteristics of an *n*-type MOS Transistor illustrating the dependence of the saturation voltage gain on the substrate bias.

saturation resistance and voltage gain. Additional results on typical units of two different geometries are shown in Figs.5–18, 5–19, 5–20, and 5–21. The characteristics of the two units are:

Unit 1 (Fig. 5–18): n-type unit (positive gate voltage for conduction);
channel length $= 1 \times 10^{-3}$ cm;
total channel width $= 10 \times 10^{-3}$ cm;
channel oxide thickness $= 1000$ Å $= 1.0 \times 10^{-5}$ cm;
effective electron mobility (measured) $= 220$ cm²/v-sec;
pinch-off voltage $= + 2$ v.

SOURCE - DRAIN CONTACTS

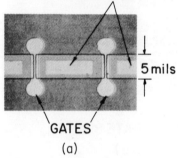

5 mils

GATES

(a)

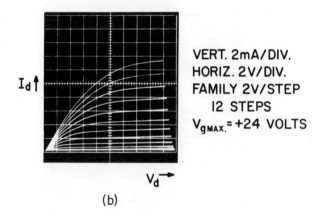

I_d

VERT. 2mA/DIV.
HORIZ. 2V/DIV.
FAMILY 2V/STEP
12 STEPS
$V_{gMAX.} = +24$ VOLTS

V_d

(b)

Figure 5–18. Photomicrograph and characteristic curves for type-1 geometry.

Unit 2 (Fig. 5–20): p-type unit (negative gate voltage for conduction);
channel length $= 1.5 \times 10^{-3}$ cm;

total channel width $= 75 \times 10^{-3}$ cm;
channel oxide thickness $= 1500$ Å;
effective hole mobility (measured) $= 170$ cm^2/v-sec;
pinch-off voltage $= -0.5$ v.

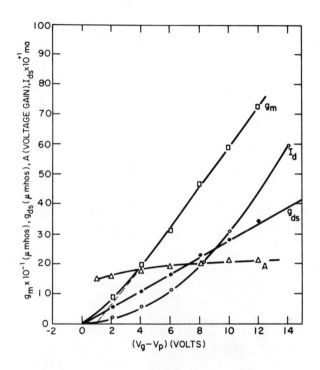

Figure 5-19. Measured values of g_m, g_{ds}, I_{ds}, and A vs. V_g for type-1 geometry.

Including the effect of the pinch-off voltage and the channel width, the reciprocal of Eq. (5–67) gives for the drain conductance:

$$g_{ds} = \frac{wC_{dc}\mu_{\text{eff}}}{l^2}(V_g - V_p) \qquad (5\text{–}71)$$

where, from Eq. (5–65), $C_{dc} \approx \epsilon_s$. Substituting the parameters for the two units listed before into this equation, we find that:

For unit 1 $g_{ds} = 2.2 (V_g - 2)$ μmhos for $V_g > + 2$v.
For unit 2 $g_{ds} = 5.5 (- V_g - 0.5)$ μmhos for $V_g < - 0.5$ v.

The experimental curves for these two units (Figs. 5–19 and 5–21) yield:

For unit 1 $g_{ds} \approx 2.8\,(V_g - 2)$ μmhos for $V_g > +2$ v.
For unit 2 $g_{ds} \approx 11\,(-V_g - 0.5)$ μmhos for $V_g < -0.5$ v.

The linear variation with gate voltage is apparent. The discrepancy in the constants is due, in part, to the simplified derivation of $C_{dc} \approx \epsilon_s$. However, considering the relative simplicity of the model, the experimental results are in good agreement with the theory.

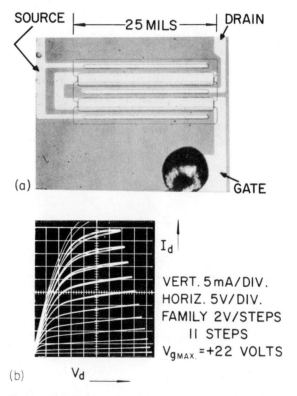

SOURCE |←——25 MILS——→| DRAIN

(a)   GATE

I_d

VERT. 5 mA/DIV.
HORIZ. 5V/DIV.
FAMILY 2V/STEPS
II STEPS
$V_{g_{MAX}}$ =+22 VOLTS

(b) V_d ——

Figure 5–20. Photomicrograph and characteristic curves for type-2 geometry.

It is interesting to note that unit 1 is a very good approximation to a square-law device for $V_g > +6$ v. From Eqs. (5–69) and (5–70):

$$A = \frac{l}{d_i} \times \frac{\epsilon_i}{\epsilon_s} \qquad (5\text{--}72)$$

Substituting the appropriate values for unit 1, we obtain $A \approx 33$. From Fig. 5–19, the measured value for A agrees with this calculated value to within a factor of 2.

Equation (5-72) points out a problem in optimizing the performance of these transistors. If the channel length is reduced to increase the frequency response of the transistor, the voltage gain will drop because of a decrease in the saturation drain resistance. This problem may be surmounted by an increase in the substrate doping level to the point where

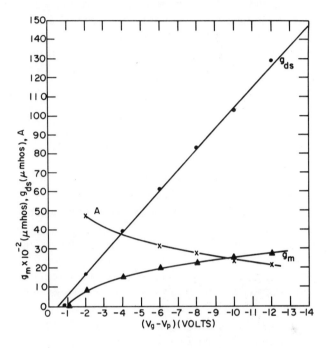

Figure 5-21. Measured values of g_m, g_{ds}, and A vs. V_g for type-2 geometry.

the substrate-to-channel depletion region is sufficiently narrow so that penetration of the drain field into the channel region is greatly reduced. In a sense, the substrate acts as a "screen grid" in capacitively decoupling the drain from the channel. The penalty is an increased drain-to-substrate capacitance. It is important to note that the drain resistance discussed so far is a low-frequency parameter. At high frequencies, particularly as one approaches the cut-off frequency of the device, the resistive component of the output impedance may become quite low due to loss mechanisms, and may be deteriorated by an increase in the substrate doping level. This phenomenon has been observed in high-frequency MOS transistors. In addition, the behavior of the drain saturation resistance as a function of gate voltage may deviate from the simple linear relationship in units where surface state effects are strong, in this case, the assumption of constant mobility is no longer valid.

3. Effect of surface states on device behavior

In general, the interface between the insulator and semiconductor possesses trapping states distributed in energy over the forbidden gap. As the applied gate voltage modulates the mobile charge in the surface region, it also modulates the amount of charge trapped in these states.

At a point x in the channel, the total charge per unit area produced by the gate voltage, V_g, is $Q(x) = C_i[V_g - V(x)]$ where $V(x)$ is the potential at the point x in the channel. A portion of this charge is trapped in surface states and cannot contribute to the conduction. The effect of surface states can be included if we define an effective mobility:

$$\mu_{\text{eff}} \equiv \left[C_i \frac{dV(x)}{dx} \frac{dV_g}{dI_d} \right]^{-1} \tag{5–73}$$

which is less than the actual mobility.

The conventional procedure for computing the charge trapped in the surface states is to determine the position of the Fermi level at the surface and apply thermal equilibrium statistics.[12] However, when the channel drift field is high enough to generate hot carriers, impact ionization of the trapped charges may become significant. The energy required for this ionization may be substantially less than that for band-to-band hole-electron pair generation. In the region of "saturated" -current operation, this ionization causes an increase in the drain current with increasing drain voltage, and decreases the saturation drain resistance. For most devices, the surface state density is sufficiently small so that this effect is not significant compared to the feedback effect described in Section 5–2.2. The surface states also play a role in determining the temperature-dependence of the transistor transfer characteristic. This is discussed in Section 5–2.8.

4. Effect of surface scattering on transistor characteristics

In this section the effect of surface scattering[17] on the behavior of the MOS transistor operating in the nondegenerate regime will be considered. If several different independent scattering mechanisms exist, the effective mobility is given by:

$$\mu_{\text{eff}} = \left[\frac{1}{\mu_a} + \frac{1}{\mu_b} + \cdots \right]^{-1} \tag{5–74}$$

where μ_a, μ_b, etc., are the mobilities associated with each individual scattering mechanism in the absence of the others. The mobilities of interest are:

μ_o = bulk mobility (constant), and

$\mu_s \approx \mu_o \left(\dfrac{\mathcal{E}_{sc}}{\mathcal{E}_s} \right)$ = surface scattering mobility [4] for perfectly diffuse

surface scattering

where:

$$\mathcal{E}_s = \mathcal{E}_s(x) = \frac{V_g - V(x)}{d_i} \times \frac{\epsilon_i}{\epsilon_s} \qquad (5\text{-}75)$$

and $\mathcal{E}_{sc}$ is that field for which the surface scattering mobility becomes equal to the bulk mobility:[4]

$$\mathcal{E}_{sc} = \frac{(m^*kT)^{1/2}}{q\tau_o} \qquad (5\text{-}76)$$

The effective mobility of the surface layer carriers is:

$$\mu_{\text{eff}} = \mu_o \left[1 + \frac{V_g - V(x)}{V_{gc}} \right]^{-1} \qquad (5\text{-}77)$$

where:

$$V_{gc} = \left(\frac{\epsilon_s}{\epsilon_i} \right) d_i \, \mathcal{E}_{sc} \qquad (5\text{-}78)$$

The channel conductance is determined by the method used in Section 5-1, except that the effective mobility must be used rather than the bulk mobility. Thus:

$$I_d = \mu_{\text{eff}} C_i [V_g - V(x)] \frac{dV(x)}{dx} \qquad (V_d < V_g) \qquad (5\text{-}79)$$

And substituting for μ_{eff}:

$$I_d = \frac{\mu_o C_i}{l} \int_0^{V_d} \frac{V_g - V(x)}{1 + [V_g - V(x)]/V_{gc}} dV(x) \qquad (V_d < V_g) \qquad (5\text{-}80)$$

We evaluate this integral by making the substitution, $Z = [V_g - V(x)]/V_{gc}$ and integrating by parts. The result is:

$$I_d = \frac{\mu_o C_i}{l} V_{gc}^2 \left\{ \frac{V_d}{V_{gc}} - \ln \frac{1 + (V_g/V_{gc})}{1 + [(V_g - V_d)/V_{gc}]} \right\} \qquad (V_d < V_g) \qquad (5\text{-}81)$$

In saturation ($V_d > V_g$), the current is:

$$I_{ds} = \frac{\mu_o C_i}{l} V_{gc}^2 \left[\frac{V_g}{V_{gc}} - \ln\left(1 + \frac{V_g}{V_{gc}}\right) \right] \qquad (V_d \geqslant V_g) \qquad \textbf{(5-82)}$$

The transconductance in saturation is:

$$g_m = \frac{\mu_o C_i}{l} V_{gc} \left[\frac{V_g/V_{gc}}{1 + (V_g/V_{gc})} \right] \qquad \textbf{(5-83)}$$

For $V_g \ll V_{gc}$, the transconductance reduces to that of the constant mobility case:

$$g_m = \frac{\mu_o C_i}{l} V_g \qquad \textbf{(5-84)}$$

A plot of the normalized transconductance as a function of normalized gate voltage given by Eq. (5–83) appears in Fig. 5–22.

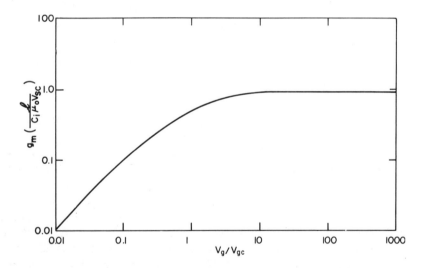

Figure 5-22. Normalized transconductance vs. normalized gate voltage for a perfectly diffuse scattering surface, nondegenerate inversion layer.

$\mathcal{E}_{sc}$ has been defined as that field for which the surface scattering mobility becomes equal to the bulk mobility. It is of interest to determine the order of magnitude of this field. For the two mobilities to be equal, the surface and bulk scattering times, and hence the surface and bulk mean-free-paths must be equal. Assuming $\mu_o = 1200$ cm²/v-sec, and an effective mass for the electrons of 0.36 of the free electron mass, the mean collision time in silicon is:

$$\tau = \frac{m^*}{q}\mu_o \approx 2 \times 10^{-13} \text{ sec}$$

For an average thermal speed of 10^7 cm/sec, the mean-free-path is:

$$\lambda_{mfp} \approx 2 \times 10^{-6} \text{ cm} = 200 \text{ Å}$$

For this particular system, surface scattering becomes significant only for fields in excess of that required to make the surface Debye length less than 200 Å. For a Si–SiO₂ structure, Eq. (5–76) gives $\mathscr{E}_{sc} = 5 \times 10^4$ v/cm.

EXPERIMENTAL OBSERVATIONS OF SURFACE SCATTERING EFFECTS IN A SILICON MOS TRANSISTOR. A silicon MOS transistor was fabricated with a thermally grown SiO₂ insulating layer 1000 Å thick. From Eq. (5–75) with $\mu_o = 1200$ cm²/v-sec, the calculated surface scattering mobility is:

$$\mu_s = \frac{6 \times 10^7}{\mathscr{E}_s} \text{ cm}^2/\text{v-sec}$$

and the calculated effective surface mobility is:

$$\mu_{\text{eff}} = \frac{6000}{5 + \mathscr{E}_s \times 10^{-4}} \qquad \text{for } \mathscr{E}_s > 5 \times 10^4 \text{ v/cm}$$

This effective surface mobility[15] varies over the range from 600 cm²/v-sec to 12 cm²/v-sec as $\mathscr{E}_s$ varies from 5×10^4 v/cm to 5×10^6 v/cm.

The actual behavior of the device depends strongly on the conditions at the Si–SiO₂ interface. The characteristics of the n-type unit studied are shown in Fig. 5–19. The transconductance is a linear function of the gate voltage over a rather wide range of gate voltages and, hence, over a wide range of surface fields. From Eq. (5–10), upon inserting the pinch-off voltage and channel width, we obtain:

$$g_m = \frac{\mu_{\text{eff}} C_i w}{l}(V_g - V_p) \tag{5-85}$$

If the theoretical slope of the g_m vs. V_g curve given by Eq. (5–85) is equated to the slope of the experimental curve, it is found that:

$$\frac{\mu_{\text{eff}} C_i w}{l} = 65 \ \mu\text{mhos/volt}$$

From the geometry of this particular unit, $w/l \approx 10$. Hence, $\mu_{\text{eff}} = 220$ cm^2/v-sec.

From the experimental curve, this mobility is constant for gate fields extending into the 10^6 v/cm range. It is apparent that the mean-free-path for carrier scattering in the inversion layer is on the order of 30–40 Å and is independent of the gate field. This indicates that either the effective potential well for surface scattering is much larger than the assumed value based on the surface Debye length or that the surface is acting primarily as a specular scatterer. Experimental results[16] indicate that both conditions probably exist. The failure of the simple linear potential-well theory to quantitatively predict surface scattering is not too surprising when the simplicity of the assumptions is considered. The primary purpose has been to give the reader an understanding of the physics involved.

5. Influence of parasitic source and drain resistance

In this section, the influences of parasitic source and drain resistance and of surface scattering will be examined theoretically and found to be qualitatively similar. Both cause a "saturation" in the transconductance vs. applied gate-voltage curve. Experimentally, it is shown that pure surface scattering does not appear to play a dominant role and that μ_s, the mobility in the surface region, is nearly constant with gate voltage and is lower than the bulk mobility, μ_b, (e.g., $\mu = 200$ cm^2/v-sec versus $\mu_b = 1300$ cm^2/v-sec for electrons in silicon at room temperature) due to some undetermined scattering mechanism.

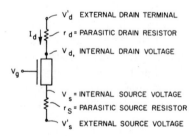

Figure 5–23. First-order model for the analysis of the effect of parasitic source and drain resistances.

The model to be analyzed is shown in Fig. 5–23. The "internal" transistor (i.e., not including r_s and r_d) will be considered a square-law device. The characteristic equations for this "internal" transistor, derived in Section 5-1 are:

$$I_d = \frac{\mu_o C_i}{2l}[V_g^2 - (V_g - V_d)^2] \qquad (V_d < V_g) \tag{5-86}$$

$$I_{ds} = \frac{\mu_o C_i}{2l} V_g^2 \qquad (V_d > V_g) \tag{5-87}$$

In terms of the voltages of Fig. 5-23, the drain saturation current is:

$$I_{ds} = \frac{\mu_o C_i}{2l}[V_g - V_s]^2 \tag{5-88}$$

If the voltage reference is taken as $V_s' = 0$, then:

$$V_s = I_{ds} r_s \tag{5-89}$$

and

$$I_{ds} = \frac{1}{\alpha}(I_g - I_{ds})^2 \tag{5-90}$$

I_g is not an actual gate current but is defined as:

$$I_g \equiv \frac{V_g}{r_s} \tag{5-91}$$

and

$$\alpha \equiv \left[\frac{\mu_o C_i}{2l} \times r_s^2\right]^{-1} \tag{5-92}$$

The solution of the quadratic equation (Eq. 5-90) for I_{ds} is:

$$I_{ds} = \tfrac{1}{2}[2I_g + \alpha - \sqrt{4\alpha I_g + \alpha^2}] \tag{5-93}$$

The transconductance is:

$$g_m = \frac{\partial I_{ds}}{\partial V_g} = \frac{1}{r_s} \times \frac{\partial I_{ds}}{\partial I_g}$$

so that:

$$g_m r_s = 1 - \left(\frac{V_g}{V_o} + 1\right)^{-1/2} \tag{5-94}$$

where:

$$V_o \equiv \frac{\alpha r_s}{4} = \frac{l}{2\mu_o C_i r_s} \tag{5-95}$$

A plot of $g_m r_s$ as a function of V_g/V_o appears in Fig. 5–24. If $V_g/V_o \ll 1$, then $g_m r_s \approx V_g/2V_o$ and:

$$g_m \approx \frac{\mu C_i}{l} V_g$$

In other words, the series resistance is negligible compared to the channel resistance.

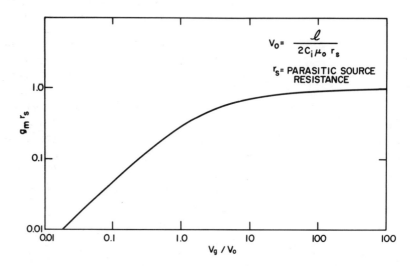

Figure 5–24. Normalized transconductance vs. normalized gate voltage including the effect of parasitic source resistance.

The effect of the parasitic source resistance on the transconductance is qualitatively very similar to the effect of surface scattering considered in Section 5–2.4 and illustrated in Fig. 5–22. In practice, one must be careful in determining which of these two phenomena may be causing saturation of the transconductance.

6. Substrate doping and substrate bias effects

The substrate for the MOS transistor is doped to form a junction with respect to the source-drain contacts and channel. This junction acts as a gate on the channel in the same fashion as the junction in the junction-gate field-effect transistor. If the substrate is left unconnected, its potential will float slightly above that of the source contact so that the back current flow of the drain-to-substrate diode is exactly counterbalanced by an equal forward current flow from the substrate to the source.

Reverse bias may be applied to the substrate to deplete the channel and cause an effective shift in the pinch-off voltage as seen from the metal gate. The shift in pinch-off voltage for a uniformly doped substrate is:

$$\Delta V_p = 2\left(\frac{\epsilon_s}{\epsilon_i}\right)\left(\frac{N_a q d_i^2}{\epsilon_s}\right)^{1/2} [(V_{su} + \psi_{cs})^{1/2} - \psi_{cs}^{1/2}] \qquad (5\text{--}96)$$

where: V_{su} is the applied substrate bias; and ψ_{cs} is the "built-in" channel-to-substrate potential (approximately 0.5 v–0.8 v for silicon, depending on the doping level).

This analysis is based on a one-dimensional field distribution. If the channel-to-substrate depletion-region depth becomes comparable to the channel length, the one-dimensional model becomes inaccurate and the effect of the substrate bias begins to decrease. The shift in pinch-off voltage as a function of substrate bias and substrate doping level is shown in Fig. 5–25 for silicon – silicon dioxide. An additional effect of the substrate gating action is to cause pinch-off at the drain for drain voltages less than V_g, reducing the transconductance.

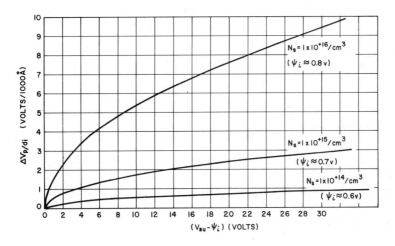

Figure 5–25. Shift in pinch-off voltage vs. applied substrate reverse bias (silicon substrate).

In the section on voltage gain, the effect of capacitive feedback from the drain to the source region of the channel through the substrate was examined. It was found that if the substrate was conducting sufficiently, the substrate gate would act as a screen grid to shield the channel from the drain. For the shielding to be effective, the channel-to-substrate depletion-region depth should be significantly smaller than the channel length.

This requirement must be balanced against the undesirable increase in drain-to-substrate capacitance.

7. Impurity surface inversion layer (doped channel)

In the fabrication of field-effect transistors, one alternative is to dope the surface of the semiconductor so that a conducting inversion layer is formed without the application of an external electric field. This layer may be modulated by application of the electric field. A uniform p-type background with n-type surface doping will again be considered.

It is assumed that the mobile charge density follows the spatial distribution of the diffused impurity centers exactly. For the case at hand:

$$n(y) = N_d(y) - N_a \tag{5–97}$$

This is accurate only if the dimensions involved are large compared with the characteristic Debye length, $\lambda_o = [\epsilon_s kT/q^2 n(y)]^{1/2}$ based on $n(y)$. Consider the case of a total sheet density, ΔN_d per unit area, of n-type impurity distributed over a depth, d, where $d \to 0$. The effect of the doping is to act as a surface sheet charge of $Q_s = q\Delta N_d$, and to add a component to the surface field of $\mathscr{E}_{sd} = q\Delta N_d/\epsilon_s$. For no applied external (gate) field, there will be an internal field, $\mathscr{E}_{sd}$, terminating at the surface of the charges $q\Delta N_d$. The effect of this surface charge is identical to the effect of an applied gate field of $(\epsilon_s/\epsilon_i)\mathscr{E}_{sd}$. To a good approximation, the mobile electron distribution is characterized by the Debye length:

$$\lambda = \left[\frac{\epsilon_s kT}{q^2 n_s}\right] = \frac{kT/q}{\mathscr{E}_{sd}} \tag{5–98}$$

where n_s is the mobile electron density at the surface and $qn_s\lambda = Q_s$. The approximation, $d \to 0$ is equivalent to setting $d \leq \lambda$. This states that, for purposes of fabrication of a shallow doped channel, the distribution of the diffused impurities is unimportant so long as the total sheet density is at the proper value, and the diffusion depth is much less than the characteristic length:

$$d_c = \frac{kT/Q}{q\Delta N_d/\epsilon_s} \tag{5–99}$$

8. Temperature dependence of the MOS transistor characteristics

Temperature-dependence of the carrier mobility and pinch-off voltage will now be considered. It will be pointed out that, for units using an induced (rather than doped) channel, operation at temperatures as low as liquid helium is possible. It also will be shown that, for a unit in which the surface mobility is significantly lower than the bulk mobility, the effect of lattice thermal scattering is reduced.

The major temperature-dependent mechanisms in the MOS transistor are:

1. Carrier mobility in the channel.
2. Surface state contributions to the transfer characteristic.
3. Drain-diode leakage current.

1. The carrier mobility in the channel generally decreases with increasing temperature because of increased carrier-phonon scattering. If the channel is a surface inversion layer produced by an external gate field, operation at temperatures as low as that of liquid helium is possible since the channel carriers will not "freeze out." This contrasts with the behavior of the bipolar transistor in which operation ceases when the mobile carriers "freeze out" into the impurity centers. The actual temperature-dependence of the surface mobility differs from that in the bulk because of the complex nature of the surface region. The effect of lattice thermal scattering becomes apparent only when the lattice-scattering mobility decreases to the point where it is less than the mobility due to surface and the surface-region scattering. If $\mu_b \approx 1300$ cm²/v-sec, $\mu_s \approx 600$ cm²/v-sec, and the lattice scattering mobility varies as $T^{-3/2}$, the temperature variation of mobility due to the bulk lattice scattering will be small even up to $T = 200°C$.

2. The temperature-dependence of the surface states and their influence on the transfer characteristics of the MOS transistor have been considered by Heiman and Miiller.[13] A good semiquantitative understanding may be obtained from the following. Setting the current from source to drain constant, we may investigate the effect of variations in temperature on the gate voltage required to maintain this current constant.

For the total charge in the channel inversion layer to stay constant with temperature variation, the Boltzmann factor $e^{-(E_{cs}-E_F)/kT}$ must be constant, (E_{cs} is the energy of the conduction band at the surface, and E_F is the Fermi level). Hence, $(E_{cs} - E_F) \propto kT$, and the Fermi level moves linearly with temperature. As the Fermi level moves, it may sweep through surface state levels and change Q_{ss}, the net charge in the surface states, and hence the field in the oxide. A change in gate voltage is required to maintain a constant current. For most cases, the surface state distribution (in energy) may be considered uniform over the range of energy variation of the Fermi level (e.g., $\Delta E_F \approx 2kT$ for $\Delta T \approx 100°C$). The change in gate voltage is simply $\Delta V_g = C_i \Delta Q_{ss}(T)$, and:

$$\frac{dV_g}{dT}\bigg|_{I_d} = C_i \frac{dQ_{ss}}{dE_F} \times \frac{dE_F}{dT} = \gamma_T \tag{5-100}$$

where γ_T is a constant dependent on the surface state density and the initial level of the gate voltage. In general, $|\gamma_T|$ increases with increasing surface state density and decreases with increasing channel charge (or gate voltage). A typical set of curves[16] for this effect appears in Fig. 5–26.

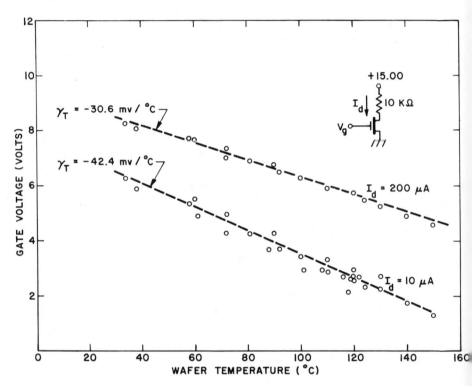

Figure 5–26. Temperature-dependence of pinch-off voltage in a typical MOS transistor.

3. In the conventional MOS transistor structure, the drain contact forms a back-biased diode with respect to the substrate. The temperature performance of this diode is conventional and is not influenced by *Beta* multiplication effects observed in the bipolar transistor when the base is not grounded to the emitter.

POWER LIMITATIONS. The power limitations of the MOS transistor are nearly identical to those of the bipolar transistor. The dissipation of power is limited primarily by the thermal resistance of the transistor-package combination. For channel lengths much smaller than the wafer thickness, the conduction of heat from the channel into the substrate is radial (cylindrical) and leads to a logarithmic dependence of temperature on power dissipation rather than the linear dependence characteristic of planar heat flow.

For large-area junction-gate devices, Dacey and Ross[20] calculate a maximum permissible power dissipation of several hundred watts/cm². Measurements on small-area silicon MOS transistors, in which the heat flow is radial from the channel into the substrate, indicate that power dissipation per unit area of channel may run as high as 10,000 watts/cm² without limiting transistor performance.

THERMAL RUNAWAY AND INSTABILITIES. In the MOS transistor, the net drain current decreases or increases only slightly with increasing temperature. The power dissipation has either a negative or small positive temperature coefficient, and thermal runaway of the type exhibited by the bipolar transistor does not occur. Early MOS silicon transistors, under the influence of applied positive gate voltage, exhibited a temperature-dependent instability which took the form of a shift in the I_d vs. V_g transfer characteristic along the V_g axis (i.e., a shift in the pinch-off voltage) with time. The direction of the shift was opposite to the sign of the gate voltage and was enhanced by elevated temperature. The cause of this instability is a motion of charged centers in the oxide. Modification of the chemical structure of the oxide has largely eliminated this instability.

5-3 JUNCTION-GATE FIELD-EFFECT TRANSISTOR

The junction-gate unipolar transistor was described by Shockley[19] in 1952. It is a means of obtaining a practical field-effect device without the need to solve the surface state problem. Figure 5-27 shows the

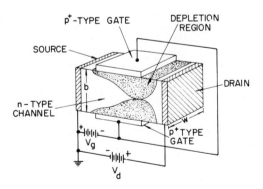

Figure 5-27. Junction-gate field-effect transistor.

structure. The mechanism for charge control is the capacitance of the reverse-biased *p-n* junction. Since the electric field now is completely immersed in the semiconductor, the surface plays no part in the device operation, and the problem of surface states is avoided. The use of a *p-n* junction allows only depletion of charge from the channel, as reversing the applied gate voltage forward biases the p-n junction and results in heavy current flow. Extensive analyses of this device have appeared in the literature,[20,21,22,23] and only the more significant aspects of its behavior will be reviewed.

1. Basic device equation.

The n-type channel will be considered to be uniformly doped. The cross-sectional area available for conduction at a point x along the channel is then:

$$A(x) = [b - 2d(x)]w \qquad (5\text{–}101)$$

where: b = total depth of the bar of semiconductor;
  d = depth of the depletion region; and
  w = width of bar of semiconductor.

The pinch-off voltage is that gate-to-channel voltage for which $d = b/2$. An analysis[19] of this case yields the following characteristic equation:

$$I_d = \frac{wb}{l\rho_o}V_p\left[\frac{V_d}{V_p} + \frac{2}{3}\left(\frac{V_g - V_d}{V_p}\right)^{3/2} - \frac{2}{3}\left(\frac{V_g}{V_p}\right)^{3/2}\right] \quad \left|V_d\right| \leq \left|V_g - V_p\right| \quad (5\text{–}102)$$

$$I_d = \frac{wb}{l\rho_o}V_p\left[\frac{V_g}{V_p} - \frac{1}{3} - \frac{2}{3}\left(\frac{V_g}{V_p}\right)^{3/2}\right] \quad \left|V_d\right| > \left|V_g - V_p\right| \quad (5\text{–}103)$$

$$V_p = \frac{\rho}{8\epsilon_s\mu_o}b^2 \qquad (5\text{–}104)$$

and

$$g_m = \frac{wb}{l\rho_o}\left[1 - \frac{V_g}{V_p}\right]^{1/2} \qquad (5\text{–}105)$$

where a constant mobility, μ_o, has been assumed. The effects of mobility variation may be computed in a fashion similar to that for the MOS transistor.[20]

2. Power dissipation limitations

Dacey and Ross[20] have computed that it is not feasible to operate the junction-gate field-effect transistor in the regime of square-root field-dependent mobility because of excessive power dissipation. The upper limit of power dissipation was set at several hundred watts/cm² based on a large-area device.

For present planar-type devices (a typical structure is illustrated in Fig. 5–28), the power dissipation into the substrate is "cylindrical" as in the MOS case discussed in Section 5–2. The effective *area* used in

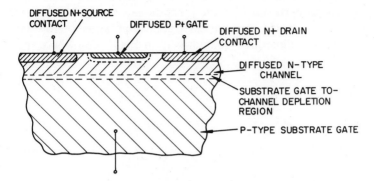

Figure 5–28. Planar p^+-n junction-gate field-effect transistor.

computing the power density is significantly larger than the actual active channel area. In general, the maximum allowable power density is on the same order as that for a bipolar transistor of equivalent over-all area. Typical values for this power are on the order of hundreds of watts/cm², consistent with the predictions of Dacey and Ross. The same power *density,* computed in terms of the active channel area, may be as high as 10^4 watts/cm².

3. Temperature performance

The temperature performance of the junction-gate field-effect transistor is somewhat poorer than the equivalent MOS structure due to the degradation in input impedance of the reverse biased *p-n* junction. The behavior of the drain-to-substrate junction (in the planar-type unit) is basically identical to that in the MOS structure. An advantage of the junction-gate field-effect transistor is the lack of a surface-state component in the temperature-dependence of the threshold voltage as observed in the MOS transistor.

4. Frequency response

The fundamental frequency response of the junction-gate unit is controlled by the same factor as in the MOS transistor, i.e., carrier transit time from source to drain. In the junction-gate field-effect transistor there is a more significant problem with the parasitic source resistance. This resistance arises from the necessity of spacing the highly-doped gate region away from the highly-doped source region to maintain a reasonably high gate-breakdown voltage. This portion of inactive channel length acts as a degenerative resistance. The effects of a resistance of this type on the device current-voltage characteristics have been briefly considered in Section 5–2 for the MOS transistor. A similar analysis may be performed for the junction-gate unit. This degeneration often results in a device having a fairly good approximation to square-law behavior. This is illustrated qualitatively in Fig. 5–29, where the effect

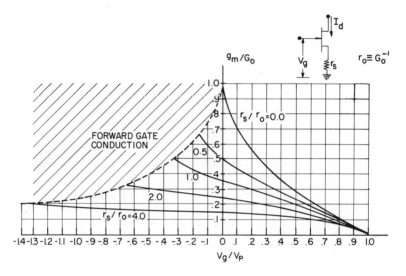

Figure 5–29. Normalized transconductance vs. normalized gate voltage as a function of degenerative source resistance for junction-gate transistor.

of the resistance is to cause the normally concave upward g_m vs. V_g curve to become more convex. For the appropriate r_s, this can result in approximate square-law behavior over a reasonably wide range of gate voltages.

REFERENCES

1. S. R. Hofstein and F. P. Heiman, Proc. IEEE **51**, 1190 (1963).

2. G. T. Wright, *Solid State Electronics* **7**, 167 (1964).

3. S. R. Hofstein, Ph.D. thesis, Princeton University, May, 1964.

4. J. R. Schrieffer, *Phys. Rev.* **97**, 641 (1955).

5. W. Shockley, *Bell Syst. Tech. J.* **30**, 990 (1951).

6. E. J. Ryder, *Phys. Rev.* **90**, 766 (1953).

7. A. C. Prior, *J. Phys. and Chem. of Sol.* **12**, 175 (1959).

8. J. Grosvalet, C. Motsch, and R. Tribes, *Solid State Elec.* **6**, 65 (1963).

9. J. Hilibrand, to be published.

10. C. D. Root *et al.*, *IRE Trans. on Elec. Dev.* **ED–7**, 257 (1960).

11. S. R. Hofstein and G. Warfield, *IEEE Trans. on Elec. Dev.* **ED–12**, 66 (1965).

12. L. M. Terman, *Stanford Res. Tech. Rept.*, No. 1655–1, Stanford University, Calif. (Feb., 1961).

13. F. P. Heiman and H. Miiller, *IEEE Trans. on Elec. Dev.* **ED– 12**, 142 (1965).

14. R. F. Greene *J. Phys. Chem. Solids* **14**, 291 (1960).

15. C. D. Root and L. Vadasz, *IEEE Trans. Elec. Dev.* **ED–11**, 294 (1964).

16. A. B. Fowler, F. F. Fang, and F. Hochberg, to be published.

17. F. P. Heiman and S. R. Hofstein, *Electronics* (Nov., 1964).

18. H. C. Nathanson, R. Szedon, and N. A. Jordan, Electron Devices Meeting, Washington, D.C. (Oct., 1963).

19. W. Shockley, Proc. *IRE* **40**, 1365 (1952).

20. G. C. Dacey and I. M. Ross, *Bell Syst. Tech. J.* **34**, 1149 (1955).

21. R. C. Prim and W. Shockley, *IRE Trans. Elec. Dev.* **ED–4**, 1 (1953).

22. R. R. Bockemuehl, *IEEE Trans. Elec. Dev.* **ED–10**, 31 (1963).

23. A. van der Ziel and J. W. Ero, *IEEE Trans. Elec. Dev.* **ED–11**, 128 (1964).

6

Noise in Field-Effect Transistors

Harwick Johnson

6-1 NOISE IN ELECTRON DEVICES

Exhaustive studies of the noise behavior of field-effect transistors, particularly in the case of insulated-gate transistors, have not yet been made. This chapter deals with the first-order principles of the more significant noise sources to provide an understanding of the basic noise behavior of field-effect transistors. Parasitic series source and drain resistance are not included as sources of thermal fluctuations in the noise analysis. These can readily be added to the basic behavior by suitable manipulation of the equivalent circuit representations.

Consideration of the noise behavior of any solid-state active device involves the evaluation of the contribution of three types of noise. These are generally denoted as thermal noise, shot noise, and 1/f noise. *Thermal noise* is due to the thermal agitation of carriers in conducting media under conditions of thermal equilibrium. This is the familiar noise of a resistance and may be represented by a mean-square current generator:

$$\overline{i^2} = \frac{4kT\Delta f}{R} \tag{6-1}$$

in parallel with the resistance R. kT is the Boltzmann energy and Δf is the frequency bandwidth. Reference to thermal fluctuations according to the conventional formulation applies strictly to systems in thermal equilibrium. Application to portions of active semiconductor devices, such as the channel of a field-effect transistor with voltage applied, implicitly assumes that the thermal distribution of charge is not significantly altered. This situation has been discussed in connection with the use of Boltzmann statistics in the analysis of device behavior.[1,2] (See Chapter 5.) The use of Boltzmann statistics was found justified for the induced-channel field-effect transistor and this transistor model will be used in the following analysis.

Shot noise has its origin in the discreteness of the charge carriers and the random manner in which they are produced. These are the individual events of generation and recombination of carriers, which are statistically averaged to measure such properties of semiconductors as lifetime, surface recombination velocity, junction currents, and diffusion constant. These phenomena generally give rise to mean-square current fluctuations proportional to the current flow, I, and are represented by:

$$\overline{i^2} = \gamma 2qI\Delta f \qquad (6\text{-}2)$$

where γ is unity for purely random events but may be less for physical mechanisms involving a smoothing effect. Hence, we have the term *shot noise* by analogy to the fluctuations in current flow in a vacuum tube.

The term *1/f noise* refers to a type of noise whose power density varies inversely with frequency. The inverse linear relationship is loosely applied and any noise having a spectrum of this general nature is often called 1/f noise. This type of noise is also referred to as flicker or scintillation noise. In practical devices, this noise is predominant only at low frequencies. It is perhaps the least understood of the various types of noise mechanisms but is often ascribed to some local alteration of the electrical properties of a material through some physical–chemical action. Surfaces are particularly prone to give rise to 1/f noise as are regions of the material which are highly stressed by electrical fields giving rise to *leakage* currents. Historically, it appears that almost all active devices have suffered from large amounts of 1/f noise in their early stage of development. The field-effect transistor has not been an exception. Also, historically, continued refinement of device processing and quality improvement has invariably reduced 1/f noise to insignificant levels at the frequency of most applications.

6–2 NOISE SOURCES IN FIELD-EFFECT TRANSISTORS

In a field-effect transistor, thermal noise will be produced by the channel resistance and by parasitic source and drain resistances. In the first case, the fluctuations interact with the transistor control mechanism to produce output current fluctuations other than that which would be indicated by the thermal noise of the output resistance itself. Indeed, van der Ziel[3] has concluded that, in junction-gate transistors at low frequencies, this is the predominant noise source in the absence of 1/f noise. At somewhat higher frequencies, the channel fluctuations are coupled through the gate capacitance into the gate circuit, which further affects the noise performance of the transistor.

In the junction-gate field-effect transistor, the gate junction is reverse biased. Guggenbuehl and Strutt[4] have shown that current fluctuations in the current flow through a reverse biased *p-n* junction can be expressed as shot noise. The numerical coefficient, γ, in the shot noise expression depends on the physical mechanism predominant in the current flow in the space-charge region. The physical mechanism may be diffusion in the case of germanium junctions or generation and recombination in the case of silicon junctions. Other possible noise contributions which may appear in the form of shot noise are those caused by the generation and recombination of carriers in the channel, and current flow through the space-charge region of the pinched-off channel. In the first instance, the noise contribution is expected to be negligible because the channel in practical field-effect devices is heavily doped. In the second instance, experimental evidence has not yet shown that this effect is of significance in comparison with the noise due to thermal fluctuations in the channel discussed earlier. However, most measurements have been made below or near saturation where first-order analyses apply. Both experiment and analysis need to be extended into the saturation region to conclusively evaluate the significance of this possible noise mechanism.

At low frequencies, 1/f noise is by far the most important noise source in field-effect transistors. The frequency below which 1/f noise is dominant may be less than 10^3 cps or may be greater than 10^6 cps, depending on the state of the development. For example, early germanium units[5] had noise factors of 68 db at 10^3 cps while modern junction-gate silicon units[5] have single-frequency noise factors of less than 1 db at this frequency. This improvement is due to the improved quality of the *p-n* junction, minimizing leakage currents and charge trapping centers both on the surface and the transition region of the junction. In modern silicon junction-gate transistors Sah[7] suggests that the major contribution to l-f noise is due to the fluctuation of charge in the recombination-generation centers in the transition region. These are the centers responsible for the reverse bias current as well.[8]

In contrast to junction-gate transistors where the junction can be imbedded in the bulk of a homogeneous material, the insulated-gate transistor is a surface-controlled device where the control action occurs at the interface between two dissimilar materials, the insulator and the semiconductor. As discussed in Chapter 2, high concentrations of surface states are often found at interfaces. In addition, the insulator structure is noncrystalline (Chapter 3) and contains defect states which may exchange charge with the semiconductor. In insulated-gate transistors utilizing polycrystalline semiconductors, there is the additional concern of localized states at the crystalline boundaries. As a consequence, the insulated-gate transistor is susceptible to 1/f noise generated through charge exchange with these states in a manner analogous to that given by Sah[7] for the case of the junction-gate transistor. Current modulation by charge exchange with surface states is discussed by McWhorter[9] as a source of 1/f noise. These surfaces or interface states also are of importance in the control action of the transistor (Chapter 2) and must be minimized for that purpose as well. As transistor quality and performance are improved, it is reasonable to expect less 1/f noise in insulated-gate transistors.

The quality of the insulator in insulated-gate field-effect transistors can be made very good so that gate leakage currents are very small. Input resistances of 10^{15} ohms have been measured in silicon devices. The 1/f noise contribution of leakage currents is insignificant in such units.

The measured noise distribution for a silicon insulated-gate transistor is shown in Fig. 6–1. Although the actual noise is a function of the current

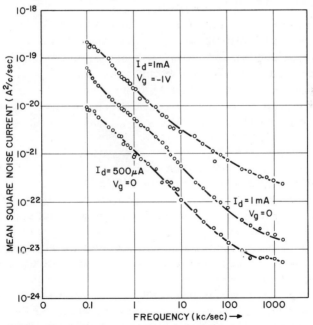

Figure 6–1. Typical 1/f noise characteristic for a silicon insulated-gate field-effect transistor.

and voltage applied to the device, the equivalent mean-squared input voltage at 10^3 cps is on the order of 10^{-14} to 10^{-13} v²/cps for silicon insulated-gate units, 10^{-16} to 10^{-15} v²/cps for silicon junction-gate units, and about the same order of magnitude for silicon bipolar transistors.

A small-signal equivalent circuit representation of the field-effect transistor is shown in Fig. 6–2 with noise generators $\overline{i_d^2}$ in the output circuit and $\overline{i_g^2}$ in the gate circuit. From the preceding discussion, the

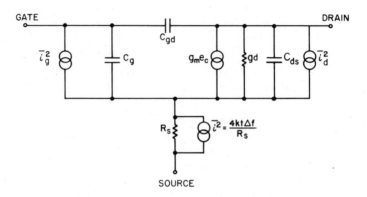

Figure 6–2. Equivalent circuit for the field-effect transistor including noise generators.

principal contribution to $\overline{i_d^2}$ will be thermal fluctuations in the channel. The principal contributions to $\overline{i_g^2}$ will be thermal fluctuations in the channel coupled into the gate circuit, shot noise of current flowing through the gate, and 1/f noise. In addition, parasitic series resistances will add thermal noise sources as indicated. The contributions of thermal fluctuations in the channel to $\overline{i_d^2}$ and $\overline{i_g^2}$ are calculated in the following section.

6–3. THERMAL NOISE FLUCTUATIONS IN THE CHANNEL

The principal contribution to the output noise generator $\overline{i_d^2}$, is from the thermal noise fluctuations in the channel modified by the transistor control mechanism. This has been analyzed in detail for the junction-gate field-effect transistor by van der Ziel.[3] An analogous calculation for the insulated-gate field-effect transistor using the first-order transistor model of Hofstein and Heiman[1] is given below. This model is shown in Fig. 6–3 and the relationships are applicable to first-order in either the MOS or TFT structures. The thick oxide case is assumed and parasitic series resistances are neglected. The necessary transistor relations from

Chapter 5 are as follows. (Absolute quantities are given per unit channel width.)

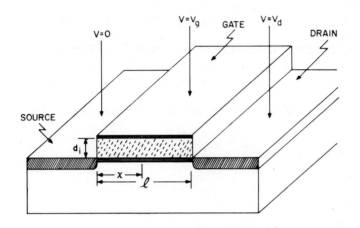

Figure 6–3. Model for an MOS field-effect transistor.

Surface charge density in channel [from Eq. (5–1)]:

$$\sigma(x) = \frac{\epsilon_i}{d_i}\left\{V_g - V_p - V(x)\right\} \qquad V(x) < (V_g - V_p) \tag{6–3}$$

Surface conductivity of channel:

$$\mu\sigma(x) \tag{6–4}$$

Differential channel resistance:

$$dr = \frac{dx}{\mu\sigma(x)} \tag{6–5}$$

Channel current from Eq. (5–79):

$$i_d = \mu\sigma(x)\,\mathcal{E}(x)$$
$$= \frac{\mu\epsilon_i}{d_i}\left[V_g - V_p - V(x)\right]\frac{dV}{dx} \tag{6–6}$$

Drain current from Eq. (5–2):

$$I_d = \frac{\beta_s}{l}\left[(V_g - V_p)V_d - \tfrac{1}{2}V_d^2\right] \tag{6–7}$$

where $\beta_s = \epsilon_i\mu/d_i$ is the field-effect surface conductivity-to-voltage ratio and where the pinch-off voltage has been inserted according to the discussion of Chapter 5.

At drain current saturation, $V_d = V_g - V_p$, and the drain current from Eq. (5–9) is:

$$I_{ds} = \frac{1}{2}\frac{\beta_s}{l}(V_g - V_p)^2 \tag{6-8}$$

The transconductance at drain-current saturation from Eq. (5–10) is:

$$g_{ms} = \frac{\beta_s}{l}(V_g - V_p) \tag{6-9}$$

By differentiation of Eq. (6–5), the drain conductance, dI_d/dV_d, at $V_d = 0$ is:

$$g_{do} = g_{ms} = \frac{\beta_s}{l}(V_g - V_p) \tag{6-10}$$

and at $V_d = 0$, $V_g = 0$ it is:

$$g_{doo} = -\frac{\beta_s}{l}V_p \tag{6-11}$$

To find the drain current change due to a voltage perturbation in the channel, consider the channel voltage distribution shown in Fig. 6–4.

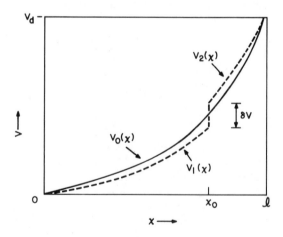

Figure 6–4. Channel-voltage distribution in the presence of a voltage perturbation δV.

If $V_o(x)$ is the normal equilibrium distribution, then a perturbation δV introduced at $x = x_o$ will alter the potential distribution somewhat in the manner shown. Since the channel current is given by Eq. (6–6), the current change will be:

$$\Delta i = i_1 - i_0 = \beta_s \left\{ [V_g - V_p - V_1(x)]\frac{dV_1}{dx} - [V_g - V_p - V_0(x)]\frac{dV_0}{dx} \right\}$$

$$0 < x < x_0$$

$$\Delta i = i_2 - i_0 = \beta_s \left\{ [V_g - V_p - V_2(x)]\frac{dV_2}{dx} - [V_g - V_p - V_0(x)]\frac{dV_0}{dx} \right\}$$

$$x_0 < x < l$$

(6–12)

Integrating between the indicated limits, imposing the condition that Δi is constant throughout the channel, and adding, we find that:

$$\Delta i = -\delta V \frac{\beta_s}{l} \{ V_g - V_p - V(x_0) \}$$

(6–13)

where $\delta V = V_2(x_0) - V_1(x_0)$.

The thermal noise fluctuation in the differential channel resistance, dr, gives rise to a mean-squared voltage fluctuation:

$$\overline{\delta V^2} = 4kT\Delta f dr = \frac{4kT\Delta f}{i_d} dV$$

(6–14)

upon using Eqs. (6–5), (6–3), and (6–6). Then, since i_d is constant in the channel:

$$\overline{\Delta i^2} = 4kT\Delta f \frac{\beta_s^2}{I_d l^2} \{ V_g - V_p - V(x_0) \}^2 dV$$

(6–15)

is the mean-squared current fluctuation in the drain current due to a voltage fluctuation at $x = x_0$. Integrating over the entire channel, we find the output noise current squared:

$$\overline{i_d^2} = 4kT\Delta f g_{ms} \frac{1 - \eta + \frac{1}{3}\eta^2}{1 - \frac{1}{2}\eta} = 4kT\Delta f g_{ms} f_1(\eta)$$

(6–16)

where the relative drain voltage, $\eta = V_d/(V_g - V_p)$, is a measure of approach to saturation ($\eta = 1$). Beyond $\eta = 1$ the relations no longer apply. Experiments indicate that no large error is introduced on applying values for the saturation condition for a reasonable distance into the saturation region. The function, $f_1(\eta)$, is shown in Fig. 6–5.

At saturation ($\eta = 1$), Eq. (6–16) reduces to:

$$\overline{i_d^2} = \tfrac{2}{3} \times 4kT\Delta f g_{ms}$$

(6–17)

At $V_d = 0$:

$$\overline{i_d^2} = 4kT\Delta f g_{do} = 4kT\Delta f g_{ms} \qquad (6\text{-}18)$$

and at $V_d = 0, V_g = 0$:

$$\overline{i_d^2} = 4kT\Delta f g_{doo} \qquad (6\text{-}19)$$

that is, the thermal noise of the unbiased channel as would be expected.

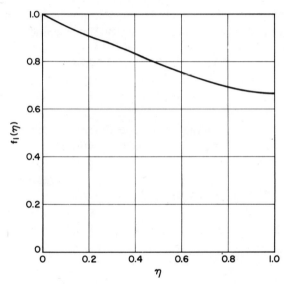

Figure 6–5. Plot of the function $f_l(\eta)$, where $\eta = V_d(V_g - V_p)^{-l}$.

6–4 NOISE INDUCED IN THE GATE CIRCUIT

The thermal fluctuations in the channel which give rise to the output noise generator discussed previously are coupled to the gate circuit by virtue of the gate-to-channel capacitance. This causes a contribution to the input noise generator, $\overline{i_g^2}$. Since this phenomenon underlies both $\overline{i_d^2}$ and $\overline{i_g^2}$, the input and output noise generators will be partly correlated. Because of this correlation, the output noise will not be the simple sum of contributions from $\overline{i_d^2}$ and $\overline{i_g^2}$ calculated separately. The correlation between these noise generators must be taken into account in determining the total noise output.

The contribution of thermal fluctuations in the channel to $\overline{i_g^2}$ has been given by van der Ziel[10] for the junction-gate field-effect transistor. An analogous calculation for the insulated-gate field-effect transistor will be made continuing the first-order analysis given before.

The channel charge may be considered as the charge on one plate of a capacitor whose dielectric is the insulator (assuming the thick oxide case) and whose other plate is the gate electrode. A fluctuation in the channel charge will induce an equal and opposite fluctuation in charge on the gate electrode, causing a fluctuation current in the short-circuited gate circuit of:

$$i_g = j\omega q \tag{6-20}$$

The central calculation is, therefore, to obtain the change in the channel charge to a voltage perturbation, δV, at $x = x_0$.

Using Eq. (6–3) to express the channel charge density appropriate to the voltage distributions in the channel for the perturbed and unperturbed distributions of Fig. 6–4, we find the incremental change in charge density:

$$\begin{aligned}
\Delta\sigma(x) &= \sigma(x) - \sigma_0(x) \\
&= \frac{\epsilon_i}{d_i}\{V_0(x) - V_1(x)\} \qquad 0 < x < x_0 \\
&= \frac{\epsilon_i}{d_i}\{V_0(x) - V_2(x)\} \qquad x_0 < x < l
\end{aligned} \tag{6-21}$$

The net change in charge per unit channel width is then:

$$\Delta q = \int_0^l \Delta\sigma(x)\,dx = \frac{\epsilon_i}{d_i}\left\{\int_0^l V_0(x)\,dx - \int_0^{x_0} V_1(x)\,dx - \int_{x_0}^l V_2(x)\,dx\right\} \tag{6-22}$$

Using Eq. (6–6) to integrate over the channel voltage:

$$\begin{aligned}
\Delta q = \frac{\epsilon_i}{d_i}\beta_s\Bigg\{ &\int_0^{V_d} \frac{[V_g - V_p - V_0(x)]V_0(x)}{i_0}\,dV \\
&- \int_0^{V(x_0)} \frac{[V_g - V_p - V_1(x)]V_1(x)}{i_0 + \Delta i}\,dV \\
&- \int_{V(x_0)}^{V_d} \frac{[V_g - V_p - V_2(x)]V_2(x)}{i_0 + \Delta i}\,dV\Bigg\}
\end{aligned} \tag{6-23}$$

where i_0 and $(i_0 + \Delta i)$ are the channel currents corresponding to the equilibrium and perturbed distributions, respectively. Integrating and neglecting product terms in δV and Δi, we find that the change of channel charge due to a voltage perturbation, δV, at $x = x_o$ is:

$$\Delta q = \frac{\Delta i}{I_d}\left\{Q_o - \frac{\epsilon_i l}{d_i}V(x_o)\right\} \tag{6-24}$$

where:

$$Q_o = \frac{\epsilon_i \beta_s}{d_i}\frac{1}{I_d}\left\{(V_g - V_p)\frac{V_d^2}{2} - \frac{V_d^3}{3}\right\} \tag{6-25}$$

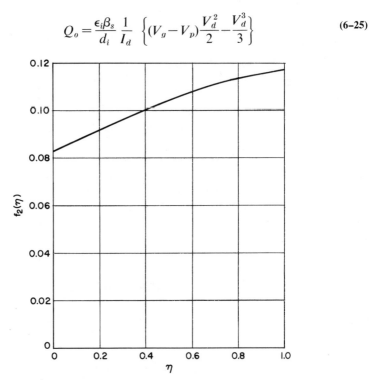

Figure 6-6. Plot of the function $f_2(\eta)$, where $\eta = V_d(V_g - V_p)^{-1}$.

Note that Δq is correlated with Δi. Squaring and substituting Eqs. (6-11) and (6-12), we find the mean-squared charge fluctuation:

$$q^2 = \left(\frac{\epsilon_i l}{d_i}\right)^2 4kT\Delta f\frac{\beta_s^2}{l^2 I_d^3}\int_0^{V_d}\{V_g - V_p - V(x)\}^2\left\{\frac{Q_o d_i}{\epsilon_i l} - V(x)\right\}^2 dV \tag{6-26}$$

Upon integrating:

$$\overline{q^2} = 4kT\Delta f\frac{C^2}{g_{ms}}\times f_2(\eta) \tag{6-27}$$

where $C = \epsilon_i l/d_i$ is the gate-to-channel capacitance per unit channel width and the function:

$$f_2(\eta) = \frac{1}{(1-\frac{1}{2}\eta)^3}\left\{\frac{(\frac{1}{2}-\frac{1}{3}\eta)^2}{(1-\frac{1}{2}\eta)^2}(1-\eta+\frac{1}{3}\eta^2)-\frac{(\frac{1}{2}-\frac{1}{3}\eta)}{(1-\frac{1}{2}\eta)}(1-\frac{4}{3}\eta+\frac{1}{2}\eta^2)\right.$$

$$\left. + (\frac{1}{3}-\frac{1}{2}\eta+\frac{1}{5}\eta^2)\right\}$$

(6-28)

is shown in Fig. 6-6.

At saturation $\eta = 1$ so that:

$$\overline{q^2} = 0.12 \times 4kT\Delta f \frac{C^2}{g_{ms}}$$

(6-29)

and

$$\overline{i_g^2} = 0.12 \times 4kT\Delta f \frac{\omega^2 C^2}{g_{ms}}$$

(6-30)

At $V_d = 0, \eta = 0$ and:

$$\overline{q^2} = \frac{1}{12} \times 4kT\Delta f \frac{C^2}{g_{ms}} = \frac{1}{12} \times 4kT\Delta f \frac{C^2}{g_{do}}$$

(6-31)

At $V_g = V_d = 0$:

$$\overline{q^2} = \frac{1}{12} \times 4kT\Delta f \frac{C^2}{g_{doo}}$$

(6-32)

To evaluate the significance of correlation between the drain and gate-circuit noise generators, the cross-product fluctuation must be known. To find $\overline{i_g^* i_d}$, multiply Eq. (6-24) by Δi_d and use Eq. (6-15):

$$\Delta q \Delta i_d = 4kT\Delta f \frac{\beta_o^2}{l^2 I_d^2}\left\{V_g-V_p-V(x_o)\right\}^2\left\{Q_o-\frac{\epsilon_i l}{d_i}V_o(x)\right\} dV$$

(6-33)

Integrating over the channel and multiplying by $j\omega$:

$$\overline{i_g^* i_d} = 4kT\Delta f \times j\omega C f_3(\eta)$$

(6-34)

where the function:

$$f_3(\eta) = \frac{1}{(1-\tfrac{1}{2}\eta)^2}\left\{\frac{(\tfrac{1}{2}-\tfrac{1}{3}\eta)}{(1-\tfrac{1}{2}\eta)}\,(1-\eta+\tfrac{1}{3}\eta^2)-(\tfrac{1}{2}-\tfrac{2}{3}\eta+\tfrac{1}{4}\eta^2)\right\} \tag{6–35}$$

is shown in Fig. 6–7.

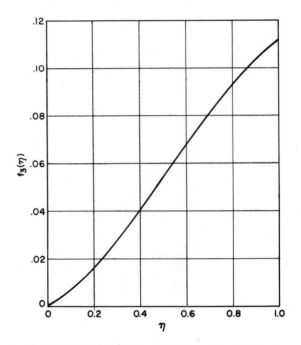

Figure 6–7. Plot of the function $f_3(\eta)$, where $\eta = V_d(V_g - V_p)^{-1}$.

At saturation, $\eta = 1$ and:

$$\overline{i_g^* i_d} = 4kT\Delta f \times 0.11j\omega C \tag{6–36}$$

Defining a complex correlation coefficient,[11]

$$c = \frac{\overline{i_g^* i_d}}{\sqrt{\overline{i_g^2 i_d^2}}} \tag{6–37}$$

This may be evaluated at saturation from Eqs. (6–17), (6–30), and (6–36), and it is:

$$c = j0.39 \tag{6–38}$$

6-5 NOISE FACTOR AND EQUIVALENT NOISE RESISTANCE

The noise representation of any two-port can be reduced to that shown in Fig. 6–8. The relations for the minimum noise factor are:[11]

$$F_{\min} = 1 + 2R_n(G_v - G_o) \qquad \text{(6-39)}$$

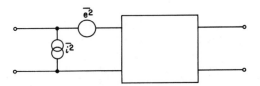

Figure 6-8. General noise representation of a two-port.

where R_n is an equivalent noise resistance, G_v is the correlation conductance, and G_0, the optimum source conductance, is given by:

$$G_o = \left(\frac{G_u + R_n G_v^2}{R_n}\right)^{1/2} \qquad \text{(6-40)}$$

where G_u is an equivalent noise conductance for the uncorrelated component of the noise-current generator. For a first-order consideration of the noise in insulated-gate field-effect transistors, R_n may be identified with $\overline{i_d^2}$ by:

$$\overline{e^2} = \frac{\overline{i_d^2}}{g_m^2} = 4kT\Delta f R_n \qquad \text{(6-41)}$$

assuming the transadmittance is essentially real and the current generator, $\overline{i^2}$ of Fig. 6–8, is identified with the gate noise, $\overline{i_g^2}$.

  The induced gate noise varies as ω^2 from Eq. (6–30), and in the presence of a series source resistance it will be further modified to become important when $\omega > 1/RC$. If $R_s = 100$ ohms and $C = 10^{-11} f$, this corresponds to frequencies above 100 mc/sec. Therefore, at frequencies below which the induced gate noise can be neglected, both G_u and $G_v \rightarrow 0$, and, as for a vacuum tube, there is no minimum noise factor until other considerations are introduced to limit the source conductance. It should be recalled that only channel thermal fluctuations are being considered. The equivalent noise resistance then completely characterizes the noise performance of the device. From Eqs. (6–41) and (6–17) at saturation:

$$R_n = \frac{2}{3g_{ms}} \qquad (6\text{–}42)$$

This is about one-fourth of the equivalent noise resistance of a vacuum tube having equal transconductance. For the vacuum tube:[12]

$$R_n = \frac{5}{2g_m} \qquad (6\text{–}43)$$

At frequencies where the gate noise is important, it is necessary to evaluate the cross-product fluctuations. By definition[11] of the correlation admittance:

$$\overline{ei^*} = \gamma^* \overline{e^2} \qquad (6\text{–}44)$$

But from Eq. (6–34), the cross product $\overline{i_g^* i_d}$ is reactive; so with e^2 being identified with $\overline{i_d^2}$, the correlation admittance will be essentially susceptive so long as the transadmittance is essentially real. Then, the correlation conductance, G_v, is approximately zero and the minimum noise factor is:

$$F_{\min} = 1 + 2\sqrt{R_n G_u} \qquad (6\text{–}45)$$

To find the uncorrelated noise current:

$$\overline{i_u^2} = \overline{i_g^2} - \overline{i_{\mathrm{corr}}^2} = \overline{i_g^2} - \gamma\gamma^* \overline{e^2} \qquad (6\text{–}46)$$

whence by manipulation of Eq. (6–44) and $\overline{e^2} = \overline{i_d^2}/g_m^2$

$$\overline{i_u^2} = \overline{i_g^2} - \frac{\left|\overline{ei_g^*}\right|^2}{\overline{e^2}} = \overline{i_g^2}\left(1 - |c|^2\right) \qquad (6\text{–}47)$$

and, by definition:

$$G_u = \frac{\overline{i_g^2}}{4kT\Delta f}(1 - |c|^2) \qquad (6\text{–}48)$$

At saturation, from Eqs. (6–30) and (6–38):

$$G_u = 0.102\omega^2\frac{C^2}{g_{ms}} \qquad (6\text{–}49)$$

and

$$F_{\min} = 1 + 0.52\omega\,\frac{C}{g_m} \qquad (6\text{–}50)$$

If, for example, $C = 10^{-11} f$ and $g_m = 2000 \, \mu$mhos, then at 100 mc/sec, $F_{min} = 4.2$ db.

Measured noise factors of insulated-gate field-effect transistors are given in Chapter 11. For a high-frequency transistor, typical noise factors are 4.5 db at 10 mc/sec and 6 db at 60 mc/sec. For an ultra-high-frequency transistor, noise factors of 3.5 db at 200 mc/sec and 4 to 5 db at 400 mc/sec were measured.

REFERENCES

1. S. R. Hofstein and F. P. Heiman, *Proc. IEEE* **51**, 1190 (1963).

2. H. K. S. Ihantola, *Stanford Res. Tech. Report* No. 1661–1, Stanford University, California (February, 1961).

3. A. van der Ziel, *Proc. IRE* **50**, 1808 (1962).

4. W. Guggenbuehl and M. J. O. Strutt, *Proc. IRE* **45**, 839 (1957).

5. G. C. Dacey and I. M. Ross, *Proc. IRE* **41**, 970 (1953).

6. P. O. Lauritzen and O. Leistika, Jr., 1962 International Solid-State Circuit Conference, *Technical Digest* **5**, 62 (1962).

7. C. T. Sah, *Proc. IEEE* **52**, 795 (1964).

8. C. T. Sah, R. N. Noyce, and W. Shockley, *Proc. IRE* **45**, 1228 (1957).

9. A. L. McWhorter, *MIT Technical Rep.* No. 80, Lincoln Lab (1955).

10. A. van der Ziel, *Proc. IEEE* **51**, 461 (1963).

11. H. A. Haus *et al.*, *Proc. IRE* **48**, 69 (1960).

12. W. A. Harris, *RCA Review* **5**, 505 (1941).

7

Radiation Tolerance of Field-Effect Transistors

S. M. Christian

7-1. FACTORS AFFECTING TRANSISTOR DECAY UNDER BOMBARDMENT

1. Types of radiation; equivalence factors; effects on materials

For both military and civilian applications, active solid-state devices are needed which will operate despite the radiation encountered in outer space or in terrestrial nuclear environments. Because field-effect devices are relatively insensitive to radiation compared to conventional transistors, an evaluation of the effect of radiation on their performance is particularly appropriate.

Intense radiation may occur near a radioactive material or chain reaction. Neutrons from reactors are especially damaging. In space, men and equipment may encounter (1) a small flux of galactic cosmic-ray protons, (2) damaging electrons and protons trapped in the Van Allen belts, and (3) very damaging protons from brief solar flares. As an example of the severity of environment which exists, consider a satellite whose orbit intersects a Van Allen belt. The integrated flux bombarding its surface may amount to 10^{11} fast protons and 10^{15} fast electrons/cm^2 per year at the middle of the belt, but only 1% as much during most of its path.[1] The dosage reaching a transistor is greatly reduced by shielding.

The possible combinations of different types of radiation striking

176

devices of different materials and designs are so numerous that it would be an excessive task to measure the damage in each case of interest. Semiquantitative comparisons, in the form of approximate equivalents, may be given for the relative amounts of damage caused in solids by common types of radiation. The damaging effects of the elementary particles generally follow the order of severity:

$$\text{proton} \; > \; \text{neutron} \; > \; \text{electron} \; > \; \text{gamma photon}$$

Table 7-1 shows the relative damage produced in germanium by typical particles.[2, 3]

Table 7-1 Relative Damage Per Particle in Germanium

Particle	Energy	Source	Effects	
			Displacement	Ionization
Proton	20 Mev	inner Van Allen belt	300	100
Proton	200 Mev	solar flare	75	15
Neutron	1 Mev	reactor	100	0.3
Electron	0.6 Mev	inner Van Allen belt	1	20
Gamma photon	1.25 Mev	reactor	0.004	0.04

Gamma-ray doses are usually given not in photons, but in rads of absorbed energy. One rad is defined as 100 ergs/gram, and it is roughly equivalent to a roentgen, that quantity of radiation which will produce 1 e.s.u. each of positive and negative ion charges per cm^3 of air.

In transient ionization effects, 1 rad of gamma rays is roughly equivalent to 10^9 fast neutrons/cm^2. Near nuclear power plants, gamma-ray damage may be comparable to that from neutrons.[4] The neutron energies cover a broad spectrum, including both slow or thermal and fast neutrons with energies above 1 Mev. The degradation for a given dosage is often not the same at different reactors, probably because of variations in the neutron spectra.[10]

Damage also varies with the target material. Silicon is damaged more than germanium, having a lower energy threshold for the displacement of atoms in the crystal lattice. A few elements, notably boron and cadmium, have very large absorption cross sections for thermal neutrons.

2. Transient versus integrated dose

The difference between transient and permanent effects is often of critical importance. In general, the amount of permanent damage is proportional to the integrated incident dose and independent of dose rate.

The transient damage is often proportional to instantaneous dose rate and independent of integrated dose. An exception is the transient surface ionization of bipolar transistors, which increases with the integrated dose.[5] No such behavior is found in insulated-gate field-effect transistors, since they have no *p-n* junction exposed to surface leakage.

Some field-effect transistor constructions may be subject to excessive self-heating in an intense flux of thermal neutrons. At the core face of a typical research reactor, the flux is about 10^{13} n/cm²/sec and is strongly absorbed by borosilicate glass. The glass substrate of a typical thin-film transistor in this flux will generate possibly more than 10 watts of heat, and certainly enough to damage the unit permanently.

Transient effects are greater per rad for gamma exposure than for particle irradiation. A pulse of radiation absorbed by a semiconductor releases free holes and electrons, causing a pulse of added conductivity which vanishes when these carriers recombine. A gamma pulse of 10^6 roentgen/sec may cause disruptive leakage current across an insulator.[6] Majority-carrier devices, particularly field-effect transistors and tunnel diodes, are expected to be more resistant to rate effects than bipolar transistors.

3. Modes of damage in semiconductor devices

To analyze specific cases, the various mechanisms that cause damage must be considered. Collisions of fast neutrons or protons with nuclei are usually elastic, displacing atoms to form relatively permanent lattice vacancies and interstitials, or displacing electrons to cause ionization or emission. The ionization is transient and is limited to about 1 millisec by carrier recombination. The displaced atoms act as traps or recombination centers to reduce carrier concentration, and as scattering centers to reduce mobility. Both effects result in lower conductivity and smaller current gain. Collisions of slow neutrons are often inelastic, add permanent impurity atoms by transmutation, and induce radioactivity.

Damage may occur in the bulk semiconductor, on its surface, or in the supporting structure. High-frequency thin-base bipolar transistors are less vulnerable than thick-base types, because the carrier recombination increases as the square of the base width.[7] An unshielded, thin-base germanium transistor may operate usefully 1 year in outer space but only 3 days at the center of a Van Allen belt.[8]

Semiconductors are more vulnerable than metals or insulators. Above 10^{14} neutrons/cm², all conventional semiconductor devices deteriorate and only special types remain useful.[4] In comparison, ceramic capacitors and some ceramic vacuum tubes[9] are operable above 10^{18} neutrons/cm².

Bipolar transistors are injured chiefly through reduction of minority-carrier lifetime. For example, the lifetime in intrinsic germanium was decreased[6] almost two orders of magnitude by 3×10^{13} fast neutrons/cm². Since field-effect transistors are majority-carrier devices, their action should not be greatly impaired by loss of lifetime.

Both theory and experiment[7] have shown that in bipolar transistors the degradation, measured by an increase in the reciprocal of the current gain, β, follows the equation:

$$\frac{1}{\beta} = \frac{1}{\beta_o} + K\phi \qquad (7\text{–}1)$$

where ϕ is the integrated flux of bombarding particles. Except for differing values of K, this simple function holds for irradiation by neutrons, protons, alpha particles, electrons, and gamma rays. This indicates that one basic cause of degradation, reduction of minority-carrier lifetime, is involved.[3] No corresponding principle applies to field-effect transistors.

Neutron-irradiated bipolar transistors show complete recovery of reverse current, I_{cbo}, in two days, partial recovery of β, but no recovery of switching time in a week.[8] No analogous generalization has been found for field-effect transistors.

Surface effects are transient and understood less than bulk effects. Devices of different types respond differently and there are wide variations within a type. The Telstar experiment[5] demonstrated the practical importance of surface effects in bipolar units. Surfaces are greatly affected by doses below the threshold of bulk damage. The chief mechanism is the formation of ions on the surface to induce a channel for reverse current. Exposure to 10^4 rads increased the reverse current of silicon transistors 50% in gas-filled cans. 10^5 rads changed germanium units similarly. Yet 10^7 rads caused no surface effects to an evacuated unit.

Similar effects are anticipated in any field-effect device which has a high potential gradient at a surface exposed to air.

7–2. EXPERIMENTAL RESULTS

1. Comparison of field-effect transistors with bipolar transistors

An exemplary investigation has been made of the relative tolerance of bipolar and field-effect silicon transistors to 1-Mev electron bombardment.[11] The FE200 is an *n*-type junction-gate field-effect transistor. The 2N930 is an *n-p-n* bipolar transistor with similar low-power, high-gain characteristics. Forty units of each were irradiated and the degraded gain, reverse-biased junction current and saturation voltage were measured. Figures 7–1 and 7–2 show the results. Gain was measured by the current transfer ratio, h_{fe}, for the bipolar, and by the transconductance g_m, for the unipolar transistors.

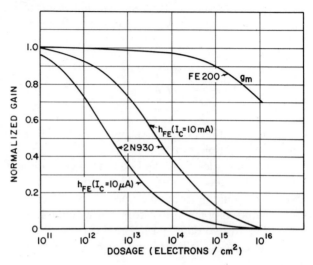

Figure 7–1. Degradation of current gain in bipolar units and transconductance in junction-gate field-effect units by 1–Mev electrons (after Roberts and Hoerni).

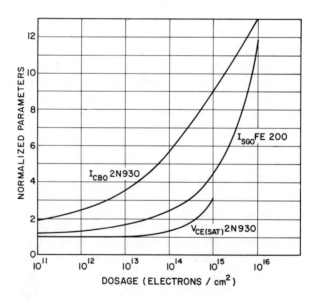

Figure 7–2. Degradation of leakage current and saturation voltage by 1–Mev electrons (after Roberts and Hoerni).

The field-effect transistor was still useful after a dosage 1000 times that which rendered the bipolar units unusable. The 2N930 tolerated more radiation if operated with high collector current, but the high input impedance was lost under this condition. After a dose of 10^{16} electrons/ cm^2 the gate current of the FE200 had increased relatively more than the reverse current of the 2N930; but the input impedance of the former was still usefully high. The increased gate current of the FE200 is explained by the increase of generation-recombination states in the reverse-biased junction.

The increase in saturation voltage, $V_{ce(sat)}$, of the 2N930 resembles the decrease in g_m of the FE200. This indicates that both effects are due to one mechanism, a reduction in majority-carrier conductivity.

Another study[12] extended the dosage to 2×10^{16} electrons/cm². Three other field-effect transistors were degraded slightly more than the FE200, losing half their transconductance after 1.3×10^{16} electrons/ cm². Some of this damage was annealed out by heating at 100 to 300°C, and very slow recovery occurred at room temperature.

To simulate space effects, transistors were bombarded with 22 to 440 Mev protons.[13] Damage appeared above a threshold of 10^{11} protons/ cm². It then varied directly with integrated flux and inversely with proton energy, following the trend seen in Table 7–1. A 2N2497 silicon field-effect transistor lost 25% of its drain current at fixed voltage after 3.4×10^{13} protons/cm². Bipolar transistors are severely damaged[14] by proton doses above 10^{12}/cm².

Several comparative studies have been made of field-effect and bipolar transistors in the mixed flux of nuclear reactors. In each case the unipolar device is more resistant because it does not suffer from loss of minority-carrier lifetime. The field-effect device seems to suffer primarily from loss of conductivity. In one case,[15] while the g_m decreased 9.1%, the channel conductance decreased 16.7% per 10^{13} neutrons/cm². This suggests that field-effect transistors with higher initial majority-carrier concentration would have greater tolerance to neutrons. Also 3.5×10^7 rads of gamma rays caused excessive gate leakage through ionization.

A similar study[10] comparing five different shapes of junction-gate field-effect transistors showed that the degradation depends less on the geometry than on the doping. It was also found that 10^{15} neutrons/cm² raised the resistivity of silicon by a factor of about 30, agreeing roughly with the loss of drain current in transistors of the same kind of silicon. These units (e.g., 2N2608 and 2N2386; Fig. 7–4) tolerated on the average 10^{14} fast neutrons/cm² before losing 30% of the initial g_m, and herein equal or excel the most resistant bipolar transistors.

A third study[16] compared 10 developmental field-effect units with 100 bipolar units of various types, measuring several parameters inter- mittently during irradiation. The unipolar transistors were by far the most tolerant, surviving 10^{15} fast neutrons/cm² before losing 30% of their g_m. Next most tolerant were the high-frequency germanium bipolar units, losing 30% of their gain at 6×10^{14} n/cm². Least resistant were the low-frequency silicon bipolar transistors, which failed the 70% gain test at 3×10^{13} n/cm².

The gate current also was measured on these field-effect units. It increased about a decade with the first 10^{13} neutrons/cm², remained nearly constant to 7×10^{14} n/cm², and then decreased by half at 10^{15} n/cm².

These comparisons were made between separate field-effect and bipolar units; so it is uncertain to what extent differences in dimensions or doping caused the observed differences in radiation tolerance. The following experiment[17] employed MM765 silicon hybrid tetrodes, which can be operated alternatively as either bipolar or unipolar devices. Connected through one set of 3 contacts, the device is a *p-n-p* bipolar transistor; using another 3 contacts, it is a field-effect unit. The semiconductor region which serves as the base in the bipolar mode of operation acts as the channel in the unipolar mode.

These units were exposed to successively larger doses of reactor neutrons plus gamma rays, and the characteristics were noted after each exposure. Figure 7–3 gives a series of oscillograms with the bipolar mode exhibited to the left and the unipolar mode to the right, all on the same voltage and current scale.

While the bipolar mode is already affected by a dose of 10^{12} n/cm², the field-effect mode is almost unchanged by 10^{14} n/cm². Gate leakage remained below 1 microampere even after the 10^{15} dose. However, above 10^{14}, the g_m of the unipolar mode fell much faster with added flux than did the h_{fe} of the bipolar mode. This bears out the earlier suggestion[18] that bipolar units, although affected by a lower dosage, will retain some performance at a very high dose where field-effect units have declined even more. A careful analysis has recently been published[22].

2. Insulated-gate silicon transistors

The foregoing field-effect transistors were of the junction-gate type. Several developmental types of insulated-gate units have also been irradiated by a reactor[17] with similar results. MOS units will be compared in this section, the thin-film type being treated in Section 4. Two different geometries of silicon MOS transistors were tested and show large differences in radiation tolerance.

A series of symmetrical MOS transistors[17] were exceptionally resistant to radiation. In this construction, the gate electrode covers the entire channel (Chapter 5). Figure 7–4 shows the average of three units: after 10^{15} mixed neutrons/cm² one unit was almost inoperable; whereas the

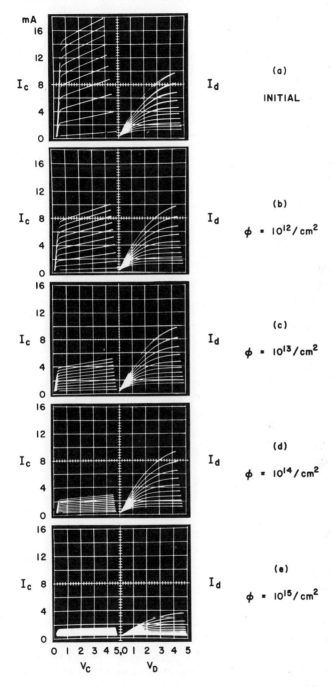

Figure 7–3. Degradation of integrated bipolar (left) and field-effect (right) transistor by neutron flux, ϕ.

other two showed considerable gate leakage and hysteresis, but had lost only 20% of their g_m. Few active semiconductor devices are so little deteriorated after such a high radiation dosage. Comparison with the 2N2608 and 2N2386 junction-gate units in Fig. 7–4 supports an earlier indication[19] that insulated-gate units are more radiation-resistant.

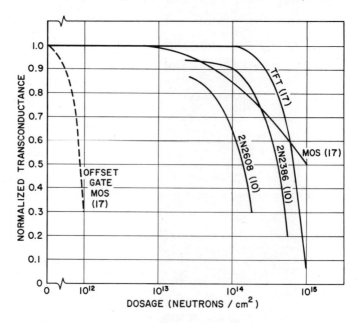

Figure 7–4. Degradation of transconductance by neutrons, comparing a thin-film transistor with MOS units and junction-gate units.

The other set consisted of three experimental depletion units with an offset gate (see Chapter 8). These transistors[17] lost 50 to 90% of their drain current after 10^{12} mixed neutrons/cm² (see Fig. 7–4). The damage was permanent with no change after many weeks on the shelf at room temperature. This sensitivity probably results from the production of positive charges in the insulator, causing the bands at the surface of the silicon to bend towards p-type, so that the unit becomes inoperable in the depletion mode.

3. Gallium arsenide transistor

The damage by 1-Mev electrons to an experimental gallium arsenide field-effect transistor has been measured.[12] After bombardment by 5×10^{17} electrons/cm², the unit had lost only 35% of its drain current. This is the highest known tolerance of any transistor, presumably because of the extremely thin channel and independence of lifetime.

4. Thin-film transistors

Evaporated transistors (Chapter 9) may be expected to be even more radiation-resistant than MOS units. Evaporated films are highly disordered, and damage to crystal structure should make little difference in the operation of the device, which is designed to function in an imperfect medium. The structure of a thin-film transistor (TFT) resembles that of a capacitor, which is two orders of magnitude more tolerant of radiation than bipolar transistors.

An early study[20] showed that thin-film transistors are highly resistant to transient gamma radiation. Some of these units were almost unaffected by 3×10^8 roentgen/sec. This is an order of magnitude greater than the dose rate which injected an excessive current pulse in the best bipolar transistor tested.

Twenty TFT's (Fig. 9-4a) have been studied after irradiation by neutrons and gamma rays.[17] Some of these units were destroyed by melting of the indium contacts. Most of the remainder survived 10^{14} n/cm² nearly unchanged. However, 10^{15} neutrons/cm² reduced the transconductance to 5% of the initial value, as in Fig. 7-4.

Some of this damage may be due to thermal shock from neutron absorption in the borosilicate glass substrate. Most of the damage is attributed to crystal defects in the CdS, caused by recoil of cadmium nuclei after reacting with thermal neutrons. It is known[21] that exposure to 10^{15} neutrons/cm² decreases the conductivity of n-type CdS by a factor of 5. The failure of these TFT's may be due to the large capture cross section of the cadmium atoms. TFT's made of other materials may yet prove to be among the most tolerant semiconductor devices.

REFERENCES

1. W. L. Brown, J. D. Gabbe, and W. Rosenzweig, *Bell Syst. Tech. J.* **42**, 1505(1963).

2. P. H. Miller, Jr. and V. A. J. van Lint, ASTM Symposium on Space Radiation Effects, Atlantic City, 1963. To be published in ASTM Special Technical Publication 363.

3. G. L. Keister, ASTM Symposium on Space Radiation Effects, Atlantic City, 1963. To be published in ASTM Special Technical Publication 363.

4. D. J. Niehaus and F. Larin, *Nucleonics* **22**, 85 (May, 1964).

5. D. S. Peck, R. R. Blair, W. L. Brown, and F. M. Smits, *Bell Syst. Tech. J.* **42**, 95 (1963).

6. V. R. Honnold and C. W. Perkins, *Electronic Industries* **21**, 99 (February, 1962).

7. J. J. Loferski, *Jour. Appl. Phys.* **29**, 35 (1958).

8. L. B. Gardner and J. R. Coss, ASTM Symposium on Space Radiation Effects, Atlantic City, 1963. To be published in ASTM Special Technical Publication 363.

9. R. E. Moe, *Electrical Design News* **9**, 4 (June, 1964).

10. A. B. Kaufman, *Electronics* **35**, 56 (July 13, 1962); *Electronic Industries* **23**, 94 (March, 1964).

11. C. S. Roberts and J. A. Hoerni, *Amelco Semiconductor Technical Bulletin,* No. 1 (1963).

12. B. A. Kulp, J. P. Jones, and A. F. Vetter, Proc. *IRE* **49**, 1437 (1961).

13. E. Rind and F. R. Bryant, IEEE International Convention, New York, 1964; *IEEE Spectrum* **1**, 62 (1964).

14. W. E. Chapin, D. J. Hamman, E. N. Wyler, and D. Jones, Radiation Effects Information Center, Report No. 32, Battelle Memorial Institute, 1963.

15. R. V. Babcock, *Transactions, American Nuclear Society* **4**, 60 (1961).

16. L. Taylor, Texas Instruments, Inc., Technical Report (March. 1962).

17. S. M. Christian, RCA Laboratories, to be published.

18. V. H. Grinich, *Solid State Design* **5**, 8 (March, 1964).

19. J. T. Wallmark, *RCA Review* **24**, 649 (1963).

20. R. W. Marshall, IEEE 10th Annual East Coast Conference on Aerospace and Navigational Electronics, Baltimore, 1963.

21. C. Kikuchi and R. B. Oswald, Amer. Phys. Soc., Buffalo, 1963; Bull., *APS,* **8**, 443 (1963).

22. B. L. Gregory and F. M. Smits, *IEEE Trans. on Electron Devices* **12**, 254 (1965).

8

MOS Field-Effect Transistors

Fred P. Heiman

8-1 INTRODUCTION

The development of the MOS (Metal-Oxide-Semiconductor) insulated-gate field-effect transistor came at a time when semiconductor device technology was well advanced. In fact, the use of silicon for many commercial semiconductor devices produced the wealth of technology concerned with the preparation of clean, passivated silicon surfaces which made this transistor possible. Techniques for the reduction of surface state densities and the control of fine dimensions played a major role in the development of MOS devices.

This chapter is concerned with aspects of fabrication and technology which apply to the field-effect transistor. Some of the limitations on performance set by practical considerations will be given.

1. Control of surface states

Bound electronic states located at the surface of a semiconducting material originate from the discontinuity of the crystal structure (see Chapter 2). These surface states acting as either donor or acceptor sites can trap electrons or holes from the semiconductor bulk. Very little is known about the control of these states, but it has been demonstrated experimentally that a significant decrease in the density of surface states on silicon can be achieved by properly producing a thermally grown silicon dioxide layer[1,2] over the surface of chemically etched silicon. It is this reduction that allows the electric field produced by the gate potential to penetrate the silicon surface and modulate its conductivity. The exact mechanism associated with this improvement in the surface properties of silicon is unknown; but it is felt that the smooth transition between pure silicon and pure silicon dioxide eliminates unsaturated, or dangling, bonds commonly associated with surface states. Also, the clean conditions under which the oxide layer is grown eliminates contamination of the silicon surface by undesirable ambient constituents.

A surface state density of less than 3×10^{11} cm^{-2} can be obtained with present-day technology, whereas workers in this field a decade ago[3-11] reported densities as high as 10^{13} cm^{-2}. An electric field in the silicon dioxide layer of 10^6 v/cm terminates in an electronic charge layer corresponding to 2×10^{12} electrons cm^2. Since the dielectric breakdown strength of silicon dioxide is approximately 5×10^6 v/cm, a surface state density less than 5×10^{11} cm^{-2} is necessary for satisfactory device operation. The 1/f noise associated with surface devices has been correlated with the transfer of carriers in and out of surface states[12] and a reduction of the 1/f noise in this transistor requires an even further reduction of surface states.

2. Control of dimensions

Another technological advance that proved to be necessary for the development of this transistor was the refinement in the control of small dimensions that came with the development of photographic techniques[13,14] for the electronics industry. The use of photosensitive lacquers allows one to define a pattern as fine as 1.6 μ as shown in Fig. 8-1. Although poor uniformity would be expected in dimensions as small as this, excellent results are obtained with dimensions on the order of 5 to 6 μ. It will be shown below that this range is more than adequate for the fabrication of high frequency transistors.

It has been demonstrated by Johnson and Rose[15] that the carrier transit time in a charge-controlled triode (such as a bipolar or field-effect transistor) is a good measure of the speed of the device. Parasitic elements and external circuitry reduce the actual speed of operation, but the transit time, which is equal to the C/g_m ratio for an ideal field-effect transistor, is a useful figure of merit.

The transit time for a bipolar transistor is simply the diffusion time for minority carriers across the base of the transistor. In a field-effect device, current is carried by majority carriers which drift across the channel under the force of the drain-to-source field. Using the simplest type of analysis, one may estimate the transit time, τ_r, for a field-effect transistor under the assumption of constant channel mobility, μ.

$$\tau_r = \frac{l}{v_d} = \frac{l^2}{\mu V_d} \tag{8-1}$$

where v_d is the average drift velocity in the channel and V_d/l is the average drift field. To achieve a transit time of one nanosecond at a drain voltage of 10 v requires a channel length of no more than 15 μ. This calculation

Figure 8–1.   Magnified view of photo-resist pattern showing a line whose width is 1.6 microns.

assumes an average drift mobility of 225 cm²/v-sec, which is a typical value when the carriers flow near the silicon surface. The bulk mobility for electrons in high-purity silicon at room temperature is approximately 1350 cm²/v-sec.

Reproducible control of a 15-μ channel length is readily achieved with today's technology; but the alignment of one pattern over another within close tolerance requires a skilled operator working with precision equipment. This problem will become apparent when the enhancement-type transistor is discussed in the next section.

8–2 ENHANCEMENT-TYPE TRANSISTORS

The enhancement-type transistor is ideally suited for digital circuit applications (see Chapter 12) because direct-coupled inversion is possible without the need for level-shifting between stages. This device exhibits very low drain current at zero gate bias; the current increases with positive gate voltage for an electron conduction (n-type) device and increases with negative gate voltage for a hole conduction (p-type) device.

One salient feature of this type of transistor is that the gate electrode must cover the entire channel, overlapping both source and drain regions.

Any channel region left exposed will contribute a very high series resistance to the device, since there are few carriers in the channel region at zero gate bias. This overlap results in a substantial capacitance from gate-to-source (C_{gs}) and gate-to-drain (C_{gd}) unless special provisions are made to increase the thickness of the oxide over the heavily doped regions. Since the feedback capacitance, C_{gd}, is amplified by the Miller effect[16] when reflected to the input, this parasitic element poses a limitation to the speed at which the transistor can operate.

If the feedback capacitance is to be minimized, the overlap of the gate electrode over the drain region must be small. The smallest overlap feasible is 2.5 μ, and it requires considerable skill in aligning a large array of transistors. For a transistor having a 15-μ channel length, the ratio of feedback to useful capacitance is 1:6. Due to the Miller effect, the total input capacitance will be twice as large as the useful capacitance if this transistor operates with a voltage gain of 5. The method discussed below for increasing the oxide thickness over the source and drain regions results in a significant improvement in device performance.

1. Ladder geometry

Figure 8–2 shows a plan view of the ladder-geometry array of enhancement-type transistors; the cross-sectional view through one unit

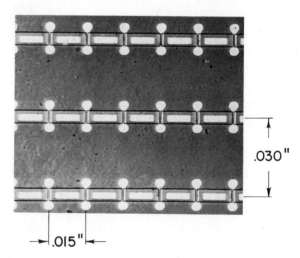

Figure 8–2. Plan view of enhancement type transistors fabricated in the ladder geometry. Packing density is 2200 transistors per square inch, which leaves ample room for interconnection wiring.

.030"

.015"

is shown in Fig. 8–3. The transistors are arranged in tandem; the drain of one unit is the source of the adjacent unit. This geometry was selected to simplify the interconnection of many transistors in an integrated circuit and to reduce the capacitance at each node. However, the dimensions for this geometry were chosen to minimize alignment difficulties and not to optimize high-frequency performance. A channel length of 15 μ and a channel width of 125 μ were chosen.

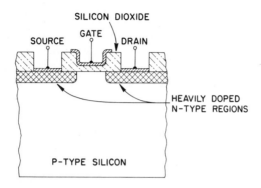

Figure 8–3. Cross-sectional view of ladder-geometry transistor showing raised oxide over source and drain regions.

Controlled impurity diffusion into silicon[17] makes possible a simple fabrication scheme which reduces the feedback capacitance by increasing the oxide thickness over the heavily doped regions, as shown in Fig. 8–3. This scheme involves the deposition of a thin film of silicon dioxide over the surface of a silicon substrate by the pyrolysis of tetraethyl orthosilicate. The deposited oxide is similar in structure to thermally grown silicon dioxide and possesses similar insulating properties. If trimethyl phosphate is added to the orthosilicate solution, phosphorus-rich oxide is deposited; if trimethyl borate is added, boron-rich oxide is deposited. Phosphorus and boron are *n*- and *p*-type dopants, respectively, when substitutionally added to the silicon lattice. These *doped* oxides are commonly referred to as *n*- and *p*- type.

Consider the following sequence of operations for the fabrication of *n*-type enhancement-transistors employing the ladder geometry shown in Fig. 8–2.

1. *N*-type oxide is deposited over the entire surface of a clean, chemically polished silicon wafer by the cracking method described above. The thickness of the deposited layer is approximately 10,000 Å (1 μ).

2. A suitable photosensitive lacquer is coated over the surface of the deposited oxide, and a pattern is exposed and developed to leave rectangular blocks of the lacquer over the source and drain regions, as shown in Fig. 8–4a. The exposed oxide is then removed in dilute hydrofluoric acid and the lacquer dissolved.

3. The wafer is now cleaned and placed in a dry oxygen atmosphere at 1050°C for one hour. This heating step allows the phosphorus to diffuse into the silicon from the *n*-type oxide to form the source and drain regions. At the same time, silicon dioxide thermally grows on the exposed silicon surface, covering the channel region with 1300 Å of oxide.

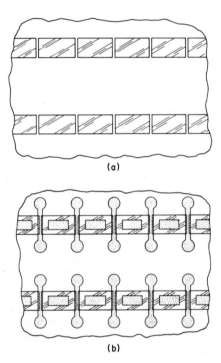

Figure 8–4. Fabrication sequence for ladder-geometry transistors (a) after first photosensitive lacquer step and (b) after final metalization.

4. Another photosensitive lacquer step is now employed to open holes in the deposited oxide, exposing portions of the heavily doped source and drain regions. After metallization, the finished array appears as shown in Fig. 8-4b, with a portion of the gate electrode separated from the heavily doped regions by the thick deposited oxide.

A cross-sectional view through a completed transistor is shown in Fig. 8-5a. This photograph was obtained after lapping through the center of the transistor at a 3° angle with respect to the silicon surface. All vertical dimensions must be multiplied by sin 3° = 0.052 to get their true values with respect to the horizontal dimensions. The difference in thickness between the channel oxide and the oxide deposited over the source and drain regions is clearly visible in the detailed photomicrograph shown in Fig. 8–5b. The horizontal lines through the oxide layers are optical interference fringes caused by the wedge shape which the oxide assumes after angle-lapping.

(a)   (b)

Figure 8–5. Cross-sectional view of finished transistor showing thick oxide layers over source and drain regions. Angle lap was at 3^0. (a) Magnification = 250X; (b) Magnification = 1000X.

This innovation reduces the feedback capacitance by a factor of 8 and relaxes the tolerance on the length of the gate electrode which overlaps the source and drain regions. The output characteristics of a typical enhancement transistor fabricated by the above process appears in Fig. 8–6. The effect of substrate bias on the electrode capacitances and

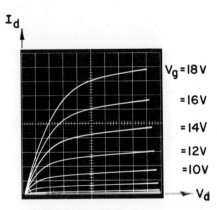

Figure 8–6. Output characteristics of typical ladder-geometry enhancement transistor. Vertical scale: 1ma/division; horizontal scale: 2v/division. Source and substrate are at ground potential.

output characteristics is discussed in Section 8–4. These transistors can tolerate a transient voltage of ± 65 v on the gate electrode; the maximum allowable gate voltage is limited by the dielectric breakdown strength of the oxide layer which is approximately 5×10^6 v/cm. The maximum allowable drain voltage is 35 v and is limited by the onset of avalanche multiplication in the channel region adjacent to the drain.

2. Diffusion depth and oxide thickness

The time and temperature needed for the diffusion-oxidation step must be selected to simultaneously yield proper values for the channel oxide thickness as well as the diffusion depth for the source and drain regions. The effective channel depth for the enhancement-type transistor, where the channel charge is induced by the gate potential, may be defined as the mean value of the electron distribution for an n-type transistor.

Under the approximation of a very lightly doped substrate material, it can be shown that the effective channel depth, d_c, defined by:

$$d_c = \frac{\int_0^\infty z\, n(z)\, dz}{\int_0^\infty n(z)\, dz} \tag{8-2}$$

is given by:

$$d_c = \left(\frac{\epsilon_s}{\epsilon_i}\right)\frac{\psi_s}{\mathscr{E}_i} \tag{8-3}$$

where ϵ_s and ϵ_i are the permittivities of the silicon and oxide, respectively, ψ_s is the potential of the silicon surface with respect to the bulk, and $\mathscr{E}_i$ is the electric field in the oxide. The definition given in Eq. (8–2) is the average value of z (the distance perpendicular to the silicon surface) weighted by the electron concentration, $n(z)$. Typically, these devices operate at oxide fields greater than 3×10^5 v/cm, where ψ_s is approximately 0.6 v and $d_c \leqslant 600$ Å.

If Poisson's equation is solved for the electron distribution, $n(z)$, corresponding to the lightly doped substrate case, it indicates that half of the electrons are contained in a distance equal to one Debye length from the surface. The Debye length, λ_s, is based on the surface concentration of electrons and is given by:

$$\lambda_s = \left(\frac{\epsilon_s}{\epsilon_i}\right)\left(\frac{kT}{q}\right)\frac{2}{\mathscr{E}_i} \tag{8-4}$$

where $kT/q = 0.026$ v at room temperature. For an oxide field of 3×10^5 v/cm, $\lambda_s = 50$ Å. Thus, most of the electrons are concentrated close to the surface, but the distribution exhibits a long tail extending deep into the bulk. A few thousand Ångstroms suffices for the depth of the source and drain regions.

The diffusion of phosphorus into the silicon from the phosphorus-rich oxide is not entirely understood. The exact concentration of free phosphorus at the silicon surface is unknown, and the oxide does not act as an infinite source. A useful quantity for estimating the diffusion depth is $\sqrt{Dt}$, where D is the diffusion constant in cm²/sec and t is the diffusion time. Figure 8–7 shows the variation in D with temperature for

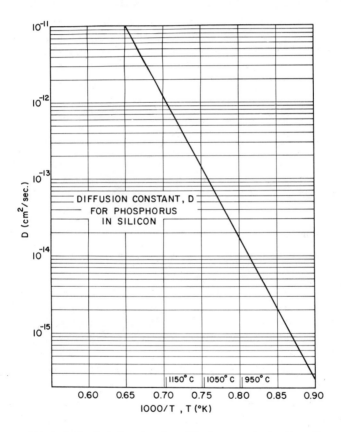

Figure 8–7. Variation in the diffusion constant, D, with temperature for the diffusion of phosphorus in silicon.

the diffusion of phosphorus in silicon. (If the diffusion proceeds from an infinite source, the profile follows a complementary error function, and the concentration drops to one-half of its value at the surface at a distance equal to $\sqrt{Dt}$.) For $T = 1050°C$, $D = 1.2 \times 10^{-13}$ cm²/sec, the diffusion depth after one hour is 2100 Å. This is satisfactory for the operation of enhancement-type transistors since the space-charge induced channel is very close to the silicon surface. A deeper diffusion depth may be obtained by a change in the furnace atmosphere to nitrogen after one hour (to inhibit further oxidation) and continuation of diffusion.

For oxidation in dry oxygen, the growth of silicon dioxide approximately follows a parabolic law (for further details, see Chapter 4), i.e.:

$$d_i^2 = Kt \tag{8-5}$$

where d_i is the oxide thickness and K is the proportionality constant. A plot of K vs. temperature is shown in Fig. 8-8 for growth in dry oxygen. The addition of water vapor to the system enhances the growth rate but

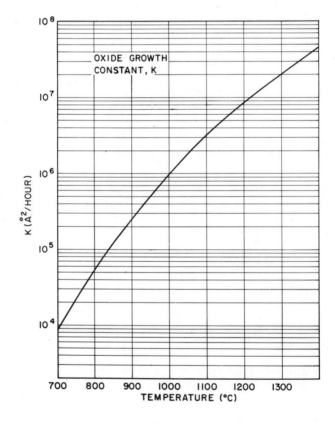

Figure 8-8. Oxide growth constant, K, in Å²/hr. vs. temperature for oxidation of silicon in dry oxygen at atmospheric pressure.

introduces an undesirable n-type skin on the silicon surface. For $T = 1050°C$, $K = 1.8 \times 10^6$ Å²/hr and 1340 Å of silicon dioxide are grown in one hour.

1. Maze geometry

A limitation to the use of deposited n-type oxide for the source of phosphorus is the fact that a very high surface concentration of electrically active donor atoms cannot be produced in the silicon surface. Conventional gas phase diffusion techniques can yield a surface concentration in the range of 10^{21} atoms/cm³. The heavier doping in the source and drain regions reduces the series resistance associated with the corresponding output electrodes. This is important for high-current transistors used in memory driver application. Figure 8-9 is a plan view of an

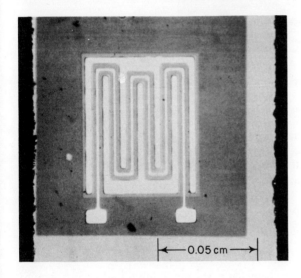

←— 0.05 cm —→

Figure 8-9. Silicon chip containing maze-geometry enhancement transistor.

enhancement transistor fabricated in the "maze" geometry by conventional oxide-masked diffusion techniques. The long gate electrode snakes between the fingerlike source and drain electrodes producing a channel width of 0.3 cm. The output characteristics of this device are shown in Fig. 8-10; drain current in excess of 100 ma can be supplied by a gate voltage of 4.5 v. The reduced channel length of 7.5 μ employed in this geometry is responsible for the very high transconductance but limits the operating drain voltage to 15 v.

8-3   DEPLETION-TYPE TRANSISTORS

This type of transistor is fabricated with the source, drain, and channel regions of the same conductivity type to yield substantial drain current for zero gate bias. The free-carrier concentration in the channel is much lower than the source or drain doping level so that complete pinch-off is obtained with a moderate oxide field. Unlike its vacuum-tube counterpart, the gate draws no current when biased positively, allowing linear

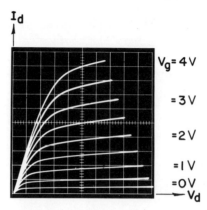

Figure   8–10. Output   characteristics of   a   maze-geometry   enhancement transistor. Vertical scale: 10 ma/division; horizontal: 1   v/division.   Source   and substrate are grounded.

amplification at zero gate bias. This transistor finds wide application as a small-signal linear amplifier over a wide frequency range and the geometry chosen for the transistor described next yields high performance up to a frequency of 150 mc at a moderate power level.

1. Offset-gate geometry

Unlike the enhancement transistor, the depletion unit does not require the gate electrode to overlap both source and drain regions. A significant improvement in high-frequency performance can be obtained with the offset-gate geometry shown in Fig. 8–11. The unmodulated portion of the channel near the drain electrode introduces a tolerable series resistance in the saturation region. The addition of a series drain resistance merely increases the drain voltage at which drain current saturates. As long as the small signal output resistance of the transistor is large with respect to the unmodulated drain resistance, little deterioration in circuit gain will result. However, any series source resistance will be multiplied by $A + 1$, where A is the voltage amplification factor of the transistor, when it is reflected to the output and cannot be tolerated. If the gate electrode must overlap, it should overlap the source region.

The offset-gate electrode significantly reduces the feedback capacitance because the active channel length is forced to coincide with the portion of the gate electrode which lies over the channel. The only inactive input capacitance is due to the overlap of the source electrode.

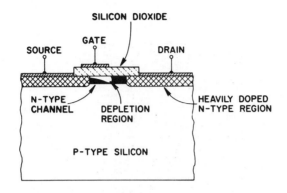

Figure 8–11. Offset-gate geometry used in depletion-type transistors to reduce the feedback capacitance from drain-to-gate when the device is operating under current-saturation conditions.

The exact distribution of active gate capacitance between source and drain is difficult to determine, but the depletion of majority carriers near the drain end of the active channel reduces the feedback capacitance when the device is in saturation.

Figure 8–12 is a photograph of an experimental depletion-type transistor which employs the offset-gate geometry just discussed. The active channel length is 10μ and the effective channel width is 0.125 cm. Conventional oxide-masked diffusion techniques were employed to define the source and drain regions and chrome-silver is used for the metallized areas. The gold wires that connect to the transistor header posts were attached by thermal-compression bonding. The output characteristics of a typical transistor are shown in Fig. 8–13 and the interelectrode capacitances of a packaged device are $C_{gs} = 4.8$ pf, $C_{gd} = 0.3$ pf, and $C_{ds} = 1.1$ pf with $I_d = 5$ma and $V_d = 15$v. A power gain of 10 db at 200 mc/s is obtained in a properly neutralized circuit, and the noise figure of this transistor under optimum conditions can be as low as 3.5 db.

2. Channel doping

The doping density of the n-type channel does not itself affect the device performance: it is the total carrier density per unit channel area that determines the pinch-off voltage and channel conductance of a depletion transistor. It can be shown that optimum performance is achieved

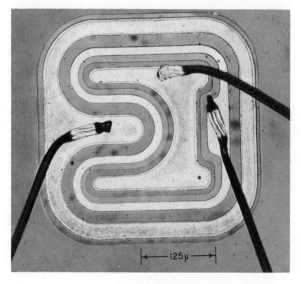

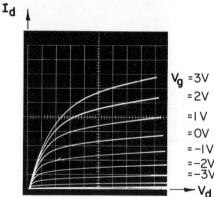

Figure 8–12. Silicon chip containing a depletion-type transistor. The drain (inner region), gate (middle region), and source (outer region) leads shown are gold wires which are attached to the transistor by thermal-compression bonding.

Figure 8–13. Output characteristics of a depletion-type transistor. Vertical scale: 2ma/division; horizontal scale: 5 v/division.

with a shallow, heavily doped channel, and complete pinch-off with a reasonable oxide field (i.e., less than 10^6 v/cm) requires a sheet charge corresponding to about 2×10^{12} carriers/cm². This can be satisfied with a donor concentration of 5×10^{17} atoms/cm³ diffused to a depth of 400 Å. However, the control of a shallow diffusion is poor when an oxide layer is to be thermally grown on the diffused region. A much more reproducible method for obtaining a shallow n-type channel under an oxide will be discussed in the next paragraph.

Baking an oxidized silicon wafer in dry hydrogen at 400°C for 15 minutes introduces positive charge in the silicon-dioxide layer which is compensated by negative charge in the silicon surface. Prolonged time and/or higher temperature increases the charge density. The net effect of this treatment is to introduce an electric field at the silicon surface which bends the bands toward n-type, creating an inversion layer on one ohm-cm p-type silicon. The electron distribution is identical to that produced by a gate field of the same magnitude, and the transfer characteristic of an n-type transistor is shifted to the left by the hydrogen treatment, as shown in Fig. 8–14, producing the desired depletion-unit characteristic.

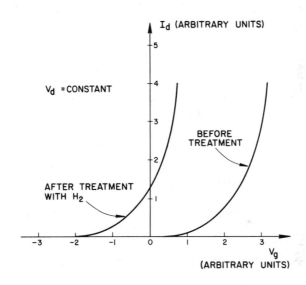

Figure 8–14. Transfer characteristics of a transistor before and after hydrogen bake at 400°C for 15 minutes.

When a shallow n-type channel is obtained with the hydrogen treatment, the entire surface of the p-type substrate is inverted to n-type, making selective channel formation difficult. For this reason, the outer diffused region of a construction such as shown in Fig. 8–12 must comprise the source, and not the drain, of the transistor. The entire n-type inversion layer of the wafer is ohmically connected to the outer diffused region; and since the drain-to-substrate junction is reverse-biased during normal operation, excessive back current would be obtained if the drain were the outer electrode. The gate must entirely enclose the inner drain region of a depletion unit because any uncovered channel will introduce a parallel, unmodulated resistance between source and drain. This is in contrast to the ladder geometry used for the enhancement transistor (see Fig. 8-2).

8-4 DESIGN CONSIDERATIONS BASED ON EXPERIMENTAL RESULTS

The variations in device performance with the dimensions of the transistor were discussed previously. A higher gain-bandwidth product is obtained with a small channel length. This figure of merit is independent of channel width and oxide thickness. A *wider channel* or *thinner oxide* produces a transistor with increased transconductance and input capacitance, leaving the C_{in}/g_m ratio unchanged. These units can deliver more current (at fixed drain and gate voltages) because of the lower impedance level of the device. However, the probability of fabricating a transistor with a defective gate is enhanced by these modifications. There is more chance that the gate electrode will cover a defect (pinhole) in the oxide layer if the gate is wider, and it is more probable to grow a defective oxide in a thin layer. A lower impedance level can be had at the sacrifice of transistor yield and reliability; these aspects will be discussed in detail in Section 8-5.

1. Substrate resistivity

At first glance, a high resistivity (preferably intrinsic) substrate would appear desirable. A low drain-to-substrate capacitance would be obtained without affecting the transistor characteristics since all channel conduction occurs at the semiconductor surface. However, transistors fabricated on a 1000 ohm-cm p-type silicon base wafer exhibited a poor amplification factor whereas transistors fabricated on 1 ohm-cm silicon demonstrated good saturation, as shown in Fig. 8-15. The explanation is based on fundamental considerations, which apply to all charge-controlled devices.

When the field-effect transistor is operated in the saturation portion of the output characteristics, the average drift velocity, v_d, for the channel carriers is approximately:

$$v_d \approx \mu \frac{(V_g - V_p)}{l} \tag{8-6}$$

since the source region of the channel has a potential difference of $(V_g - V_p)$ applied across it, and the additional drain voltage, $(V_d - V_g + V_p)$, appears across a very small fraction of the channel length. If the change in channel charge, ΔQ, per unit channel width is given by:

$$\Delta Q = C_{gc}\Delta V_g + C_{dc}\Delta V_d \tag{8-7}$$

where C_{gc} and C_{dc} are the gate-to-channel and drain-to-channel capacitances per unit width, respectively, then the change in drain current, ΔI_d, per unit width is simply:

$$\Delta I_d = \frac{\Delta Q v_d}{l} = (C_{gc}\Delta V_g + C_{dc}\Delta V_d)\,\frac{v_d}{l} \tag{8-8}$$

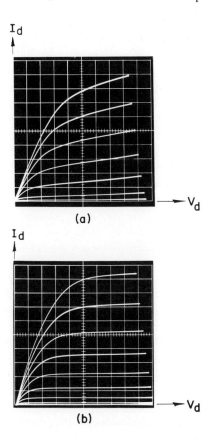

Figure 8–15. Effect of substrate resistivity on the amplification factor of a transistor. (a) 1000 ohm-cm p-type substrate: vertical scale 5ma/division; horizontal scale is 2v/division; $l = 20$ microns; $w = 2500$ microns; (b) 1 ohm-cm p-type substrate: vertical scale is 1ma/division; horizontal scale is 2v/division, $l = 10$ microns, $w = 125$ microns.

The amplification factor, A, is defined by:

$$A \equiv -\frac{\Delta V_d}{\Delta V_g}\bigg|\Delta I_d = 0 \tag{8-9}$$

and is simply the ratio of capacitances:

$$A = \frac{C_{gc}}{C_{dc}} \tag{8-10}$$

which is independent of channel width.

The addition of a screen grid in a vacuum tube electrostatically shields the plate from the cathode and lowers the plate-to-cathode capacitance, producing the high amplification factor associated with a pentode. Similarly, the substrate of an MOS transistor functions as an inefficient gate electrode, and a more heavily doped substrate electrostatically shields the drain from the channel, producing a higher amplification factor. This improvement is obtained at the cost of increasing the drain-to-substrate capacitance and a compromise must be reached for each application. Depletion units show optimum high-frequency power gain when fabricated on 20–25 ohm-cm material.

2. Substrate bias

The drain-to-source capacitance of the transistor is a function of drain voltage since the major contribution to it comes from the reverse-biased drain-to-substrate diode. The substrate is effectively at source potential. Since the shallow, highly doped drain region forms an abrupt junction to the substrate, the capacitance should vary as $(V_d + \phi)^{-1/2}$, where ϕ is the contact potential and is approximately 0.75v. However, as the drain voltage is increased, the peripheral capacitance around the shallow junction dominates, and the capacitance approaches a minimum value as shown in Fig. 8–16. This curve is for a ladder-geometry enhancement transistor fabricated on 10 ohm-cm p-type silicon. Similar curves for transistors having different drain geometries verified the empirical equation for the drain-to-substrate capacitance:

$$C_{d-\text{sub}} = A\left[\frac{K_1}{(V_d+\phi)^{1/2}} + K_2\left(\frac{P}{A}\right)\right] \tag{8-11}$$

This is the equation for two capacitors in parallel, where A is the drain area, P is the drain perimeter, and K_1 and K_2 are constants which have been evaluated for 10 ohm-cm p-type material:

$$K_1 = 1.17 \times 10^4 \ \text{pf v}^{1/2}/\text{cm}^2$$

$$(8\text{–}12)$$

$$K_2 = 3.78\text{pf/cm}$$

This discussion suggests the use of an additional battery to bias the substrate at a negative voltage to reduce the output capacitance.

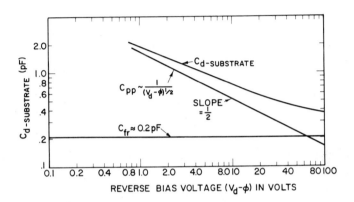

Figure 8–16. Variation in drain-to-substrate capacitance with reverse bias.

Substrate bias will affect the operating characteristics since the substrate acts as an additional gate electrode. The transfer characteristic of a depletion unit controlled from the substrate is shown in Fig. 8–17 with

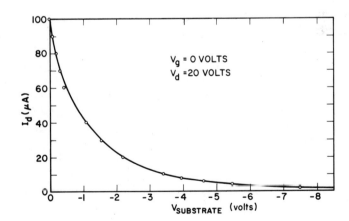

Figure 8–17. Transfer characteristic of a depletion-type transistor operated from the 10 ohm-cm resistivity substrate. The metal gate electrode is at source potential.

the metal gate connected to the grounded source and the transistor operated as a junction-type unipolar device. This curve most closely approximates an exponential because depletion of channel charge proceeds from the low density in the bulk to the high density at the silicon surface. The pinch-off voltage of a transistor controlled from the metal gate is a function of the substrate bias; a convenient way of controlling this parameter is thus established. It is desirable to have a positive pinch-off voltage (for an n-type transistor) or threshold voltage in digital applications and this may be conveniently achieved with a negative bias on the substrate. Figure 8–18 shows a graph of the effective pinch-off voltage,

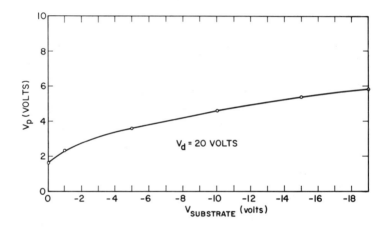

Figure 8–18. Effective pinch-off voltage of enhancement-type transistor as a function of substrate bias.

for control by the metal gate, as a function of substrate bias. Pinch-off was defined as the gate voltage necessary to produce $10\mu a$ of channel current for this curve.

The addition of a negative bias to the p-type substrate of an n-type transistor lowers the drain-to-substrate capacitance and produces the desirable threshold voltage. It has very little effect on the maximum allowable drain voltage, since drain-to-channel breakdown is caused by the electric field pattern under the gate electrode and occurs at a lower value of drain voltage than direct drain-to-substrate breakdown. This is true as long as the substrate resistivity is greater than 1 ohm-cm. The amplification factor will be lowered by the addition of substrate bias because the additional depletion region below the drain reduces the shielding action of the substrate. This is of little consequence in large-signal switching circuits.

3. Series source resistance

Parasitic source resistance, r'_s, due to contact resistance between the source region and the metal electrode, or due to insufficient doping of the source region, results in a degeneration of the transconductance of the transistor by the factor $1 + g_m r'_s$. Hence, r'_s must be small in comparison to the reciprocal of the transconductance. Since g_m varies linearly with gate voltage, this condition imposes one restriction on the maximum usable gate voltage.

Measurements performed on a large diffused n-type area produced by the deposited-oxide technique indicate a sheet resistivity of 40 ohms/ square, and a contact resistance between chrome-gold and the heavily doped silicon of approximately 25 ohms per contact. The contact area and diffusion conditions were identical to that used in the fabrication of ladder-geometry devices. From this information, a total parasitic source resistance of about 50 ohms is expected in a ladder-geometry transistor. To confirm this, transistors of differing channel lengths were fabricated and the low voltage drain-to-source resistance was measured as a function of channel length. The linear variation expected is shown in Fig. 8–19, and the intercept of the extrapolated curve indicates a total series

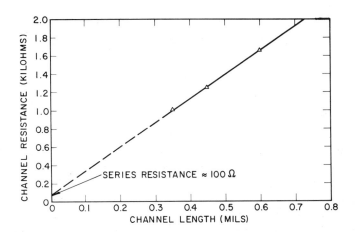

Figure 8–19. Experimental determination of series-source resistance by extrapolation of linear channel resistance vs. channel-length plot.

resistance of about 100 ohms. Since this is equally divided between the source and drain ends of the channel, a parasitic source resistance of 50 ohms is indicated, which agrees with the predicted value.

Other effects also tend to degenerate the transconductance of the transistor when operated at substantial drain and gate voltages. A fall-off of carrier mobility with increased drift field (velocity saturation) or increased surface potential (due to increased surface scattering) are two such phenomena. Their influence is very similar to that of a nonlinear source resistance.

8–5 YIELD CONSIDERATIONS

The MOS transistor is an attractive element for integrated circuits. In this application, a knowledge of the possible failure mechanisms is particularly useful because the entire circuit must be discarded when one or more transistors is inoperable. Questions of failure in fabrication and use will be treated here but will be limited to those mechanisms which are specific to these devices.

Since this transistor utilizes an insulating material as an integral part of the charge-control mechanism, major differences in yield considerations from junction devices will center around the quality of this insulator. The effects of structural imperfections and ionic conduction on the failure of MOS transistors will now be discussed.

1. Defective gate insulation

One of the possible causes of malfunctioning of MOS field-effect transistors is a faulty gate insulator, which may be caused by pinholes in the thermally grown oxide layer, yielding a short circuit between gate and channel. Direct measurements on a clean, oxidized silicon wafer indicate that the oxide defects are usually randomly distributed on the silicon surface and are most probably caused by irregular oxide growth in the neighborhood of surface imperfections. If the area of the pinhole is much smaller than the area of the gate electrode, a model of randomly distributed points may be postulated. The probability, P, of covering k pinholes with an electrode of area A is given by the Poisson distribution:

$$P(k, A) = \frac{(nA)^k e^{-nA}}{k!} \tag{8–13}$$

where n is the average surface density of pinholes. The probability of success, P_s, is just the probability of covering zero pinholes and is given by:

$$P_s = P(0, A) = e^{-nA} \tag{8–14}$$

Since the pinholes are assumed to be randomly distributed, the success of one transistor is independent of the success of an adjacent one (uncorrelated events), and the probability of obtaining N good transistors for an integrated circuit array is simply:

$$P_c \equiv (P_s)^N = e^{-n(NA)} \tag{8-15}$$

and depends only on the total active area of the circuit, NA. The same considerations apply to the fabrication of a high-current (wide-channel) transistor. It is just as difficult to fabricate a 0.1 cm-wide channel device as it is to integrate 10 transistors, each having a channel width of 100μ.

The average pinhole density for a 1000 Å oxide layer has been determined by experimental verification of Eq. (8-14). The value varied markedly from wafer to wafer, being 1000 cm^{-2} in the worst case. Thus, a transistor having a gate electrode area of $6 \times 1 \times 10^{-6}$ in.$^2 = 3.87 \times 10^{-5}$ cm^2 has a probability of success equal to $P_s = 0.968$, and an array of sixteen such transistors has a probability of success equal to $P_c = 0.538$ for this value of n.

To further investigate the feasibility of fabricating integrated circuits, assume that a logic circuit containing sixteen transistors is desired. When room for wiring and dicing is taken into account, a normal 1-inch diameter silicon wafer will easily accommodate twenty such circuits. The probability, P_m, of obtaining exactly m operative circuits (i.e., no defective gate electrodes) out of 20, with a probability of success for each circuit given by P_c, is simply:

$$P_m = \frac{(20)!}{m!(20-m)!} P_c^m (1-P_c)^{20-m} \tag{8-16}$$

The probability of having at least r operative circuits is the sum of P_m for $r \leqslant m \leqslant 20$:

$$P_{m \geqslant r} = \sum_{m=r}^{20} \frac{(20)!}{m!(20-m)!} P_c^m (1-P_c)^{20-m} \tag{8-17}$$

The plot of $P_{m \geqslant r}$ as a function of r (with $P_c = 0.5$) is shown in Fig. 8-20.

Although the over-all yield of operative circuits is 50%, there are occasions when a certain minimum number of operative circuits per wafer becomes the governing parameter. As an example, consider the case in which it is desired to integrate r circuits from the twenty on each wafer, and assume that any pattern of the r circuits may be integrated just as easily. The total yield of useful wafers is then given by the factor $P_{m \geqslant r}$. If it is desired to integrate five circuits out of the twenty then Fig. 8-20 gives a total yield of successfully integrated wafers in excess of 99.4%. Each wafer now contains an 80-transistor circuit.

These calculations illustrate that perfect gate insulation is not required to produce high-yield integrated circuits through a judicious choice of subcircuit integration.

At least two other factors may contribute to short-circuited gates. One is the large electrostatic voltage produced across the channel oxide

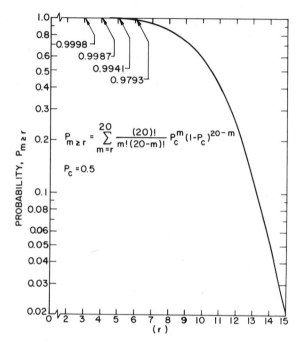

Figure 8–20. Probability of obtaining at least r operative circuits out of 20 when the only failure mechanism is a defective gate. Each circuit utilizes 16 transistors.

when the transistor is suddenly inserted or withdrawn from the poly-styrene foam (snow) commonly used to package transistors. The second cause is attributed to cracks in the oxide layer introduced during thermal-compression bonding of the lead wire to the gate electrode. Careful control of temperature and pressure during this operation can minimize this problem.

2. Instability of characteristics

Semiconductor devices such as the insulated-gate field-effect transistor, operating in the presence of high electric fields,[18] have shown instability of characteristics related to the motion of ions and molecules in silicon dioxide[19] and other insulating films[20] (see also Chapter 3). The enhancement transistor used in digital-circuit applications generally operates at an oxide field greater than 10^6 v/cm, which is close to the dielectric breakdown strength of the silicon dioxide layer. The depletion transistor is usually operated near zero gate voltage in small-signal amplifier applications, and the oxide field can be on the order of 10^5 v/cm. Thus, instability due to migration of ions in the bulk of the oxide layer is more pronounced in the enhancement transistor.

The mechanism of this instability is as follows. Assume that the oxide layer contains mobile, polyatomic molecules which may be easily dissociated. The application of a positive potential to the gate electrode of an n-type transistor will tend to move the negative ions toward the gate electrode and the positive ions toward the silicon surface, as shown in Fig. 8–21a. With zero gate bias, there remains an electric field pointing

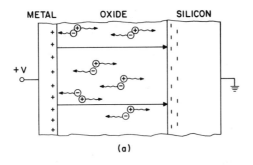

(a)

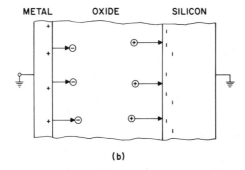

(b)

Figure 8–21. Migration of ions in the bulk of the silicon dioxide layer can cause a drift in the transistor characteristics. (a) Oxide field causes ions to drift; (b) finite electric field exists when gate potential is reduced to zero.

into the silicon which terminates on negative charge (see Fig. 8–21b). When the gate bias is removed from an enhancement transistor that has been "on" for an extended period, the transistor does not turn "off." The "off" current has changed with time.

The details of this mechanism are not well-understood and the foregoing discussion indicates, in schematic form, what might be happening. It has been suggested[21] that the ion moving in the silicon dioxide layer is a positively charged oxygen vacancy, which allows only positive charge in the insulating layer.

Another way of observing this effect is to examine the transfer characteristic of an *n*-type enhancement transistor before and after the application of a large positive gate bias for an extended period of time. Initially, the transfer characteristic appears as shown in the right-hand curve of Fig. 8–22. After the application of gate voltage, the curve drifts

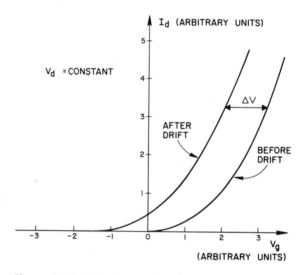

Figure 8–22. Shift in transfer characteristics of *n*-type enhancement transistor after extended application of positive gate bias.

to the left and the instability can be quantitatively characterized by the voltage shift, ΔV. This quantity increases with temperature, time of application, and electric field strength. In some units, drift is observed until a maximum value of ΔV is observed, while in others, ΔV seems to continually increase with time.

When this type of instability was first observed, values of ΔV as large as 5–6 v were observed; now it is possible to limit the drift to less than 0.5 v by diffusing phosphorus into the oxide layer before metallization of the transistor. Silicon dioxide is an open-lattice structure having a mean lattice spacing of about 8 Å. The addition of phosphorus forms a glass-like structure which is more dense than silicon dioxide. This may reduce the mobility of the ions, producing a more stable oxide.

While this type of drift can be explained by other mechanisms, other experimental and theoretical results make them unlikely. The rotation of polarized molecules trapped in the oxide lattice will produce an effect which is qualitatively similar to the one just discussed; but it can be shown[22] that an unusually high density of dipoles must be assumed to account for the large values of ΔV that have been observed. Electronic trapping in the oxide layer near the silicon and metal surfaces will also show up as a drift in the transfer characteristic but can be eliminated on the following grounds:

1. If some of the electrons induced in the silicon surface by the gate field were trapped in the oxide near the silicon surface and remained after the gate voltage was reduced to zero, they would introduce an electric field opposite to that observed and cause a shift to the right of the transfer characteristic.

2. If a net positive charge were introduced into the oxide near the metal surface due to the trapping of holes from the gate electrode, an inordinately high trap density must be assumed to produce the observed shift because most of the electric field produced by these charges terminates on the gate electrode. Also, this effect should be temperature-independent because the trapping is a tunneling process.

Although the depletion transistor operates at a low oxide field so that bulk ion migration is not a problem, it utilizes the offset-gate geometry which exposes a portion of the channel oxide near the drain end of the channel. This introduces an additional source of instability because of the finite sheet conductivity of the oxide surface. Between gate and drain, one may draw an equivalent distributed RC network as shown in Fig. 8-23. With the gate negative and the drain positive, a potential gradient

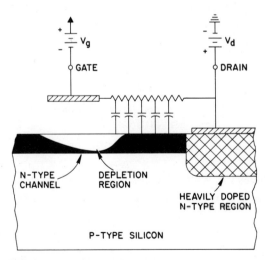

Figure 8-23. Equivalent circuit used to explain the drift in the characteristics of an offset-gate-geometry transistor.

will exist across the resistive surface and current will start to flow. This will charge the distributed oxide capacitance in a time which may be quite long (seconds to weeks) because of the large value of surface resistance. The surface next to the gate electrode will be negatively charged, causing depletion of channel charge beyond the gate geometry. When the gate potential is reduced to zero, this charge will continue to exist and a portion of the channel will remain partially depleted, adding a series resistance to the channel. This lowers the zero-bias channel current when the gate potential is reduced to zero after a prolonged negative bias. Proper packaging and surface treatments can eliminate this form of instability.

REFERENCES

1. M. M. Atalla, E. Tannenbaum, and E. J. Scheiber, *Bell Syst. Tech. J.* **38**, 749(1959).

2. M. M. Atalla, E. J. Scheiber, and E. Tannenbaum, U. S. Patent No. 2, 899, 344 (1958).

3. H. Staatz, L. Davis, Jr., and G. A. deMars, *Phys. Rev.* **98**, 540 (1955).

4. R. H. Kingston and A. L. McWhorter, *Phys. Rev.* **103**, 534 (1956).

5. S. R. Morrison, *Phys. Rev.* **102**, 1297 (1956).

6. H. C. Montgomery, *Phys. Rev.* **106**, 441 (1957).

7. W. L. Brown, *Phys. Rev.* **91**, 518 (1953).

8. E. O. Johnson, *J. Appl. Phys.* **28**, 1349 (1957).

9. E. O. Johnson, *Phys. Rev.* **111**, 153 (1958).

10. G. C. Dousmanis, *Phys. Rev.* **112**, 369 (1958).

11. W. Shockley and G. L. Pearson, *Phys. Rev.* **74**, 232 (1948).

12. A. L. McWhorter, "1/f Noise and Related Surface Effects in Germanium," Sc. D. thesis, E. E. Dept., MIT, 1955.

13. Eastman Kodak Co., *Photosensitive Resists for Industry,* Rochester, New York (1962).

14. Eastman Kodak Co., *Kodak Metal-Etch Resist,* Rochester, N.Y. (1959).

15. E. O. Johnson and A. Rose, *Proc. IRE* **47**, 407 (1959).

16. See, for instance, J. Millman and H. Taub, *Pulse and Digital Circuits,* New York (McGraw-Hill Book Company, 1956), p. 214.

17. J. Scott and J. Olmstead, *Solid-to-Solid Diffusion Technique,* to be published.

18. M. F. Goldberg and J. Vaccaro, "Physics of Failure in Electronics," *RADC Series in Reliability,* Vol. II.

19. W. Shockley, H. J. Queisser, and W. W. Hooper, *Phys. Rev. Letters* **11**, 489 (1963).

20. M. H. Pilkuhn, *J. Appl. Phys.* **34**, 3302 (1963).

21. D. R. Kerr, J. S. Logan, P. J. Burkhardt, and D. R. Young, *Stability of Silicon-Silicon Dioxide and Silicon-Glass Interfaces,* to be published.

22. F. P. Heiman, "Surface States and Related Effects Associated with a Metal-Oxide-Semiconductor Structure," Ph.D. thesis, E. E. Dept., Princeton University, 1964.

9

Thin-Film Transistors

Paul K. Weimer

9-1 INTRODUCTION

The all-thin-film approach to integrated circuits utilizes an inert insulating substrate in place of the single-crystal silicon chip used in the MOS transistor. Complete electrical isolation of individual components is readily obtained in circuits covering large areas. The common parts of the active and passive elements can be deposited simultaneously, permitting complex circuits to be fabricated in fewer processing steps.

The critical problem in thin-film circuits is to produce thin-film transistors (TFT's) having adequate performance. In thin-film transistors,[1, 2] the semiconductor material, as well as the metal electrodes and insulator, is deposited in selected areas upon an insulating substrate such as glass. In Fig. 9–1 the structure of an all-evaporated TFT is compared with that of the silicon MOS transistor.[3] Both transistors yield the typical field-effect characteristics of the insulated-gate device with minor differences arising from variations in materials and structure. The absence of the underlying slab of semiconductor in the TFT eliminates the need for back-biasing the substrate to minimize resistive and capacitive coupling between elements. The semiconductor layer in the thin-film transistor is normally a polycrystalline layer, although single-crystal layers may be capable of higher performance. The gate-insulator layer in the all-evaporated TFT consists of a separate material deposited independently either on top or underneath the semiconductor layer. The electrodes are of metal such as aluminum or gold.

Although the thin layers in the TFT can be deposited by various techniques, evaporation in vacuum has been most widely used. Complex circuits incorporating hundreds or thousands of active and passive components can be deposited upon a single glass substrate during one pump-down of the vacuum system. This chapter will discuss the TFT from the standpoint of fabrication, performance, and application in thin-film circuits.

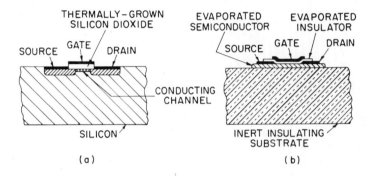

Figure 9-1. Two forms of the insulated-gate field-effect transistor. (a) An MOS transistor formed on the surface of a block of silicon; (b) an all-evaporated TFT deposited upon an insulating substrate.

9-2 DESCRIPTION OF THIN-FILM TRANSISTOR STRUCTURES

An advantage of the all-evaporated thin-film transistor is that it can be constructed in a variety of forms upon an inexpensive insulating substrate. Figure 9-2 shows a group of TFT's with interconnections deposited upon a glass plate. Figures 9-3 and 9-4 show cross-sectional drawings of four types of structures. The thickness of each film is greatly exaggerated in the cross-sectional drawings. The metal electrodes are several hundred Ångstroms in thickness, the insulator layer ranges from 200 to 2000 Å, and the semiconductor ranges from a few hundred Ångstroms to one or more microns. The source and drain electrodes are usually of aluminum or gold. Cadmium sulfide and selenide films have been used most frequently for the semiconductor, but other materials of both n- and p-type are also suitable. Typical insulating materials which can be readily evaporated are silicon monoxide, magnesium fluoride, and zinc sulfide. An encapsulating overcoat consisting of a nonporous layer of a material such as silicon dioxide, selenium, or arsenic trisulfide can be deposited over the top of the entire structure for protection against the effects of air.

In the staggered structure of Fig. 9–3a, the metal source and drain electrodes are deposited first upon the glass substrate with a gap spacing of approximately 10 μ. Following the semiconductor deposition, the insulator layer is evaporated, and finally the gate strip is put down in

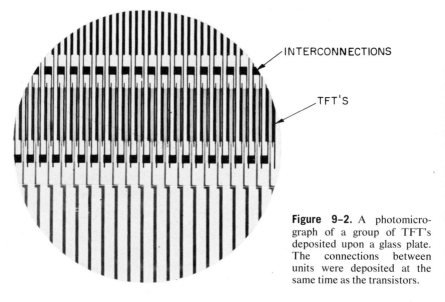

Figure 9–2. A photomicrograph of a group of TFT's deposited upon a glass plate. The connections between units were deposited at the same time as the transistors.

registry with the source-drain gap. The gate may be permitted to overlap the source and drain slightly as shown, although this is not required. The strips forming the source and drain are typically 50 to 100 thousandths of an inch long. Since the substrate may be heated to several hundred degrees

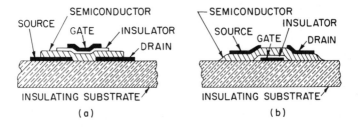

Figure 9–3. Cross-sectional diagrams of two TFT's having the *staggered-electrode* structure.

centigrade during the semiconductor deposition, it is sometimes convenient to carry out this operation in a vacuum system other than the one in which the electrodes are deposited. A precision masking jig suitable for defining the electrodes will be described in Section 9–3.

For cadmium sulfide TFT's the coplanar electrode structure[4] of Fig. 9-4a is somewhat simpler to fabricate than the staggered structure because all the evaporations requiring precision masking can be carried out in one pump-down without having to heat the substrate. Since the semiconductor is deposited before any electrodes, maximum freedom in processing the semiconductor layer is obtained.

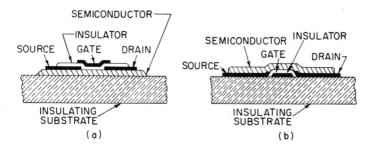

Figure 9-4. Cross-sectional diagrams of two TFT's having the *coplanar-electrode* structure.

The coplanar structure of Fig. 9-4b is of interest in that the entire circuit including the TFT electrodes and insulator layers are deposited upon the substrate prior to any semiconductor deposition. This structure allows maximum freedom in the choice of fine-pattern deposition techniques without fear of damage to the semiconductor.

9-3 FABRICATION OF THIN-FILM TRANSISTORS

The advantage of thin-film transistors for cost reduction of integrated circuits can be realized only if their fabrication procedure is compatible with that of the passive components. To reduce the total number of steps in building the complete circuit, similar parts of all components should be deposited simultaneously. The construction of successful thin-film circuits requires a compatible solution to two basic problems:

1. the deposition of thin films having the required electrical properties;

2. the precise geometrical control of the dimensions of each layer.

Although evaporation in high vacuum is customarily used for deposition of the layers, other methods such as sputtering, chemical decomposition, and electroplating are also useful. A most critical step in the construction of the TFT is the deposition and treatment of the semiconductor layer, discussed in the next section. The choice of a suitable method of pattern delineation is equally important in determining the economic significance of the thin-film transistor.

1. Deposition of semiconductor films suitable for thin-film transistors

Polycrystalline semiconductor films deposited by evaporation upon noncrystalline substrates have received much attention because of their promise for low-cost integrated circuits. If transistors having adequate performance can be deposited upon such substrates as glass, plastic, or ceramic, the use of integrated circuits can be greatly extended. In some applications such as the solid-state image-scanning panel discussed in Section 9–6, a large inexpensive transparent substrate may be of prime importance. Evaporated layers of cadmium sulfide,[2, 4, 5, 6, 7, 8] cadmium selenide,[9, 10, 11] and tellurium[12] upon glass substrates have been used most frequently for experimental thin-film transistors. Other polycrystalline films which have also produced operable units include zinc oxide,[13] indium antimonide,[43] cadmium telluride,[13] tin oxide,[14] and indium oxide,[14] The details of the deposition and processing techniques of each of these films is as significant as the choice of the material.

An important requirement on the characteristics of the semiconductor film is that the mobility be as high as possible for best frequency response. Although a lower mobility can be compensated to some extent by the reduction of source-drain spacings and gate width, unusually close spacings are apt to increase the cost of the device.

The high mobility must be accompanied by a carrier density which is not too large to be effectively modulated by the gate. The amount of charge the gate can control is determined by the insulator dielectric constant and breakdown strength. Although a considerable range in initial conductivity of the semiconductor film can be accommodated by adjustment of its thickness, too high a conductivity leads to poorly saturated characteristics.

The high mobilities of the III-V compounds make them of interest for TFT's, provided the initial carrier density is not too high. At the other end of the scale, wide-bandgap materials having very low initial carrier density can be used, provided the mobility is adequate. For such materials the carriers required for control would be injected from the source electrode. Alternatively, the additional carriers may be provided by doping, or an accumulation layer of higher conductivity could be formed on the surface of the insulating semiconductor by appropriate surface treatment.

For TFT's having the coplanar structure shown in Fig. 9–4a, the semiconductor is deposited first upon the glass substrate in a vacuum system separate from the one in which the electrodes are deposited. An evaporator arrangement used for cadmium sulfide is illustrated in Fig. 9–5. The vacuum system has an oil diffusion pump with a liquid nitrogen trap. The substrate heater is a glass plate coated with transparent tin oxide, permitting the monitoring of thickness by optical transmission. The crucible in which the compressed pellets of cadmium sulfide powder are heated is made of molybdenum wire coated with aluminum oxide. A quartz wool plug in the crucible prevents spattering. The charge is evaporated fairly rapidly (~3000 Å/min.) from a rather hot source onto a substrate held at about 180°C. The amount of excess cadmium in the deposited layer (and therefore its resistivity) is a function of the substrate

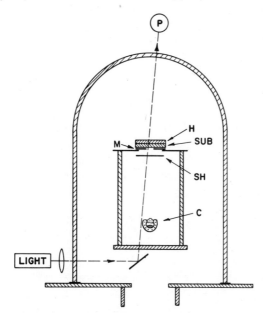

Figure 9–5. Evaporator and substrate heater set-up used in the evaporation of semiconductor layers for thin-film transistors. H is the substrate heater, M is the mask, SH is a shutter, C is the evaporator crucible, and P is the photomultiplier cell used in monitoring semiconductor thickness.

temperature. The final properties of the layer[15,16] are also affected by post-evaporative heat treatment of the layer in the presence of various gases. Good performance has been obtained with widely varying procedures of deposition[17,18] and processing, but the details of fabrication are critical. Section 9–5.2 discusses the influence of surface states, internal barriers, and electrode contacts upon performance.

Although the performance of TFT's using polycrystalline films is good, somewhat higher performance would be expected with single-crystal films. Single-crystal silicon films[19] have been deposited on sapphire by the hydrogen reduction of silicon tetrachloride. An insulated-gate thin-film transistor[20] utilizing a silicon layer pyrolytically deposited upon an oriented single-crystal substrate is described in Section 9–7.

2. Pattern delineation in thin-film devices

The production of geometrically accurate fine patterns of thin films can be carried out by either of two methods:

1. The film is prevented from coating the substrate in the undesired areas by means of masks.

2. The film is initially deposited uniformly over the entire substrate, and then selectively removed from the undesired areas.

Each method has particular advantages.

The experimental thin-film circuits described in Section 9–6 were fabricated using movable metal masks mounted close to the substrate in the vacuum chamber. A precision jig, shown in Fig. 9–6, permits the successive masks to be moved into place by means of external controls. The various steps in evaporation can be carried out in rapid sequence without exposure to air. Sample TFT's in the circuit can be monitored electrically at all stages of fabrication.

Suitable metal masks prepared by photoetching or plating are available commercially. The masks shown in Fig. 9–6 were used in depositing the

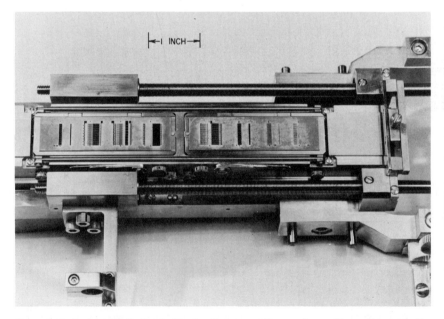

Figure 9–6. A precision jig for positioning the evaporation masks used in making a thin-film circuit. The evaporator crucibles are mounted below the jig, while the substrate (not shown) is held in a fixed position directly above the masks.

30-stage scan generator[21] described in Section 9–6. Complex circuits containing many transistors, diodes, resistors, and capacitors with their associated connections can be deposited in a short sequence of evaporations. The dimensional requirements on the photoetched masks are that they should be flat and sufficiently accurate in aperture spacing so that successive patterns will register. It is somewhat difficult to obtain photoetched masks having stable, long, narrow "lands" required to produce the 10-μ source-drain gap in the transistor. This problem can be avoided by the use of separate masks for the source and drain, or by the insertion of bridges into the mask with provision for *healing* the resulting

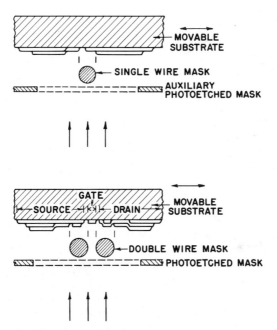

Figure 9–7. Illustration of the use of single- and double-wire masks to form evaporated patterns having spacings much less than the wire diameter. Movable photoetched masks mounted below the wire grill serve to define the less critical dimensions.

breaks in the evaporated pattern with subsequent evaporations. The total thickness of the evaporated material accumulating on the masks is sufficiently small that many evaporations can be made before the masks need to be cleaned.

Although the photoetched evaporation masks have been used for thin-film circuits having more than 1000 components/in², other types of mechanical masks are capable of greater precision and packing density.

Repetitive patterns such as the foregoing scan-generator circuit can be made in a much finer scale using a stretched wire grill[22] in combination with one or more photoetched masks. Since the most critical dimensions are determined by the grill, it is mounted closest to the substrate. The grill wires are drawn through a die as the grill is being wound, thus ensuring parallelism of the shadows cast by opposite sides of each wire. By displacement of the substrate relative to the wires for successive evaporations, as shown in Fig. 9-7, gap widths much less than the wire diameter are possible. Gaps 5 to 10μ wide are readily produced with grill wires 38μ in diameter. Such gaps are much cleaner and more reproducible than those obtained with photoetched masks. It is also easier to maintain close spacing to the substrate with grills than with photoetched masks which are not always flat. The ultimate limit in fineness of patterns which can be produced by mechanical masks appears to be set by the amount of scattered material that can be tolerated behind the mask edges.[23]

For large-scale production of integrated thin-film circuits, the mechanical masking technique just described can be automated or replaced by other methods of pattern delineation. Photoresist masking, which has been used successfully for deposition of TFT's, represents another promising approach.[14] The photoresist coating, which is deposited directly on the substrate, can be used as a mask for either chemically removing a portion of film which was previously deposited, or for preventing a subsequent deposit from sticking to the substrate in particular areas.

9-4 PERFORMANCE CHARACTERISTICS OF EVAPORATED THIN-FILM TRANSISTORS

The TFT displays the high input impedance and the well-saturated pentode-like characteristics typical of an insulated-gate field-effect transistor. Figures 9-8 and 9-9 illustrate enhancement and depletion-type characteristics for two polycrystalline cadmium sulfide TFT's. These units have the coplanar electrode structure[4] shown in Fig. 9-4a. Similar curves are obtained with the staggered-electrode structures and with other n-type semiconductors such as cadmium selenide.[10] Fig. 9-10 shows enhancement characteristics for a p-type tellurium TFT.[12] Enhancement- and depletion-type characteristics differ primarily in the value of V_p, the gate voltage required for pinch-off (or onset) of drain current. The design factors affecting the value of V_p are discussed in a later section.

The source-drain gap in each of the transistors illustrated is $10 \mu \times 0.25$ cm, with a gate width of 18μ. The CdS unit shown in Fig. 9-8 has a transconductance of 4000 μmhos at a gate bias of $+2.6$ v. The dynamic output impedance derived from the slope of the saturated portion of the curve is 40,000 ohms. The voltage amplification factor calculated from the product of these quantities is 160. The input capacitance under operating conditions is about 30 pf. CdS TFT's have been built in the same geometry with transconductances up to 25,000 μmhos.

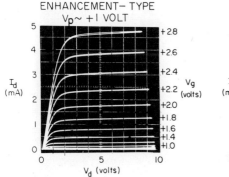

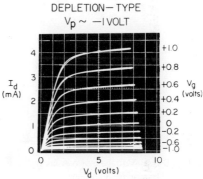

Figure 9–8. Operating characteristics for an *enhancement-type* cadmium sulfide thin-film transistor. Drain current is plotted against voltage for different values of gate voltage. The source is grounded.

Figure 9–9. Operating characteristics for a *depletion-type* cadmium sulfide thin-film transistor. Such a unit can be operated in either the enhancement or depletion mode. The TFT's illustrated in Figures 9–8 and 9–9 both have the coplanar electrode structure of Figure 9–4a.

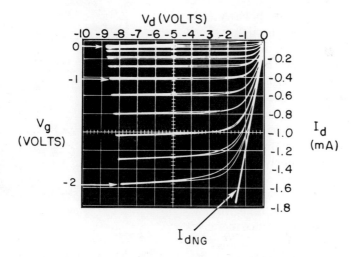

Figure 9–10. Drain characteristics of a *p*-type tellurium TFT. The straight line labelled I_{dNG} is the current-voltage curve for an identical tellurium TFT from which the gate was omitted. (See Section 9–5.2)

The gain-versus-frequency characteristics for a similar TFT are shown in Fig. 9–11. As a low-pass amplifier, it has a voltage gain of 8.5 from d-c up to about 2.6 mc/s, with a gain-bandwidth product of 22 mc/s. This test was made with a low-impedance signal source and included additional output capacitance to simulate a second TFT stage. Three

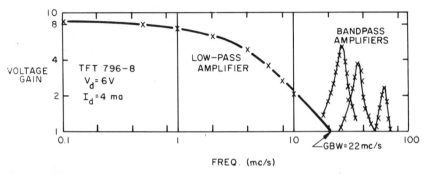

Figure 9–11. Voltage gain-versus-frequency characteristics of a CdS TFT operated as low-pass and band-pass amplifiers.

different band-pass amplifier characteristics are shown for output circuits resonant at 25, 36, and 60 mc/s. The voltage gain at 60 mc/s was 2.5, with a gain-bandwidth product of 17 mc/s. Other cadmium sulfide TFT's[21] have performed as oscillators at frequencies above 70 mc/s. As shown in Fig. 9–12 the output switching transitions are fast, occurring in less than 4 nsec measured in a circuit having 50-ohm input and output impedances. The opposite polarity transient is direct-feed-through of signal through the gate-drain capacitance.

Although very high transconductances are possible in TFT's, the gate capacitance in such units is also large. The best frequency response has been obtained in units having a somewhat thicker insulator and correspondingly lower gate capacitance. Figure 9–13 shows the measured gate capacitance as a function of gate and drain voltage. Note that the capacitance increases with positive drain voltage as the space-charge region in the semiconductor is reduced in thickness. With zero drain voltage

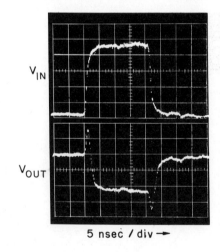

5 nsec / div →

Figure 9–12. Pulse response of a cadmium sulfide TFT. The opposite-polarity transient in the output waveform is direct feed-through of signal via the gate-drain capacitance.

applied, the total gate capacitance, C_g, divides about equally between the gate-source and gate-drain region in the symmetrical structure. However, at high drain voltage, in the current saturation region, the major portion of

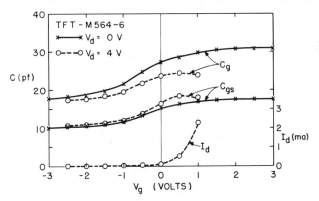

Figure 9–13. Capacitance and transfer function of a CdS enhancement-type TFT. C_g is the total gate capacitance and C_{gs} is the capacitance between the gate and the source electrodes.

the total gate capacitance exists between the gate and source electrodes. It is the gate-drain capacitance that is magnified by feedback and may restrict high-frequency performance.

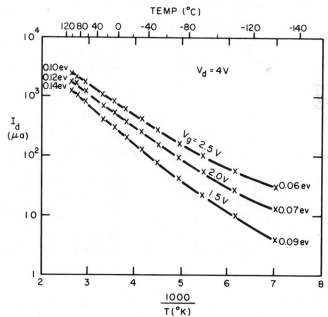

Figure 9–14. Drain current of a cadmium sulfide TFT plotted as a function of the reciprocal of the absolute temperature.

The d-c input resistance of TFT's is high (up to 10^9 ohms), but not as high as has been measured in MOS transistors. Although the insulator resistivities are very high, the presence of minute pinholes may be a source of leakage.

Figure 9–14 shows the drain current at fixed voltages in a coplanar

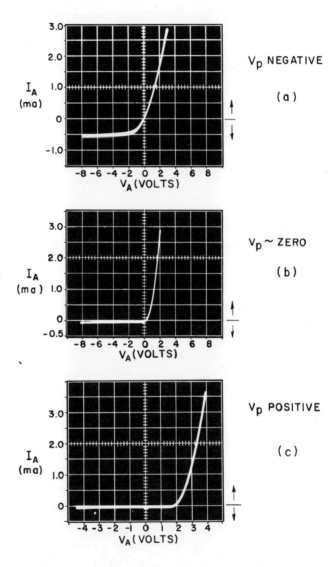

Figure 9–15. The characteristics of three cadmium sulfide TFT's having different values of V_p operated as diodes with their gates connected to their drains. The forward direction is obtained when gate-drain connection is positive relative to the source.

CdS TFT plotted as a function of the reciprocal of the absolute temperature. Note that at higher positive values of gate potential, V_g, the activation energy becomes progressively lower. This effect has been interpreted as caused by a lowering of the barriers between CdS crystallites with increasing V_g, in agreement with the experimentally observed increase in Hall mobility with V_g.[27]

A convenient feature of the insulated-gate transistor is that it can be used as a diode in integrated circuits by simply connecting the gate to the drain. Figure 9–15 shows how the resulting diode characteristics depend upon the pinch-off voltage, V_p, in the transistor. An enhancement-type TFT, with V_p near zero (as in Fig. 9–8) is preferable. A depletion-type unit (as in Fig. 9–9) will have a fairly large saturated reverse current, while a strongly enhancement-type unit may require the application of several volts in the forward direction for onset of current. In practice, the separate gate and drain electrodes may be replaced by a single electrode in which an insulating spacer separates a portion of the electrode from the semiconductor.

9-5 DESIGN CONSIDERATIONS AFFECTING THE PERFORMANCE OF THIN-FILM TRANSISTORS

The drain current, I_d, for values of drain voltage, V_d, up to the knee of the curve is given by the following approximate expression:[24]

$$I_d = \frac{\mu_d C_g}{l^2}(V_g - V_p)V_d - \frac{V_d^2}{2} \tag{9-1}$$

where: $\mu_d =$ "field-effect" mobility of the carriers;
$l =$ source-drain spacing;
$C_g =$ capacitance across the gate insulator;
$V_g =$ gate voltage (source is grounded);
$V_p =$ gate voltage required for onset or pinch-off of drain current.

Although it is based upon the simplifying assumptions of a mobility invariant with gate voltage and a semiconductor thin compared to normal space-charge layers, this expression agrees well with experiment, providing a useful means for discussing TFT characteristics.

Equation (9–1) is valid only for drain voltages up to the knee of the curve, at which point the drain voltage is given by:

$$V_{d_{\text{knee}}} = V_g - V_p \tag{9-2}$$

For $V_d > V_{d_{knee}}$ the drain current saturates at a value which is nearly constant, yielding high output impedance and high voltage gain. The saturated drain current is given by:

$$I_{ds} = \frac{\mu_d C_g}{2l^2}(V_g - V_p)^2 \tag{9-3}$$

in agreement with the square-law relationship observed experimentally.

The gain-bandwidth product for the TFT can be calculated from the ratio of transconductance to gate capacitance:

$$\text{GB} \approx \frac{1}{2\pi}\frac{g_m}{C_g} \tag{9-4}$$

where:

$$\frac{g_m}{C_g} = \frac{\mu_d V_d}{l^2} \qquad (V_d \leqslant V_{d_{knee}}) \tag{9-5}$$

or

$$\frac{g_m}{C_g} = \frac{\mu_d(V_g - V_p)}{l^2} \qquad (V_d \geqslant V_{d_{knee}}) \tag{9-6}$$

The preceding relations provide a guide to the design of TFT's for optimum characteristics. The influence of some of the fabrication parameters upon TFT performance are outlined in the following discussion.

1. Saturation of the I_d vs. V_d characteristics

As discussed in Chapter 5, saturation of drain current occurs when the depletion layer produced by the gate electrode extends completely through the conducting channel in the neighborhood of the drain. As the drain voltage is increased beyond the knee ($V_d > V_g - V_p$), the pinched-off region near the drain gradually increases in length by an amount sufficient to hold the drain current substantially constant. Under ideal conditions, the increase in drain current beyond the knee is quite small. In practice, any of the following factors can lead to unsaturated characteristics:

1. *An unmodulated parallel conductance path* between source and drain. Such a path would exist if the semiconductor were too thick to be completely pinched off by the gate field. It might also be produced in a staggered-electrode TFT by the presence of metal scattered into the gap region during the source-drain evaporation.

2. *Insufficient electrostatic shielding of the gap region* from the drain field by the gate. This might occur if the insulator were too thick or the source-drain spacing were too small. Under these conditions, no channel would

be formed, and the device could operate as a space-charge-limited triode[6, 25] provided the semiconductor resistivity was sufficiently high. The effect of the drain field in forming a weak channel on the underside of the semiconductor (see Chapter 5) has not been noted in the CdS TFT, probably because of the presence of surface states on the underside of the semiconductor layer.

3. *Internal breakdown in the semiconductor channel* in the high field region near the drain for drain voltages above the knee.

4. *Insulator breakdown* from the gate to the drain or to the channel near the drain. This effect is spurious and does not occur in a good unit operated within its specified rating. However, the fields required in the insulator to fill the traps and give adequate transconductance may be as high as 10^6 v/cm.

2. The control of the pinch-off voltage

In the fabrication of integrated circuits incorporating TFT's, it is essential that the *built-in* gate bias expressed by V_p fall within the prescribed design limits for each TFT. As indicated in Section 9-4, TFT's having a wide range of values of V_p can be made from the same semiconducting material. For example, with cadmium sulfide (*n*-type), V_p may vary from several volts negative for a depletion-type unit to several volts positive for a strongly enhancement-type unit. The value obtained depends upon the choice of materials and processing procedures, as well as upon the thickness of the layers. For most applications, a unit having V_p near zero volts and capable of operating in the enhancement mode is preferred. The value of V_p should remain constant throughout the life of the unit and should be unaffected by applied voltages, either past or present.

In the derivation of Eq. (9-1), V_p was introduced[24] into the expression through the definition:

$$V_p \equiv -\frac{N_o q}{C_g} \tag{9-7}$$

where q is the electronic charge and N_o is the total number of charges initially present in the gap region of the semiconductor.

N_o is proportional to the thickness of the semiconductor and the average volume density of donors and acceptors. The variation in charge density across the thickness of the semiconductor is ignored in the derivation of Eq. (9-1), which assumed a thin semiconductor. N_o is positive for a depletion-type unit, where it represents the total number of free carriers initially present in the film. N_o is negative for a strongly enhancement-type unit, and it represents the total number of acceptor states or traps which must be filled before the free-carrier density can be increased appreciably by field effect.

For a depletion-type unit N_o must be large enough to yield the required value of I_{do}, the saturated drain current at zero gate bias. The value of I_{do} derived from Eqs. (9–3) and (9–7) is:

$$I_{do} = \frac{\mu_d C_g V_p^2}{2l^2} = \frac{\mu_d N_o^2 q^2}{2l^2 C_g} \qquad (9\text{–}8)$$

where N_o is positive. Note that I_{do} can be small even with semiconductors having a very high carrier density, provided the semiconductor thickness is small and the insulator capacitance is sufficiently large. It is interesting to compare I_{do} with I_{dNG}, the drain current which would be observed in the same TFT if the gate electrode had been omitted. Since:

$$I_{dNG} = \frac{\mu_d q N_o V_d}{l^2} \qquad (9\text{–}9)$$

it follows that:

$$I_{do} = \frac{1}{2} \times \frac{V_p}{V_d} I_{dNG} \qquad (9\text{–}10)$$

Thus, I_{do} can be considerably smaller than I_{dNG} for all values of V_d much greater than $V_p/2$.

The tellurium TFT whose characteristics are shown in Fig. 9–10 illustrates the case where I_{do} is kept small even though the resistivity of the semiconductor is less than one ohm-cm. Although this unit is nominally a *depletion-type TFT,* its low value of I_{do} permits an excellent set of characteristics when operated in the enhancement mode. To obtain such a low I_{do}, we hold the thickness of the semiconductor to less than 150 Å, and the gate capacitance is made large enough for the gate to deplete the entire thickness of semiconductor. This requires a relatively thin gate insulator.

With cadmium sulfide and cadmium selenide the resistivity can be sufficiently high to permit the use of semiconductor layers up to several microns in thickness. By controlling the density of acceptors and donors, we can vary the TFT characteristics from depletion-type to the strongly enhancement-type. Although traps and donors throughout the thickness of the semiconductor layer may affect the performance of the TFT, those nearest the surface of the semiconductor at the semiconductor-insulator interface will have the major effect. Acceptor-like surface states will bend the bands up at the semiconductor surface, as shown qualitatively in Fig. 9–16a, whereas an excess of donor-like states would bend the bands down at the surface, as in Fig. 9–16b. The effect of a positive gate bias (in n-type units) is to produce an accumulation layer at the surface, as shown in Fig. 9–16c, but the Fermi level does not reach the conduction band until the unfilled acceptor-like states have been filled. If too large a density of surface states is present, the Fermi level is effectively clamped at the energy of the surface state, permitting no modulation of conductivity. The same is true for a unit having an excess of donors at

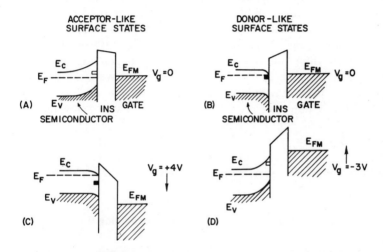

Figure 9–16. Effect of donor-like and acceptor-like surface states upon the semiconductor energy bands at the insulator interface. Although unit A, is more likely to be enhancement-type and unit B depletion type, either unit could be operated in either mode.

the interface (shown in Fig. 9–16d), where the donor-like surface states must be emptied before the negative gate can form a depletion layer at the surface. The fact that the surface-state density can be kept sufficiently small on evaporated polycrystalline surfaces to permit effective current modulation has been one of the most striking features of the TFT development.

The exact nature of the particular surface states that determine the pinch-off voltage in the CdS TFT is speculative. However, it has been possible in fabrication to control the value of V_p moderately well by the processing of the semiconductor and by choice of insulator materials. A short 500°C air bake of the cadmium sulfide layer, combined with the use of a calcium fluoride insulator, will give an enhancement-type unit. A silicon monoxide insulator evaporated in good vacuum on the same semiconductor will give a depletion-type unit. The effect of the SiO is probably to combine with absorbed oxygen on the surface of the CdS, which had been acting as acceptor states. If the SiO is evaporated in a poor vacuum, an enhancement-type unit is obtained. A glow discharge over the surface of the CdS prior to deposition of the insulator will remove oxygen or sulfur, shifting the characteristics toward depletion-type. The value of V_p is also affected to some extent by the work function of the gate material. An aluminum gate tends to give a lower value of V_p than a gold gate.

The magnitude of the surface potential at the cadmium-sulfide insulator interface in the TFT has been determined[26] by direct measurement of the surface photovoltage. A barrier height of 0.15 to 0.25 ev was found for CaF_2 or MgF_2 insulators, giving a surface state density of 2×10^{11} to 1×10^{12} states/cm². The barrier height for an SiO insulator was consistently less than that for CaF_2 by an amount depending upon the oxygen pressure at the time of evaporation. In no case were the bands actually bent down to form a built-in accumulation layer such as illustrated in Fig. 9–16b. When the CdS surface was treated with a glow discharge and covered with an SiO layer evaporated at 10^{-6} mm pressure, excellent depletion-type characteristics were obtained, and the surface was found to be nearly "flat band." These observations were made on cadmium sulfide films having carrier densities between 10^{16} and 2×10^{17} electrons/cm³.

3. Carrier mobility in polycrystalline semiconducting films

Thin films deposited by evaporation upon a noncrystalline substrate are normally polycrystalline,[16] with individual crystallites ranging from 100 Å to more than a micron in size. The influence of such a film structure upon the electrical properties of the film is of particular concern in establishing the feasibility of building a low-cost TFT having adequate performance. The carrier mobility in the film is of prime importance in determining the transconductance and the high-frequency capabilities of the device.

The *field-effect* mobility in the film can be calculated from the measured performance of the device by the relationship:

$$\frac{g_m}{C_g} = \frac{\mu_d V_d}{l^2} \quad \text{(below the knee)} \quad (9-5)$$

In materials containing traps, the field-effect mobility would be expected to be somewhat lower than the Hall mobility when the traps are only partly filled, but would approach Hall mobility as the Fermi level approaches the conduction band. In tests[2] it was found that the field-effect mobility as calculated from Eq. (9–5) for units operating in the enhancement mode was often considerably higher than the Hall mobility measured on similar films.

To resolve this apparent anomaly, a series of measurements were undertaken using a special form of TFT incorporating Hall electrodes. (See Fig. 9-17.) With this structure, the Hall mobility and field-effect mobility could be measured on the semiconductor film as a function of

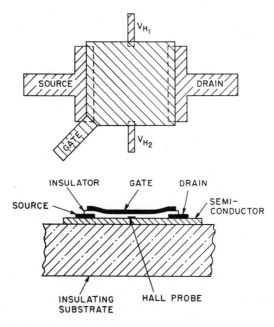

Figure 9-17. An experimental thin-film structure used in the study of mobilities in the space-charge layer of evaporated films.

gate voltage.[27] Figure 9-18 shows a typical variation of Hall mobility with gate voltage. The most striking feature of this curve is the rise in Hall mobility with gate voltage, followed by a region of substantially constant mobility. The decrease in Hall mobility at high gate voltage is ascribed to the increased effect of surface scattering as the electrons are drawn closer to the semiconductor-insulator interface. Such a decrease in mobility with surface potential was predicted theoretically for single-crystal surfaces.[28]

The observed increase in Hall mobility at low voltages is not in accord with the foregoing theory, which was derived for a homogeneous crystalline semiconductor. This increase in mobility can be explained by the assumption that the cadmium sulfide layers tested were electrically inhomogeneous, consisting of conducting crystallites separated by insulating barriers. Such a structure has been suggested by Petritz[29,30] for lead sulfide films and by Berger[31] for cadmium sulfide films. It can be shown that an increase in gate potential would depress the barriers, thus contributing to an increase in the conductivity of the films; this is in addition to the normal increase to be expected from enhancing the carrier density. Volger[32] has discussed the measurements of Hall mobilities in

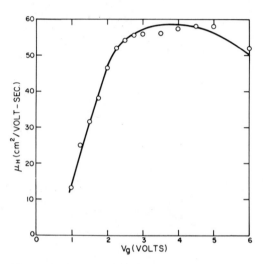

Figure 9–18. Hall mobility in evaporated cadmium sulfide films plotted as a function of the voltage applied to the gate of the structure of Figure 9–17.

inhomogeneous films, and he concluded that the measured value of R, the Hall coefficient, corresponds to that of the low-resistivity regions. Since the Hall mobility, μ_H, is equal to the product of R and the conductivity, μ_H would be expected to increase with gate voltage at low values of gate potential, and then level off at higher values when the barriers are completely depressed.[27]

Tests of the field-effect mobility and Hall mobility with the experimental structure of Fig. 9–17 gave only fair correlation between the two quantities. In most cases, the field-effect mobility was less than the Hall mobility, but occasionally the reverse was found. Both kinds of mobility increased initially with gate voltage. The rise in Hall mobility, shown in Fig. 9–18, was typical of all units tested, although in a depletion-type unit, the rise began at negative values of gate voltage.

The probable existence of intercrystalline barriers emphasizes the inexact values of both the field-effect and the Hall mobility computed by means of formulae which were derived from homogeneous semiconductors. The discrepancies observed in the two kinds of mobilities are probably no greater than the uncertainty in the experimental measurements of either quantity. The value of μ_d calculated from Eq. (9–5) can easily be too large if electrode material scattered into the gap region produces an effective source-drain spacing, l, which is actually less than the measured spacing.

A completely accurate theoretical analysis of the thin-film transistor should take into account the variation of mobility with gate voltage. An analysis of the thin-film transistor has recently been published by Haering,[33] in which the effect of traps as well as the variation of mobility with gate voltage are included. Although these factors may be significant near pinch-off, the variation of mobility in the normal operating range of the device is completely masked by the much larger variation in carrier density induced by the gate. For this reason, the simple analysis assuming constant mobility discussed earlier in this section appears to be a satisfactory approximation. No experimental evidence for an increase in transconductance with frequency as predicted for a wide bandgap semiconductor with traps[33, 25] has been noted in the measurements on gain-bandwidth characteristics described in Section 9–4. The experimental data suggest that, in the best units, the so-called fast surface states are either not present or remain filled at all times.

4. Effect of source-drain contacts upon performance

The failure to provide source and drain electrodes which make a low-impedance contact to the semiconductor can lead to distorted characteristics and poor performance. For cadmium sulfide TFT's, underlying electrodes of gold make a satisfactory contact, whereas aluminum does not. The effectiveness of the underlying gold electrodes is in agreement with the work of Dresner and Shallcross on thin-film cadmium sulfide diodes,[16] where the gold used in this manner was also found to provide an ohmic contact. The results may be contrasted with measurements by Goodman[34] who showed that gold contacts, evaporated on the surface of a single crystal of cadmium sulfide, made a blocking contact with a barrier height of 0.7 v. A blocking contact is also obtained when gold is evaporated on top of cadmium sulfide films.

The low-impedance contact produced by the underlying gold probably arises from the nonuniform composition of the evaporated layer. Chemical evidence has indicated that the first portion of the layer has an excess of cadmium.[35] It is well known that CdS tends to dissociate on evaporation. A variation in the condensation coefficient of the constituents could also contribute to a stratification of the deposit.

Aluminum electrodes evaporated over the top of the semiconductor have been found to make satisfactory ohmic contacts to CdS and CdSe in the coplanar electrode structure. In this structure, we are concerned not only with the electrode contact but also with the effect that the metal scattered into the gap region (under the mask) will have upon the surface conductivity of the semiconductor. Aluminum tends to scatter less than gold,[36] and the fraction that does scatter tends to oxidize. However, the electrical effect of the scattered aluminum is to increase the surface conductivity of the cadmium sulfide, whereas that of scattered gold is to reduce the surface conductivity. The use of an overlying gold source and drain in the coplanar structure gives an extremely low transconductance.

   Although aluminum electrodes provide suitable contacts for CdS, the aluminum evaporation is somewhat more critical to carry out. If it is deposited too slowly, a semi-insulating barrier is formed under the electrode. Figure 9–19 shows the type of characteristic[4] obtained when such a barrier exists between the source electrode and the semiconductor.

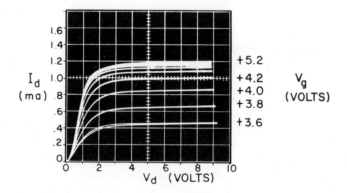

Figure 9–19. "Crowded" characteristics observed in a coplanar-electrode CdS TFT having an insulating barrier separating the source electrode from the semiconductor in the region near the source-drain gap.

The curves are crowded together at a maximum level of drain current, whose value is independent of gate voltage. A *crowded* characteristic may be found the first time the unit is operated, or it may develop after a few hours exposure to air. The mechanism of current saturation which produces crowding is the same as that producing normal saturation, except that in this case the pinch-off of current occurs under the source electrode instead of under the gate. If the insulating barrier is present at only the drain contact, the characteristics are not crowded but show an *s-shaped rise* near the origin.

   Crowded characteristics have rarely been seen in any TFT having the staggered-electrode geometry. The staggered-electrode structure puts less severe demands upon the source contact since the overlapping gate provides a larger effective area of contact.

5. Stability in thin-film transistors

Under ideal conditions, the drain current of an insulated-gate transistor should be uniquely determined by the voltages applied to the gate and drain, independently of duration of application. The drain characteristics observed on a conventional curve tracer should be stable, free of hysteresis loops, and identical to the curves obtained when measured point-by-point with d-c meters. While such stability is approached closely in some units, others exhibit gradually shifting characteristics. The family of curves may drift either up or down as more gate steps are added.

Another form of instability is noted when a reversal of the source-drain connections to a TFT (of symmetrical construction) yields non-identical characteristics. In unstable units of this type, the reversal of the source-drain connections usually leads to a drift of characteristics in a sequence which is repeated each time the connections are reversed.

Slow response and drift in field-effect measurements are normally ascribed to the slow emptying and filling of immobile states close to the surface of the semiconductor. In the TFT the presence of trapped charge in the semiconductor or insulator near the interface region has a large effect on the surface potential and on the built-in gate bias, V_p (see Eq. 9–7). The ease of transfer of charge in and out of these states determines the effect they will have upon the transistor stability. If appreciable transfer occurs in 0.01 sec, hysteresis loops may be noted in the current-voltage characteristics. If the transfer requires minutes or hours to occur, the gradual shifting of characteristics described in the preceding paragraphs will occur. Still slower rates of transfer will become apparent in life tests of the units.

The avoidance of the slow states is one of the major considerations in fabrication of thin-film transistors. The stability depends upon the choice of materials and processing procedures in ways not fully understood. If the unit is unencapsulated, the ambient atmosphere can have a strong effect on stability in some units. Considerable advance has been made in the control of these factors in fabrication.

Early experimental TFT's exhibited irreversible deterioration of transconductance over periods ranging from hours to years. The rate of degradation varied widely in units of supposedly identical design, and the deterioration at room temperature was usually independent on whether the unit was being operated or stored. The frequency of occurrence of early failure in the cadmium sulfide units was greater for the coplanar-electrode structure having overlying aluminum electrodes than for the staggered structure with underlying gold electrodes. This difficulty was traced to the formation of an insulating barrier at the contact between the aluminum electrodes and the cadmium sulfide (see preceding section).

Another typical effect of aging, which may also be affected by exposure to air, is the gradual increase in V_p toward a more strongly enhancement-type unit. In this case, the transconductance at a given drain current remains constant, but such changes are usually accompanied by increased "rubberiness" of the characteristics.

The encapsulation of the coplanar units in an evacuated enclosure is effective in extending the useful life of units to well beyond a thousand hours.[37] A more convenient type of encapsulation, particularly for integrated circuits, is to coat the TFT with a nonporous overcoat prior to exposure to air. Figure 9–20 illustrates the characteristics of two initially

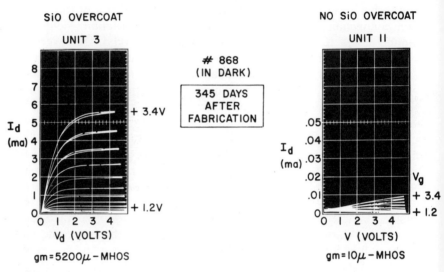

Figure 9–20. Characteristics of two initially identical CdS transistors having coplanar electrodes 345 days after fabrication. The unit on the left was encapsulated by means of an evaporated overcoat of silicon monoxide.

identical coplanar TFT's, one of which was coated with an overcoat of silicon monoxide. The coated unit had dropped only about 20% in drain current after a year, while the uncoated unit failed in a few weeks. Other vitreous layers such as evaporated selenium or arsenic trisulfide have proved to be consistently effective as a protective overcoat.

9–6 INTEGRATED CIRCUITS INCORPORATING THIN-FILM TRANSISTORS

The economic importance of thin-film transistors is based largely upon the possibility of building low-cost integrated circuits incorporating active and passive elements. The evaporated TFT offers the important advantage that it can be deposited simultaneously with the other circuit elements upon inexpensive substrates of virtually unlimited size. Entirely new applications of electronics could arise from the fabrication of complex circuits deposited in a continuous process upon a flexible roll of inert substrate material.

Experimentation on completely integrated thin-film circuits is now being actively carried on. The ease of integrating the insulated-gate transistor in circuits was demonstrated by the construction of the three-stage amplifier[38] shown in Fig. 9–21. The use of TFT's operating in

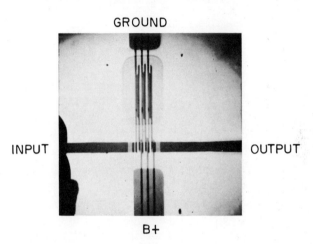

Figure 9–21. An early demonstration model of an integrated thin-film circuit incorporating TFT's. The center-to-center spacing of the three TFT's is 0.002 ".

the enhancement mode permits direct coupling between stages. The ability to deposit both n- and p-type transistors upon the same substrate with common electrodes can be utilized in the fabrication of complementary circuits. Figure 9–22 illustrates an array of low-drain flip-flops utilizing n- and p-type TFT's.

Experimental thin-film circuits incorporating many TFT's have been built in the course of research on solid-state image-scanning devices.[39,40] The replacement of the electron beam in cathode-ray tubes by an array of X-Y address strips driven by two scan generators was proposed many years ago,[41] but it was impractical at that time because of the complexity of the circuits and structures required. The advent of completely integrated thin-film circuits has reactivated interest in this approach to television pickup and display.

Figure 9–23 illustrates semischematically a solid-state image panel. This drawing could apply to either an image-sensing device or reproducing device. For the image sensor, the light-sensitive area might be an inch square, while for the display device, the light-emitting area could be several feet square. All picture elements in each panel are addressed in sequence by the proper coincidence of voltage pulses applied to the strips

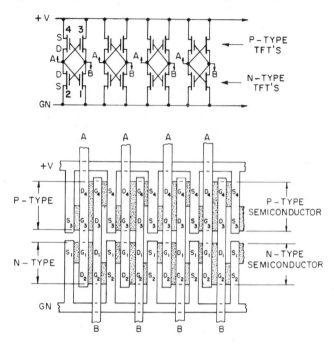

Figure 9–22. A layout for an evaporated array of flip-flops incorporating n- and p-type TFT's.

by the scan generators. Because of the large number of strips required for a high-resolution picture (~500 in each direction), it is proposed to fabricate the entire panel, including the scan generators, as a single integrated circuit deposited upon a common substrate. The insulated-gate TFT is particularly appropriate for this type of application because of the complexity of the circuit and the need for large-area substrates.

A scan generator circuit[21,40] based on the TFT which is suitable for driving the address strips in a panel is shown in Fig. 9–24. The generator is clock-driven at an elemental rate, and can provide scanning pulses of either polarity to the strips. Its operation is similar to that of a shift register in its ability to transfer any binary input. However, the circuit is simpler than a conventional shift register in that only two TFT's, two load resistors, a diode, and a capacitor are required for each output connection. Although the scanning speed is accurately controlled by the clock generator, the range of permissible scanning speeds in a particular unit is determined by the load resistor-capacitor time constant and by the loss of stored charge through the TFT in its off condition. For slow-speed operation the TFT's must have low drain current at zero gate bias.

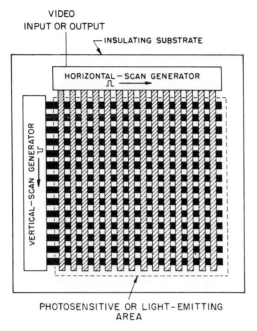

Figure 9–23. Schematic diagram of a solid-state image panel. The central portion of the panel represents either a light-sensitive or a light-emitting array.

Figure 9–25 shows an experimental model of a completely integrated 30-stage thin-film scan generator embodying this circuit. The output strips spaced 0.0125 inch apart are connected directly to 30 photosensitive elements deposited upon the same one-inch-square glass substrate. The TFT's and diodes use polycrystalline cadmium sulfide with overlying coplanar electrodes. Figure 9–26 shows an enlarged view of a portion of the TFT and diode area. Three enhancement-type TFT's are formed for each stage, with one of the three having the gate tied to the drain in order to serve as a field-effect diode. The load resistors are Nichrome strips, and the capacitors consist of aluminum electrodes separated by silicon monoxide.

The evaporation jig and the eight photoetched masks used in fabricating the circuit were shown earlier in Fig. 9–6. Following the initial deposition of the cadmium sulfide, the entire scanner is deposited in seven steps during one evacuation of the system.

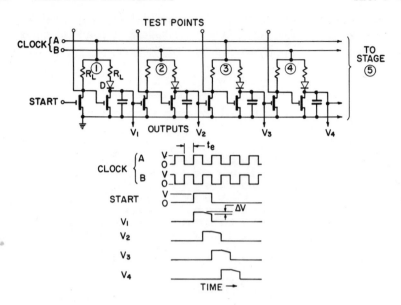

Figure 9–24. Simplified shift-register circuit suitable for driving the address strips of a solid-state image panel. Insulated-gate field-effect transistors are used as the active elements.

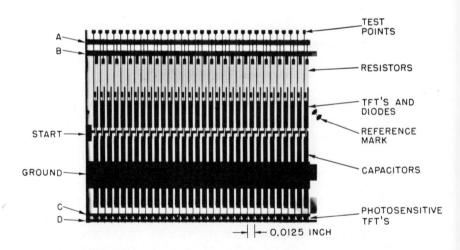

Figure 9–25. Photograph of a completely integrated 30-stage thin-film scan generator based upon the circuit of Figure 9–24.

For operation of the image scanner only five leads are required: two for the clock drive, and one each for the start pulse, the ground lead, and the video output. Tests were made using 60 evaporated fan-out

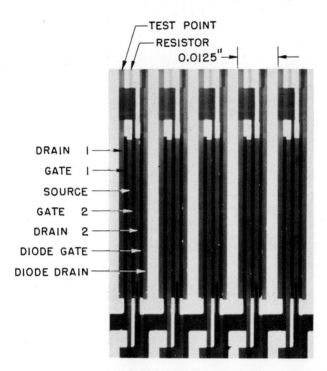

Figure 9–26. An enlarged view of a portion of the thin-film scan generator showing the TFT's and field-effect diodes for five stages.

leads connected to the drain of each TFT, as shown in Fig. 9–27. The ends of these leads were attached to a printed circuit board which was plugged into the test equipment. Figure 9–28 shows the drain characteristics of all 60 TFT's displayed on a transistor curve tracer. Good uniformity is observed from one unit to the next. The characteristics of the odd-numbered units are tipped upward because of an alternate shunt path through the load resistors to ground. There is no difference in the performance of the odd- and even-numbered units.

The fan-out connections permit the voltage pulse appearing at each output terminal of the scanner to be displayed on an oscilloscope. Figure 9–29 shows the resultant waveform at alternate output terminals for two different methods of applying the start pulse. The uniformity in timing and shape of the output pulses is apparent. In *driven* operation, shown at

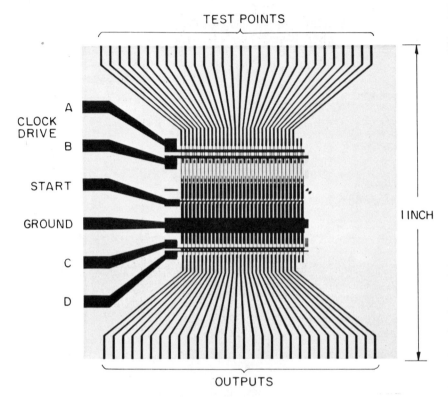

Figure 9–27. View of the 30-stage thin-film scan generator showing the evaporated fan-out connections used for test purposes.

the left, an external start pulse is applied to stage 1, while in cyclic operation the output of stage 30 is used to trigger stage 1. Three scan generators have been connected together to operate in cyclic fashion as a 90-stage ring counter. Scan generators have operated at clock frequencies ranging from 2 to 200 kc/s. Both higher and lower frequencies can be obtained with modified circuit parameters.

Laboratory models of the 30-stage scan generator have been used in research on image-sensor panels. The 30 output terminals of the generator can supply scanning pulses to a set of 30 individual photocells or to an experimental evaporated array deposited upon a separate glass blank. Improved resolution in the image sensor will require scan generators with many more output stages which are spaced much closer together. A 180-stage generator with output strips spaced 0.0021 inches apart has been built.[42] A wire grill having 480 wires/in. serves as the principal evaporation mask, as described in Section 9–3.

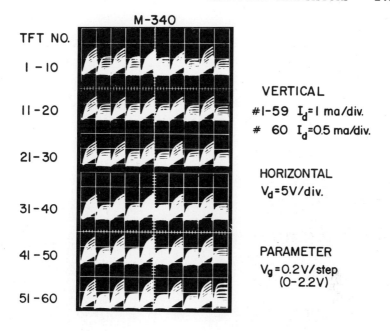

TFT NO.

I – 10

II –20

21–30

31–40

41–50

51–60

M–340

VERTICAL

#1-59 I_d=1 ma/div.
60 I_d=0.5 ma/div.

HORIZONTAL
V_d=5V/div.

PARAMETER
V_g=0.2V/step
(0–2.2V)

Figure 9–28. Drain characteristics of the 60 TFT's incorporated into the 30-stage thin-film scan generator.

9-7 GROWN-FILM SILICON MOS TRANSISTORS ON SAPPHIRE

A thin-film transistor fabricated by the application of MOS techniques to a film of silicon deposited upon a single-crystal sapphire substrate has been described by Mueller and Robinson.[20] A cross-sectional view of the insulated-gate structure is shown in Fig. 9–30. The silicon film, 12μ thick, is grown epitaxially upon an oriented, highly polished, single-crystal sapphire substrate by the pyrolytic decomposition of silane (SiH_4). The p-type films have resistivities of 1–10 ohm-cm and are metallurgically polished to a mirror surface before processing to form the MOS transistors.

The n-type source and drain regions are formed by diffusion into the silicon layer from phosphorus-doped silicon dioxide. An oxide layer about 1000 Å thick is thermally grown on the silicon. A chromium-gold gate is evaporated over this oxide. Metal contacts are evaporated for the source-drain connections. An array of transistors can be produced by standard photoresist techniques.

Figure 9–31 shows a set of drain current vs. drain voltage characteristics for one transistor in an array of 200 transistors. The source-to-drain distance is 10^{-3} cm and the active width is 1.2×10^{-2} cm. The maximum transconductance is about 1000 μmhos. This value is within a factor of 2 of the highest obtained with equal dimensions on bulk-grown single-crystal silicon.

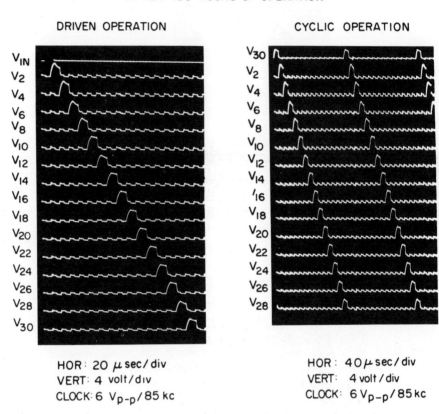

M— 355

AFTER 150 HOURS OF OPERATION

DRIVEN OPERATION   CYCLIC OPERATION

HOR: 20 μ sec/div   HOR: 40 μ sec/div
VERT: 4 volt/div   VERT: 4 volt/div
CLOCK: 6 V_{p-p}/85 kc   CLOCK: 6 V_{p-p}/85 kc

Figure 9-29. Pulse waveforms observed at alternate output strips of a scan generator which had been operated for 150 hours. In *driven* operation, shown at the left, an external start pulse is applied to the input of stage I. In *cyclic* operation, shown at the right, the output of stage 30 is used to trigger stage 1.

Figure 9-32 shows a simple switching circuit formed by evaporating interconnections between individual thin-film transistors in the array. To take full advantage of the insulating substrate, the silicon film can be confined to the transistor area by masking during deposition or by subsequent etching of the silicon.

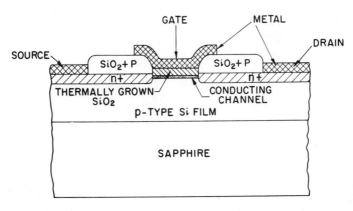

Figure 9–30. A cross section of the MOS thin-film transistor employing a silicon layer deposited upon a sapphire single-crystal substrate.

The performance of silicon thin-film transistors utilizing the sapphire substrates is generally superior to the best reported for polycrystalline cadmium sulfide TFT's on glass substrates. From the standpoint of cost, the requirement for a single-crystal substrate is a disadvantage and may limit the size of integrated circuits that can be easily constructed by this method. The relative cost of integrated-circuit fabrication utilizing MOS diffusion techniques, as opposed to all-evaporated techniques, remains to be evaluated.

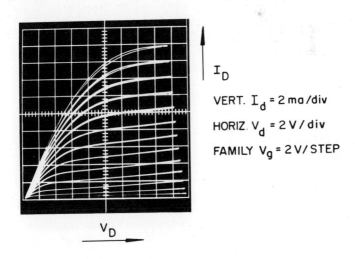

I_D

VERT. I_d = 2 ma/div

HORIZ. V_d = 2 V/div

FAMILY V_g = 2 V/STEP

V_D

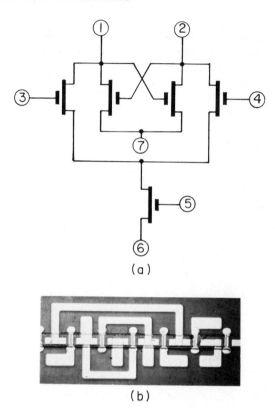

(a)

(b)

Figure 9–32. A simple circuit utilizing an array of MOS thin-film silicon transistors. (a) Switching-circuit diagram; (b) thin-film layout of switching circuit.

REFERENCES

1. P. K. Weimer, "An Evaporated Thin-Film Triode," presented at the IRE-AIEE Device Res. Conf., Stanford University, Calif., June 1961.

2. P. K. Weimer, *Proc. IRE* **50**, 1462 (1962).

3. S. R. Hofstein and F. P. Heiman, *Proc. IEEE* **51**, 1190 (1963).

4. P. K. Weimer, F. V. Shallcross, and H. Borkan, *RCA Rev.* **24**, 661 (1963).

5. H. Borkan and P. K. Weimer, "Characteristics of the Insulated-Gate Thin-Film Transistor," *NEREM Record* **4**, 158 (1962). (Paper presented at the IRE Northeast Electronics Research and Engineering Meeting, Boston, Mass., November, 1962).

6. R. Zuleeg, *Solid State Electronics* **6**, 193 (1963).

7. J. E. Johnson, "Physical processes in the CdS thin film triode," in "Thin Films for Electronic Application," 119, *Extended Abstracts of the Electrochemical Society Meeting,* Pittsburgh, Pa., April, 1963.

8. R. Zuleeg, *Solid State Electronics* **6**, 645 (1963).

9. H. L. Wilson and W. A. Gutierrez, "Cadmium Selenide Thin Film Field Effect Transistors," presented at the Electrochemical Society Meeting, Pittsburgh, Pa., April, 1963.

10. F. V. Shallcross, *Proc. IEEE* **51**, 851 (1963).

11. F. V. Shallcross, *RCA Rev.* **24**, 676 (1963).

12. P. K. Weimer, *Proc. IEEE* **52**, 608 (1964).

13. P. K. Weimer, H. Borkan, V. E. Henrich, L. Meray-Horvath, F. V. Shallcross, and A. Waxman, Scientific Reports Nos. 1–4 and Final, "Evaporated Thin-Film Devices," Contract No. AF19(628)-1617, Air Force Cambridge Research Laboratories, Bedford, Massachusetts.

14. H. A. Klasens and H. Koelmans, *Solid State Electronics* **7**, 701 (1964).

15. J. Dresner and F. V. Shallcross, *Solid State Electronics* **5**, 205 (1962).

16. J. Dresner and F. V. Shallcross, *J. Appl. Phys.* **34**, 2390 (1963).

17. R. Zuleeg and E. J. Senkovits, "A method for CdS thin-film deposition and film structure determination by X-ray and electron diffraction," in "Thin Films for Electronic Application," 110, *Extended Abstracts of the Electrochemical Society Meeting,* Pittsburgh, Pa., April, 1963.

18. I. J. Hegyi, "Preparation of CdS Films on Glass Substrates by Close-Spaced Chemical Transport," paper presented at the Electrochemical Society, Washington meeting, October, 1964.

19. H. M. Manasevit and W. I. Simpson, *J. Appl. Phys.* **35**, 1349 (1964).

20. C. W. Mueller and P. H. Robinson, *Proc. IEEE,* **52**, 1487 (1964).

21. P. K. Weimer, H. Borkan, G. Sadasiv, L. Meray-Horvath, and F. V. Shallcross, *Proc. IEEE* **52**, 1479 (1964).

22. P. K. Weimer, S. Gray, C. W. Beadle, H. Borkan, S. Ochs, and H. C. Thompson, *IRE Trans. on Electron Devices* **ED-7**, 147 (1960).

23. S. Gray and P. K. Weimer, *RCA Rev.* **20**, 413 (1959).

24. H. Borkan and P. K. Weimer, *RCA Rev.* **24**, 153 (1963).

25. G. T. Wright, *J. Brit. IRE* **20**, 337 (1960).

26. A. Waxman, "Surface Photovoltage Measurements on Evaporated CdS Films," paper presented at the IEEE Solid State Device Research Conference, University of Colorado, Boulder, Colorado, July, 1964.

27. A. Waxman, V. E. Henrich, F. V. Shallcross, H. Borkan, and P. K. Weimer, *Bull. AM. Phys. Soc.* **II, 8**, 539 (1963); *J. Appl. Phys.* **36**, 168 (1965).

28. J. R. Shrieffer, *Phys. Rev.* **97**, 641 (1955).

29. R. L. Petritz, *Phys. Rev.* **104**, 1508 (1956).

30. R. L. Petritz, F. L. Lummis, H. E. Sorrows, and J. F. Woods in *Semiconductor Surface Physics,* ed., R. H. Kingston, "Surface studies on photoconductive lead sulfide films," 229 (Philadelphia, Pa.: University of Pennsylvania Press, 1957).

31. H. Berger, *Phys. Status Solidi* **1**, 739 (1961).

32. J. Volger, *Phys. Rev.* **79**, 1023 (1950).

33. R. R. Haering, *Solid-State Electronics* **7**, 31 (1964).

34. A. M. Goodman, *J. Appl. Phys.* **35**, 573 (1964).

35. R. Zuleeg, private communication.

36. S. Chandra and G. D. Scott, *Can. J. Phys.* **36**, 1148 (1958).

37. J. Bowe, *et al.,* "Field-Effect and Space-Charge-Limited Thin Film Triodes," Final Report, July, 1964, Signal Corps Contract DA36–039-AMC-02374.

38. P. K. Weimer, "Evaporated Circuits Incorporating a Thin Film Transistor," Digest International Solid-State Circuits Conference, Philadelphia, Pa. 32, February, 1962.

39. P. K. Weimer, H. Borkan, L. Meray-Horvath, G. Sadasiv, and F. V. Shallcross, "Solid State Imaging and Sensing," Technical Documentary Report No. AL-TDR-64-56, April 15, 1964, Air Force Contract No. AF33(657)-8725.

40. P. K. Weimer, H. Borkan, L. Meray-Horvath, and F. V. Shallcross, "An Integrated Thin-Film Image Scanner," Digest International Solid-State Circuits Conference, Philadelphia, Pa., 68, February, 1964.

41. e.g., see A. M. Nicolson, U. S. Patent No. 1,779,748, October 23, 1930.

42. P. K. Weimer, L. Meray-Horvath, and W. S. Homa, "A 180-stage Integrated Thin-film Scan Generator," paper presented at the Specialists Conference on Thin-film Active devices, The Johns Hopkins University, Baltimore, Maryland, April, 1965.

43. V. L. Frantz, *Proc. IEEE* **53**, 760 (1965).

10

Applications of Field-Effect Transistors in Linear Amplifier and Attenuator Circuits

David M. Griswold

10-1 THE FIELD-EFFECT TRANSISTOR

1. Introduction

The theory of operation of field-effect transistors is discussed in the preceding chapters. It will be helpful to point out the device-operating regions of importance to amplifier and attenuator applications, and to define the device characteristics and terms which relate specifically to these applications.

At low drain-to-source potentials (region A to B in Fig. 10–1), the channel resistance is essentially ohmic in nature and current flows equally well in either direction. This is in contrast to the unilateral electron flow from cathode to plate in the vacuum tube, which the field-effect transistor otherwise resembles. Also in contrast to the vacuum tube, the field-effect transistor can use either electron flow or hole flow. The current decreases for negative bias when electron flow is used, but decreases with positive bias when hole flow is used.

253

In the pinch-off region (B to D in Fig. 10–1), a portion of the channel is depleted of charge carriers by the electric field between gate and channel, and the channel resistance becomes very large. In this region, further increases in drain-to-source potential cause relatively small changes in drain current. Variation in drain current becomes almost entirely a function of variation in the gate voltage.

In a typical sharp-cutoff depletion-type transistor, the pinch-off voltage, V_p, is defined for practical purposes as that gate-to-source voltage which will reduce the drain current to 1% of its zero-gate-voltage value at a drain-to-source voltage (C in Fig. 10–1) that is double the output characteristic-curve knee voltage. The zero-gate-voltage drain current at this reference point is designated I_{do}.

If the transistor has an insulated gate covering the entire active source-to-drain channel, the drain voltage at point B in Fig. 10–1 will have the same magnitude as the pinch-off gate voltage, V_p. The slope of the I_d vs. V_d curve between points A and B is a good approximation of the zero-bias channel resistance, r_{ds}. The reciprocal of r_{ds} is approximately equal to the maximum zero-gate-voltage transconductance of the unit in the pinch-off region. This maximum transconductance cannot always be realized in

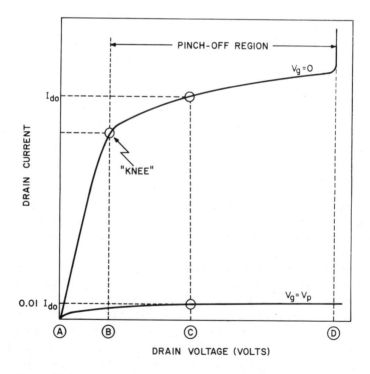

Figure 10–1. Output characteristic of a depletion-type MOS transistor.

practice because of surface effects, unmodulated series resistance, or voltage or power limitations of a particular transistor.

If the transistor has an insulated gate that overlaps the source region but does not extend all the way to the drain, it may be referred to as *half-gate, offset-gate,* or *partial-gate.* The uncovered portion of the channel, shown in the equivalent circuit of Fig. 10–2 as $r_{d'}$, causes the knee voltage

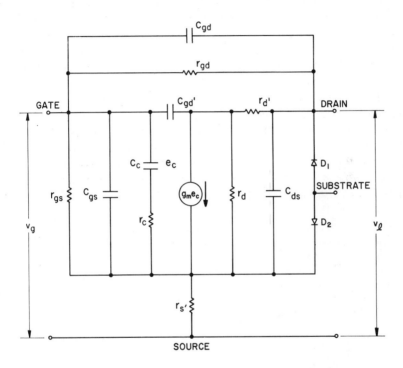

Figure 10–2. Common-source equivalent circuit of the MOS transistor.

to be higher than V_p by an amount equal to the voltage drop across $r_{d'}$. The junction-gate transistor may also have a knee voltage greater than V_p if there is any unmodulated bulk or contact resistance in series with the drain.

The pinch-off region is the region in which the device is useful as a *high-impedance voltage amplifier.* The ohmic region is the region in which the linear resistance variation, as a function of gate voltage, makes the device useful as a *voltage-controlled attenuator.*

The linear amplifier and attenuator applications of the field-effect transistor are, in many respects, similar to those which have been developed for vacuum tubes. Vacuum tubes have been designed with multiple-grid structures to reduce feedback and to provide special characteristics.

Field-effect transistors show signs of following a similar course through the addition of extra gates. The increased flexibility and unique features provided by the insulated-gate construction make such developments desirable for efficient circuit design.

2. Equivalent circuit

Figure 10–2 shows a common-source equivalent circuit of an MOS transistor operated in the region of the drain characteristic beyond channel pinch-off. If the substrate diodes, D_1 and D_2, are removed from the circuit, the equivalent circuit applies equally well to thin-film and junction-gate transistors. This equivalent circuit is useful to approximately 100 mc/s. At higher frequencies, it is necessary to modify the circuit of Fig. 10–2 by the addition of inductive elements to account for lead inductances which may resonate with device capacitances and appreciably alter the over-all performance.

r_{gs} AND r_{gd}: In the junction-gate field-effect transistor, the resistances, r_{gs} and r_{gd}, represent the reverse-biased diode resistance of the gate junction, distributed between the gate and the source or drain. Values of 10^8 to 10^{10} ohms are typical in silicon units at room temperature.

In an insulated-gate transistor, the resistances, r_{gs} and r_{gd}, represent the leakage resistance paths through and across the insulating oxide from gate to source and gate to drain, respectively. In a properly fabricated MOS transistor, these leakage resistances are very high: 10^{12} to 10^{17} ohms. The ratio between the two is mainly a function of the relative physical distances across the surface of the silicon dioxide rather than through its bulk.

C_c AND r_c: The series network formed by the capacitance, C_c, and the resistance, r_c, is a lumped approximation of the actual distributed network formed between the active channel resistance and the metalized gate. The sum total of the small capacitors distributed along the active channel resistance must charge and discharge through this resistance. Because the voltage across C_c performs the charge control, it is the important modulation parameter. The series resistance, r_c, is a lossy element. Consequently, the high-frequency performance is a function of the time constant associated with r_c and C_c.

THE TRANSCONDUCTANCE, g_m: In the pinch-off region, the drain current is relatively constant and is represented by the constant-current generator, $g_m e_c$. At low frequencies, the intrinsic $g_m e_c$ and the extrinsic $g_m e_g$ are essentially equal. The low-frequency transconductance is the slope of the $I_d - V_g$ transfer characteristic.

THE OUTPUT RESISTANCE, r_d: The resistance, r_d, shown in shunt with the $g_m e_c$ generator, represents the dynamic output resistance of the transistor. When the transistor is operated in the pinch-off region, r_d is orders of magnitude larger than $r_{s'}$ and $r_{d'}$ and is adequately approximated by the slope of the output characteristic curves. By inspection of the output characteristic curves, it can be seen that r_d increases as the channel is further depleted and decreases significantly at low values of drain and gate voltage. A unique characteristic of the insulated-gate device is that the channel conduction may also be enhanced, with the result that r_d may be reduced to a much lower value than is possible with the junction-gate transistor.

In a typical amplifier-type depletion MOS transistor, the sum of r_d, $r_{d'}$ and $r_{s'}$ may be varied from a low value of about 300 ohms to a high value of several hundred megohms, depending on whether the transistor is operated in the ohmic region or the pinch-off region, respectively.

THE SUBSTRATE DIODES, D_1 AND D_2: The diode, D_1, is the junction formed between the heavily diffused drain region and the semiconductor substrate. The diode, D_2, is the junction formed between the heavily diffused source region and the substrate. D_1 and D_2 are therefore back-to-back diodes in shunt with the channel. In some amplifier applications, the anodes of D_1 and D_2 are connected to the source. This causes D_1 to be reverse biased and tends to short out D_2. There is a distributed bulk resistance associated with these substrate diodes which cannot be entirely eliminated by an external short. In low-frequency applications it has negligible effect. At high frequencies, these diodes contribute a series RC network which alters the effective output admittance.

THE PARASITIC RESISTANCES, $r_{d'}$ AND $r_{s'}$: The resistances, $r_{d'}$ and $r_{s'}$, are those portions of the source-to-drain channel which are not controlled by the gate or gates of the transistor. In some insulated-gate depletion-type transistors, the major portion of $r_{d'}$ may be due to an intentional offset of the insulated gate away from the drain. This offset results in a greatly reduced feedback capacitance, $C_{gd'}$, and a higher source-to-drain breakdown voltage. The other resistive component, $r_{s'}$, is due to bulk resistance or contact resistance in the source, plus any unmodulated channel caused by misalignment of the insulated gate.

In the common-source configuration, $r_{s'}$ represents both a lossy element and a degenerative one. The resistance, $r_{d'}$ represents a lossy element in series with the external load impedance.

THE CAPACITANCES, C_{gd}, C_{gs}, AND C_{ds}: These capacitances include the physical case and interlead capacitances between the elements designated by the subscripts. C_{gd} and C_{gs} include any voltage-independent capacitance contributed by the physical overlap of an insulated gate over the source or drain. C_{ds} includes the capacitances associated with D_1 and D_2 in the MOS transistor, as well as the intrinsic transistor drain-to-source capacitance. The capacitance, $C_{gd'}$, is the intrinsic gate-to-drain capacitance. This capacitance decreases with increasing drain voltage in an n-channel offset-gate MOS transistor, as shown in Fig. 10–3. This decrease in feedback capacitance coincides with an increase in amplification factor and output resistance. The over-all effect is that larger values of stable voltage gain can be achieved in the offset-gate transistor than in a full-gate device having a comparable value of transconductance.

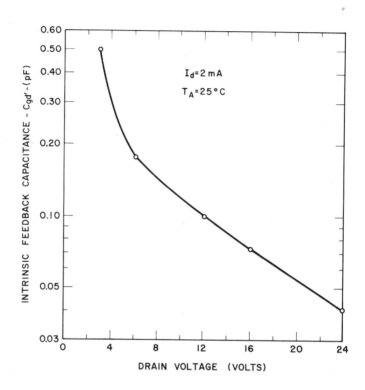

Figure 10-3. Intrinsic feedback capacitance as a function of the drain voltage of an *n*-channel MOS transistor.

SUBSTRATE: When a semiconductor material, such as silicon, is used as the substrate for an insulated-gate transistor, it cannot be assumed to have a completely passive role. (See Chapter 5.) The semiconductor substrate forms a junction with the active channel and may be utilized as a *second control electrode* in the manner of the junction-gate device. Its effectiveness, as discussed in Chapter 5, depends on the channel length and the doping level of the substrate. One commercial MOS transistor, 3N98, has an external connection to the substrate gate, which permits utilization of the substrate-to-drain transconductance. The transconductance is typically 400 to 1000 μmhos or about half of the gate-to-drain transconductance.

TYPICAL VALUES: Typical values for the small-signal equivalent circuit of Fig. 10-2 are given in Table 10-1 for a 3N98 insulated-gate transistor. The representation is valid for this transistor up to 60 mc/s.

Table 10-1 Equivalent Circuit Values for 3N98 Transistor

	$(V_d = 12v, V_g = 0v, I_d = 5.5$ ma$)$	
Symbol	Characteristic	Value
C_c	Intrinsic channel capacitance	4 pf
C_{ds}	Drain-to-source capacitance (includes approximately 1 pf drain-to-case and interlead capacitance)	2pf
$C_{gd'} + C_{gd}$	Gate-to-drain capacitance (includes 0.1 pf interlead capacitance)	0.3 pf
C_{gs}	Gate-to-source interlead and case capacitance	0.9 pf
g_m	Forward transconductance	1500 μmhos
r_c	Effective gate series resistance	100 ohms
r_d	Active channel resistance	15,000 ohms
$r_{d'}$	Unmodulated channel resistance	300 ohms
g_{os} 60 Mc	Output conductance, including the effect of the substrate diodes	200 μmhos
r_{gd}	Gate-to-drain leakage resistance	2×10^{16} ohms
r_{gs}	Gate-to-source leakage resistance	1×10^{15} ohms

3. Temperature Effects

In some field-effect transistors the drain current decreases with increasing temperature. In others, the drain current increases; and some units exhibit a zero temperature coefficient for drain current if the appropriate gate voltage is selected.

There are two ways in which the temperature can influence the drain current of field-effect transistors. First, at constant surface potential, the resistance of the channel can change as a result of a change in mobility. For many transistors this is the predominant mechanism. For insulated-gate transistors, where the current flows very close to the surface, surface and defect scattering at positive temperatures may partly compensate the negative temperature coefficient of bulk scattering.[1] However, a second effect which may be more important is a change in surface potential caused by the change in temperature. This change in surface potential, either through a change in the junction contact potential for junction-gate transistors[2] or through a change in the trap population for insulated-gate transistors, works in opposition to the mobility change. Thus, it constitutes a built-in gate-voltage compensation of the mobility change in the semiconductor. The effect is dependent on the d-c gate bias so that at a particular bias the compensation may be optimized.

Experimental insulated-gate transistors using various diffusion techniques have exhibited negative zero and positive temperature coefficients.

The transfer characteristics, shown in Figs. 10-4 and 10-5, at case temperatures of 25°C and 100°C are typical of transistors whose drain current exhibits a positive temperature coefficient at a given value of drain-to-source voltage. At a drain-to-source potential of +12 v and with

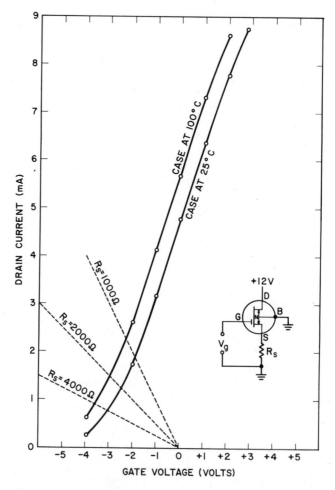

Figure 10-4. Transfer characteristic of an *n*-channel MOS transistor as a function of temperature.

fixed gate bias, the transfer characteristic shifts upward about $12\mu a$ per degree centigrade rise in case temperature. If the drain current is held constant, the transfer characteristic shifts along the negative gate-voltage axis about 8 mv per degree centigrade rise in case temperature. Figure 10-6 shows the typical linear variation of transconductance with temperature for MOS transistors.

In a silicon junction-gate transistor, type 2N2499, the gate leakage current is typically 3×10^{-9} a with a gate-to-source voltage of 10 v at an ambient temperature of 25°C. This silicon-junction reverse saturation current approximately doubles for every 8°C rise in junction temperature.

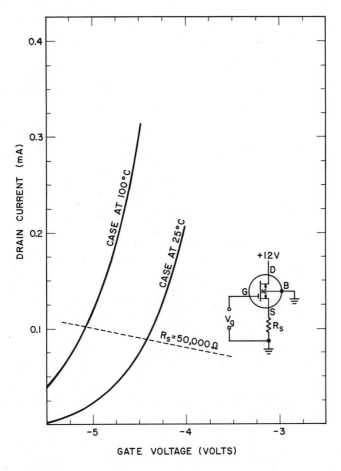

Figure 10-5. Low-current transfer characteristic of an *n*-channel MOS transistor as a function of temperature.

In a silicon insulated-gate transistor, type 3N98, the gate leakage current is typically much less than 0.1×10^{-12} a with a gate-to-source voltage of 6 v at room temperature. In contrast to the junction-gate device, the gate leakage current of this insulated-gate unit remains below 0.1×10^{-12} a at 85°C.

At temperatures above 100°C, current flowing through leakage paths across the transistor package may dominate. For example, at

150°C a group of empty TO–18 enclosures were found to have an average leakage current of about 2×10^{-9} a at an interlead potential of 45 v. This group may not be representative of all enclosures having similar dimensions and materials, but it does suggest that the enclosure leakage

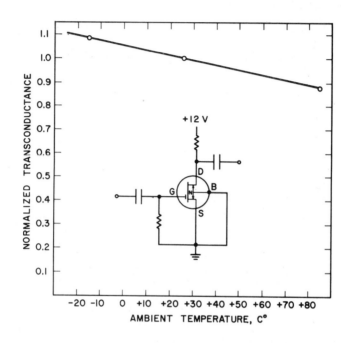

Figure 10-6. Relative transconductance of an n-channel MOS transistor as a function of temperature.

characteristics cannot be taken for granted in applications where very high input resistance is a requirement.

4. Voltage and current effects

The drain current is affected by the magnitude and polarity of both the drain-to-source voltage and the gate-to-source voltage. For a fixed value of gate-to-source voltage, an increase in the drain-to-source voltage, V_d, from zero causes the drain current to rise rapidly until channel pinch-off is reached; then it levels off and remains relatively constant. This relationship is shown in Fig. 10–7 for a typical junction-gate transistor[3] and in Fig. 10–8 for typical depletion-type and enhancement-type insulated-gate units.

Figure 10–4 shows how the drain current of a typical offset-gate depletion-type transistor varies with gate-to-source voltage at medium current levels (0.5 to 8 ma). Figure 10–5 shows the same unit at low current levels (5 to 200 μa). Figure 10–9 shows the relationship in an offset-gate depletion-type transistor between drain current, gate-to-source voltage, and drain-to-source voltage in the OFF region, which is of interest in chopper-amplifier applications.

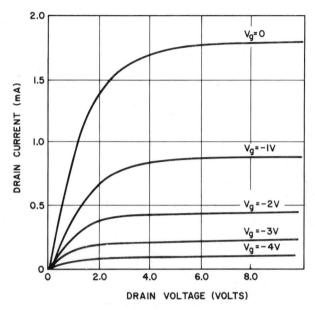

Figure 10-7. Output characteristics of an n-channel junction-gate transistor.

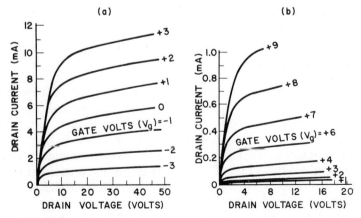

Figure 10-8. Output characteristics of an n-channel insulated gate transistor. (a) Depletion unit; (b) enhancement unit.

Figure 10–10 shows how variation in the *substrate bias* voltage affects the transfer characteristic of an offset-gate depletion-type transistor. Figure 10–11 shows how the substrate bias affects the small-signal transconductance.

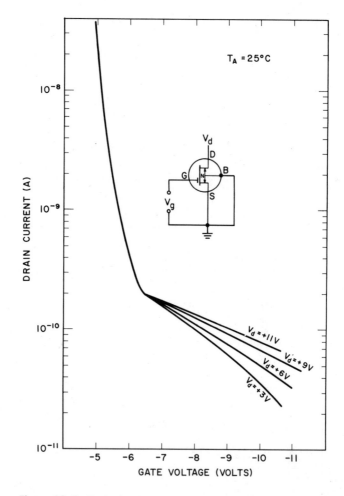

Figure 10–9. Drain current as a function of gate voltage for an *n*-channel MOS transistor with large negative gate voltages.

The *amplification factor* is affected by drain and gate voltage as shown in Fig. 10–12. Although high values of amplification factor are shown, actual stage voltage gains usually fall in the range of 5 to 50 because of circuit loading limitations.

The *dynamic output resistance*, r_d, is found from the slope of the output characteristic curves illustrated in Figs. 10–7 and 10–8. The output characteristics show that r_d increases as the channel conductivity is reduced by the depletion gate voltage. Conversely, r_d decreases as the channel conductivity is increased by an enhancement-gate voltage.

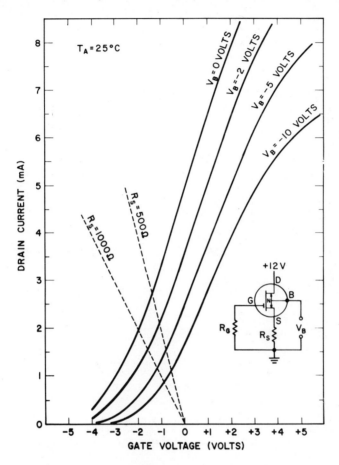

Figure 10-10. Transfer characteristic of an n-channel MOS transistor for various values of substrate bias.

The possible reduction in r_d is limited in a junction-gate transistor because the gate starts to conduct at a very low forward voltage (0.2 v in germanium; 0.6 v in silicon). By contrast, a large enhancement-gate voltage applied to an insulated-gate transistor can reduce the output resistance to a value approaching the sum of $r_{d'}$ and $r_{s'}$. The limiting factor is the gate insulation breakdown rating which may prevent the use of a gate voltage large enough to reduce r_d to its theoretical minimum. Variation of MOS transistor output resistance as a function of voltage and current is illustrated in Fig. 10-13.

In an offset-gate MOS transistor, the gating action of the substrate junction upon $r_{d'}$ (the portion of the channel not modulated by the insulated gate) actually results in an increase in $r_{d'}$ as the drain-to-source voltage is increased. As $r_{d'}$ increases, the voltage drop across it increases

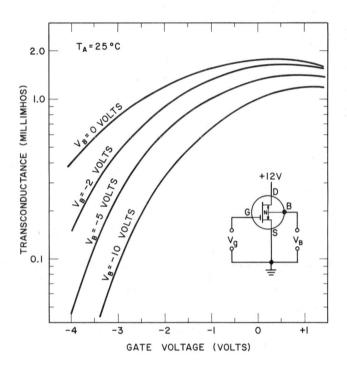

Figure 10–11. Transconductance as a function of gate voltage for an *n*-channel MOS transistor for various values of substrate bias.

and less of the applied drain-to-source voltage appears across r_d, the channel resistance which is modulated by the offset insulated gate. As the potential across r_d drops, the self-pinching action on r_d decreases and, consequently, r_d itself decreases. The net effect is that the product of drain current and drain resistance in the offset-gate MOS transistor deviates somewhat from the constant value predicted by theory in the region above the knee of the drain characteristic of a full-gate MOS transistor. However, the use of an empirically derived constant, K, provides a reasonable approximation. Figure 10–13 shows the measured I_d vs. r_d relationship of a typical offset-gate MOS transistor. Also shown is a theoretical curve for $K = 100$ v.

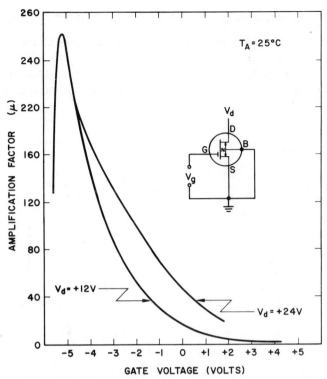

Figure 10-12. Amplification factor as a function of bias voltage of an *n*-channel MOS transistor.

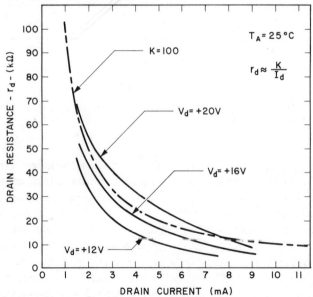

Figure 10-13. Drain resistance as a function of drain current of an *n*-channel MOS transistor.

10–2 SMALL-SIGNAL AMPLIFIERS

There are three basic single-stage amplifier configurations for field-effect transistors: common source, common gate, and common drain. Each has certain characteristics which recommend it for use in particular applications. In the examples that follow, an *n*-channel MOS transistor is used for illustration, but all statements except those relating to polarity apply equally to the *p*-channel MOS and *n*- and *p*-channel junction-gate devices unless otherwise noted.

1. Common-source operation

The grounded source or common-source arrangement is the circuit most frequently used with field-effect transistors. It is characterized by a high input impedance, medium to high output impedance, and a voltage gain greater than one. It may be used either tuned or untuned.

In this mode of operation, shown in Fig. 10–14a, the input signal is applied between gate and ground and the output signal is taken between drain and ground.

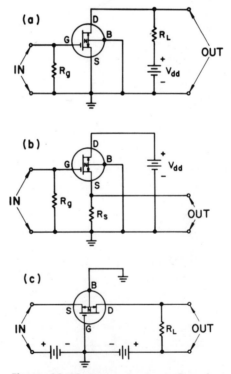

Figure 10–14. Basic circuit configurations.
(a) Common source; (b) common drain;
(c) common gate.

The common-source voltage gain, A, without feedback may be calculated from:

$$A = \frac{g_m r_d R_L}{r_d + R_L} \qquad \text{(10–1)}$$

where g_m is the gate-to-drain transconductance, r_d is the drain resistance, and R_L is the effective load resistance. If $R_L \gg r_d$, the voltage gain is approximately equal to the amplification factor, μ, of the transistor. When $r_d = R_L$, the voltage gain is $\mu/2$. If $R_L \ll r_d$, the voltage gain reduces to $g_m R_L$.

An unbypassed source resistor introduced into the common-source circuit produces negative feedback proportional to the output current. The common-source voltage gain with an unbypassed source resistor is:

$$A' = \frac{g_m r_d R_L}{r_d + (g_m r_d + 1)R_s + R_L} \qquad \text{(10–2)}$$

where R_s is the unbypassed source resistor.

The common-source output impedance is increased by the unbypassed source resistor and becomes:

$$Z_o = r_d + (g_m r_d + 1)R_s \qquad \text{(10–3)}$$

2. Common-drain operation

Common-drain operation, shown in Fig. 10–14b, is frequently referred to as a *source-follower*. In this arrangement the input impedance is higher than that of the common-source configuration. The output impedance is low and there is no polarity reversal between input and output. The voltage gain is always less than one, and distortion is low. Power gain can be very large because of the ratio of input to output impedance.

A transistor is operated as a source-follower when the application requires reduced input-circuit capacitance, downward impedance transformation, or increased input-signal handling capability.

In the circuit of Fig. 10–14b, the input signal is effectively applied between gate and drain, and the output is taken between source and drain. This circuit has 100% negative voltage feedback. The voltage gain is:

$$A' = \frac{R_s}{[(\mu + 1)/\mu]R_s + 1/g_m} \qquad \text{(10–4)}$$

or, if $\mu \gg 1$:

$$A' = \frac{g_m R_s}{1 + g_m R_s} \tag{10-5}$$

where R_s is the net effect of all resistances between source and ground, and μ is the transistor amplification factor.

If we assume a transistor g_m of 1500 μmhos and an R_s of 667 ohms, the stage gain, A', will be 0.5. With an input impedance of one megohm, the stage *power gain* will be almost 32 db. With the same R_s and a transistor g_m of 10,000 μmhos, the stage gain would increase to 0.87.

If R_g is returned to ground as shown in Fig. 10–14b, the input resistance R_i of the stage is equal to R_g. If R_g is returned to source instead of ground, the effective input resistance, R_i', may be determined from the following equation in which A' is the stage voltage amplification defined in Eq. (10–4):

$$R_i' = \frac{R_g}{1 - A'} \tag{10-6}$$

For example, if $R_g = 1$ megohm and $A' = 0.5$, R_i' would equal 2 megohms.

For the case of a resistive load, the effective input capacitance, C_i', of the source-follower is reduced by the inherent voltage feedback so that:

$$C_i' = C_{gd} + (1 - A')C_{gs} \tag{10-7}$$

If, for example, $C_{gd} = 1$ pf, $C_{gs} = 5$ pf, and $A' = 0.5$, then C_i' is 3.5 pf.

The output resistance, R_o, of the source-follower is:

$$R_o' = \frac{r_d R_s}{(g_m r_d + 1)R_s + r_d} \tag{10-8}$$

For a transistor with $g_m = 1500$ μmhos, $r_d = 10,000$ ohms and $R_s = 667$ ohms; then R_o' is 333 ohms.

The output capacitance, C_o', of the source-follower is:

$$C_o' = C_{ds} + C_{gs}\left(\frac{1 - A'}{A'}\right) \tag{10-9}$$

If $A' = 0.5$ as in the previous input-circuit example, C_o' is equal to $C_{ds} + C_{gs}$. If A' is as large as 0.9 and C_{ds} and C_{gs} are 3 pf and 5 pf, respectively, C_o' becomes 3.6 pf.

3. Common-gate operation

The common-gate circuit of Fig. 10-14c is used to transform from a low input impedance to a high output impedance. The input impedance of the common-gate circuit has approximately the same value as the output impedance of the common-drain circuit.

The common-gate configuration is also used in high-frequency circuits because its low voltage gain makes neutralization of feedback unnecessary in most applications.

The expression for common-gate voltage gain may be written as:

$$A = \frac{(g_m r_d + 1)R_L}{(g_m r_d + 1)R_g + r_d + R_L} \qquad (10\text{-}10)$$

where R_g is the generator resistance associated with the input signal.

For the typical values, $g_m = 1500$ μmhos, $r_d = 10,000$ ohms, $R_L = 2000$ ohms, and $R_g = 500$ ohms, the common-gate voltage gain is 1.6. Doubling the value of R_g reduces the voltage gain to 1.14.

If the product of g_m and r_d is very much greater than unity and r_d is very much greater than the composite load resistance, R_L, the common-gate voltage gain may be written as:

$$A = \frac{g_m R_L}{1 + g_m R_g} \qquad (10\text{-}11)$$

4. Cascaded stages

Field-effect transistors may be used in a number of different cascade arrangements, either with other field-effect transistors or with bipolar transistors or vacuum tubes. A few of the more likely combinations are shown in Fig. 10-15.

Circuit (a), using typical 3N98 transistors, will produce a voltage gain of 15 or 20 and have a low output impedance. The voltage gain is obtained in the first stage by operating at reduced drain current, with a resulting increase in the g_m/I_d figure of merit as well as a higher permissible value of load resistance. The high input impedance of the second MOS transistor is compatible with the large load resistor. The low output impedance of the pair is obtained by operating the second stage as a source-follower.

Circuit (b) is similar to circuit (a) in that the first stage is operated at a reduced level of drain current for voltage gain, and the second stage is a source-follower for low output impedance. However, all coupling capacitors have been eliminated, but a separate bias battery must be used in the first stage. Although the drain voltage of the first stage is applied directly to the gate of the second stage, its effect is partially cancelled by the increased voltage drop that appears across the 1000 ohm source resistor in the second stage. For example, if the quiescent drain voltage of the first stage is 12 v and the quiescent drain current of the second stage is

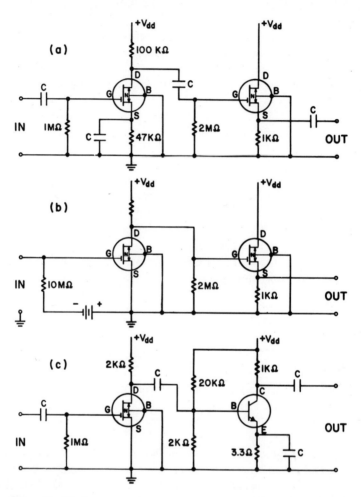

Figure 10–15. Typical cascade circuits using *n*-channel MOS transistors.

6 ma at $V_g = 0$, the second stage gate sees −6 v opposing +12 v. The gate then sees a net positive gate potential of +6 v. This enhances the drain current flow, causing a greater voltage drop across the source resistor; so the gate voltage is balanced at about half the original difference or +3 v for a unit whose $g_m = 1/R_s$.

Circuit (c) uses an MOS transistor in the first stage to provide a high input impedance and to drive the low input impedance of a bipolar power transistor. This configuration uses the MOS transistor as an impedance transformer. Although the low input impedance of the second stage bipolar transistor reduces the voltage gain of the first stage to a low value, the power gain of the first stage can be very high.

5. Cascode operation

Cascode circuit configurations are described by Wallman[4] and a particular version may be used to improve the signal-to-noise ratio and reduce the feedback capacitance of an amplifier stage. As applied to field-effect transistors, the cascode circuit consists of a transistor operating as a common-source amplifier driving a second transistor operating in the common-gate configuration. See Fig. 10-16. The transconductance

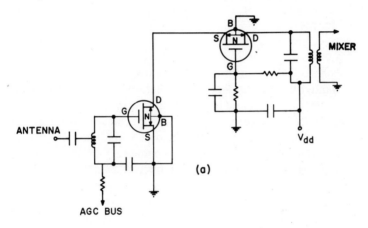

(a)

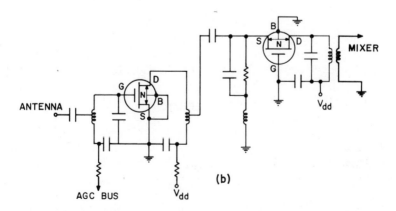

(b)

Figure 10-16. Cascode circuits. (a) Series cascode; (b) parallel cascode.

of the pair is determined by the transconductance of the driving unit so long as the driven unit does not limit the current flow through the pair. The input impedance of the pair is also determined by the driving unit. The output impedance of the pair is determined by the driven unit in all cases. If the conductivity of the driven unit is kept above that of the driving unit in direct-coupled operation so that no current limiting occurs, the output impedance of the pair will always be equal to, or greater than, the normal output impedance of the driven unit operating alone. If, on the other hand, the driven unit begins to limit, the output impedance of the pair may be increased by several orders of magnitude. This limiting results from the degenerative action of the driving unit when the pair is operated in series and the gate of the driven unit has a d-c return to some point in the circuit which is more negative than the driven unit's source. Possible return points are the source of the driving unit, ground, or a negative-bias battery.

Excessive limiting by the driven unit drastically reduces the dynamic range of the cascode pair and produces a sharp cutoff at the high-current end of the cascode drain-current–gate-voltage transfer characteristic. On the other hand, by careful selection of the gate bias of the driven unit, one can vary the high-current end of the cascode transfer characteristic over a wide range and even give it a remote cutoff characteristic; at the same time, the output impedance is maintained at a high value. This is a very significant advantage over a single unit because forward automatic gain control (AGC) reduces the output impedance of a single unit with undesirable loading on associated tuned circuits. This reduction of the output impedance of a single unit under forward AGC conditions also applies to the output impedance of a cascode pair if the gate of the driven unit is returned to its own source. The d-c output characteristics of cascode circuits using various bias arrangements are illustrated later in this chapter (see Section 10–3.2).

The possibility of tailoring the transfer characteristic of the cascode pair by biasing the gate of the driven unit is perhaps the most significant feature of this circuit configuration, although improved signal-to-noise ratio and reduced feedback capacitance are also advantages.

10–3 GENERAL OPERATING CONSIDERATIONS

1. Selection of operating point

The selection of the transistor operating point is determined by one or a combination of the following considerations:

1. Maximum output voltage.
2. Minimum power dissipation.

3. Minimum drain current drift.

4. Maximum voltage gain.

5. Availability of bias voltages.

For *maximum output voltage,* the first step is to choose the largest supply voltage consistent with the transistor drain-to-source voltage rating. To determine the load resistance that will result in maximum undistorted output voltage, subtract V_p from the supply voltage and divide by 2. This gives the optimum quiescent drain-to-source voltage. Divide this voltage by the desired value of quiescent drain current to obtain the value of the appropriate load resistor:

$$R_L = \frac{1}{2} \frac{V_{dd} - V_p}{I_d} \tag{10-12}$$

Minimum power dissipation will be obtained if both drain-to-source voltage and drain current are minimized. Minimum power dissipation is of concern in portable battery-operated equipment. Where minimum power dissipation is of paramount importance, transistors with low values of V_p should be used. Drain current can be reduced by the use of appropriate gate bias, but the related decrease in transconductance should be recognized.

Minimum drain-current drift with temperature can be achieved in some transistors if the transistor is biased to its zero temperature coefficient point. For precise compensation, interchangeability of transistors is compromised. In units which do not have a zero temperature coefficient, the drain-current drift due to temperature can be minimized by operation at reduced drain-to-source and gate-to-substrate potentials.

In general, *minimum drain-current drift with time* will result when the transistors are operated with a gate-to-substrate voltage close to zero, minimum drain-to-source voltage, and minimum temperature excursions.

Maximum voltage gain with large values of load resistance can be secured if we bias the transistor into the depletion region. This accomplishes the necessary reduction in drain current and increases the amplification factor (refer to Fig. 10-12).

Maximum voltage gain with small values of load resistance is obtained when we operate the transistor at the point of maximum transconductance. In many offset-gate transistors this point is at, or near, zero gate-to-source voltage. In full-gate transistors, the transconductance and drain current both increase with enhancement-gate voltages. The maximum transconductance operating point in these units is limited by the device dissipation ratings and the large voltage drop across the load resistor which results from the increase in drain current. The required gate bias voltage of insulated-gate transistors operating in the region above pinch-off may be determined if we assume a square-law relationship between gate voltage and drain current:

$$V_g = \left(1 - \sqrt{\frac{I_d}{I_{do}}}\right) V_p \tag{10–13}$$

Both the offset-gate and full-gate MOS transistors may deviate from this square-law relationship as illustrated in Fig. 10–17. Deviations from the square-law relationship are in the region of high dissipation and high

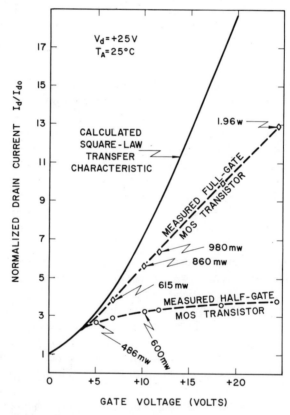

Figure 10–17. Normalized transfer characteristic at high drain current.

current, generally beyond the recommended ratings of the transistor. When operated within ratings, the transfer characteristic of the full-gate transistor of Fig. 10–17 follows the square law very closely. The offset-gate transistor deviates from square-law behavior when the drain current increases to the point at which the voltage drop across the un-modulated portion of the channel resistance, $r_{d'}$, becomes significant. This is discussed in greater detail in Chapter 5. Finally, *the availability of bias voltages* determines the extent to which fixed-bias, or fixed-bias in conjunction with self-bias, can be used to establish the optimum operating point.

2. Bias circuitry

The insulated gate of the MOS transistor makes possible a wide variety of biasing arrangements, shown in Fig. 10-18. The gate bias batteries in these circuits supply no power. In circuits (b), (c), and (h), the use of large resistances to supply the gate bias from the drain supply voltage essentially eliminates all bias-circuit power loss.

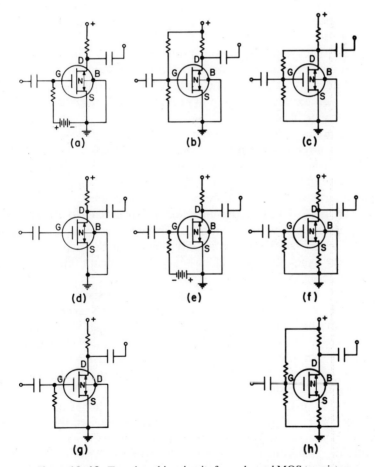

Figure 10-18. Transistor bias circuits for *n*-channel MOS transistors.

Circuits (a), (b), (c), and (d) of Fig. 10–18 may be used to obtain a quiescent operating point in the enhancement mode. Circuit (d) is a special case in which the positive gate bias is obtained from the internal voltage divider formed by the gate-to-source and gate-to-drain leakage resistances. It is a very critical circuit and should be considered only when it is necessary to utilize the maximum input-resistance capabilities of the MOS transistor. In the case of a typical offset-gate depletion-type MOS transistor with no accumulated gate charge, the floating gate attains a positive bias equal to about 5% of the drain supply voltage. It is especially important to protect the floating gate from damage due to electrostatic voltages, since this circuit provides no additional resistive paths to dissipate such charges.

Circuits (e) and (f) are used for operation in the depletion mode.

Circuit (g) is used for zero-bias operation, except in the case of a very large gate-to-source resistance ($\approx 10^{15}$ ohms). In this case, the quiescent operating point may be in the enhancement mode as explained for circuit (d).

Circuit (h) is a combination of circuits (b) and (f). This circuit may be used in situations where the desired source resistor results in too high a value of negative gate bias. The positive voltage from the divider across the supply voltage can be chosen to provide any degree of cancellation of the negative gate bias.

An additional possible bias arrangement combines the self-bias source resistor circuit (f) with the negative bias battery circuit (e). The fixed bias of the battery is used to place the transistor close to the desired operating point, and it reduces the portion of the total supply voltage which would otherwise have to be dropped across the source resistor to achieve the desired gate bias. This is important when it is necessary to use a relatively low battery supply voltage with a transistor having a high pinch-off voltage. The use of fixed bias is only feasible if the expected ambient temperature excursions would produce insignificant changes in the quiescent operating point.

The *cascode circuit* (see Section 10–2) consists of a transistor operating as a common-source amplifier driving a second transistor operating in the common-gate configuration. For bias purposes, the devices may be operated either in series or in parallel. When operated in series, the supply voltage must be approximately double that which would be required for operation of a single unit. The two basic configurations were shown in Fig. 10–16.

The output resistance of a series cascode pair reaches its high, essentially constant value, when the drain-to-source voltage of the driving unit just exceeds the sum of the enhancement voltage on the gate of the driven unit plus the pinch-off voltage of the driven unit. Any further increase in the drain voltage of the driving unit causes the gate of the driven unit to become proportionately more negative than its own source. This is illustrated in Fig. 10–19, which shows the output characteristics (a and b) of two individual *n*-channel depletion-type transistors and their composite cascode output characteristic (c) when operating with a fixed positive 10-v bias on the gate of the driven unit. Figure 10–19d shows the transfer characteristic for the pair.

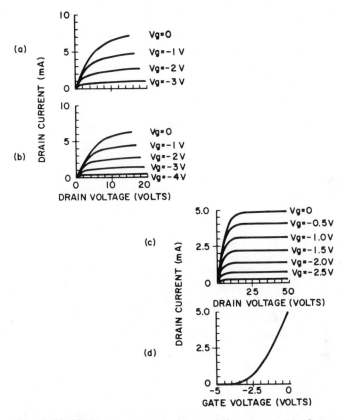

Figure 10–19. Series cascode characteristic curves. (a) Output characteristics of top cascode unit; (b) output characteristics of bottom cascode unit; (c) output characteristics of cascode pair; (d) transfer characteristic of cascode pair.

3. Circuit stability

The saturated drain current is given by $I_d = I_{do}(1 - V_g/V_p)^2$. If it is desired to maintain I_d constant when the ambient temperature changes, V_g must be varied in such a way as to provide the necessary compensation.

The circuits of Figs. 10–18c and 10–18f both provide an increased degree of stability because of the negative feedback which is present.

In circuit (c), if I_d increases due to a change in temperature, V_d decreases because of the additional voltage drop across R_d and the positive gate voltage, V_g, is decreased. This tends to cancel out the initial drain-current increase.

In circuit (f), if I_d increases due to temperature effects, V_d decreases because of the additional voltage drop across both R_d and R_s. However, the increased voltage drop across R_s makes the gate-to-source voltage more negative. Again, the net result is a tendency to cancel out the initial drain-current increase and to restore V_d to its original value.

The circuit arrangement of Fig. 10–18b may be used when the larger drain currents associated with enhancement mode operation can be tolerated, for example, with either an inductive load or a low value of resistive load. Circuit (f) may be used for low drain current applications in which the load impedance is large and the loss in d-c gain due to R_s can be tolerated or, in the case of a-c amplifier circuits, R_s can be bypassed with a capacitor.

One of the outstanding features of the MOS transistor is its very high input resistance, which may be even higher than those of the best electron tubes. However, unlike the electron tube, whose control element (grid) operates in a vacuum, the MOS transistor depends on the relative perfection of a very thin insulating layer of SiO_2 between its control electrode (gate) and the active channel. If this layer is punctured by the inadvertent application of excess voltage to the external gate connection the damage is irreversible. If the damaged area is small enough, the additional leakage may not be noticed in many circuits. Greater damage may degrade the device to the leakage levels associated with a junction-gate transistor. It is very important to take appropriate precautions to insure that MOS transistor gate-voltage ratings are adhered to.

Static electricity represents the greatest threat to the gate insulation in the MOS transistor. A large electrostatic charge can accumulate on the gate electrode if the transistor is allowed to slide around in plastic containers or if the leads are brushed against fabrics such as silk or nylon. It is possible to avoid this type of charge accumulation completely by wrapping the leads in conductive foil, using conductive containers, or otherwise electrically interconnecting the leads when the transistors are being transported.

Another source of electrostatic charge which may damage the gate insulation can be traced to personnel who handle the transistors. A human body has a capacitance of about 150 pf. Nearly everyone has noticed the spark which may be discharged between one's hand and a lamp or other metal fixture on a cold dry day. This represents a discharge of several thousand volts and is associated with relative humidity levels of about 10% or less. Even at relative humidity levels of 35%, a person may accumulate an electrostatic potential of 300 v. If an individual carrying this charge grasps an MOS transistor by the case and plugs it into a piece of test equipment, or in any other way causes the gate lead to contact *ground* before the other leads do, the accumulated electrostatic charge may break down the gate insulation. To prevent this type of damage an electrostatic *grounding strap* should be used whenever insulated-gate transistors are handled. The grounding strap may have an impedance to ground of several megohms and still accomplish its primary purpose of discharging static electricity.

10-4 APPLICATIONS OF FIELD-EFFECT TRANSISTORS

1. Electrometer

Advanced technology has greatly increased the role played by the electrometer. Because of this importance, much development work has been done to improve electrometer performance. Many sophisticated electrometer circuits have been designed for a variety of general and specialized requirements. This section will review electrometer requirements and discuss the features of the field-effect transistor which make it especially suitable for this application.

An electrometer is a d-c voltmeter used to measure potentials developed across very high impedances without loading the circuit. Used in conjunction with an accurate sampling resistor, it can measure very small currents and is called a micromicroammeter (or picoammeter).

Electrometers are used to amplify the output of high-impedance sources such as ionization gauges, photomultiplier tubes, proportional counters, ion chambers, piezoelectric crystals, high-impedance *pH* electrodes, and photoelectric cells. They are used to measure currents in vacuum gauges and in reverse-biased semiconductor junctions. They are also used to measure stored charge on capacitors.

There are two basic approaches to the use of electrometers as sensitive current-measuring instruments. One utilizes an accurate high-value resistor to produce a voltage drop proportional to the current being measured. This simple technique works, but it does have certain drawbacks. To keep the desired voltage drop across the resistor large compared to the thermal noise voltage, it is necessary to increase the size of the resistor when measuring small values of current. However, the time constant of the measuring circuit also increases proportionately. For very large values of resistance, such as 10^{13} ohms, shunted by a typical input-circuit capacitance of 30 pf, five minutes is required to reach the correct voltage reading.

The second basic approach to small-current measurement with the electrometer seeks to drastically reduce this input time constant by the use of a large amount of negative feedback. These two circuit techniques are shown schematically in Fig. 10–20.

Electrometers used as picoammeters are required to measure minute currents. Specialized expensive versions, such as the vibrating-reed type, have full-scale current ranges as low as 10^{-15} a. As voltmeters, they have sensitivities from one mv to 10 v full-scale. Drift, referred to the input, may be only 200 μv/day, noncumulative.[5]

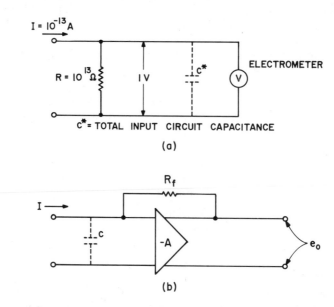

(a)

(b)

Figure 10–20. General high-impedance current-measurement techniques.

In the more common vacuum-tube electrometer, drift of 1000 μv/hr is typical and input impedances of greater than 10^{14} ohms are available. The high impedances are accomplished by the use of specially designed high-vacuum electrometer tubes coated with silicone varnish, special glass-enclosed resistors coated with silicone varnish, and Teflon-insulated cable and wiring. The effects of stray electrostatic fields are reduced by careful shielding techniques.

Response times of 30 to 50 cps have been achieved by the appropriate use of negative feedback to reduce the effective input-circuit capacitance.

Table 10–2 compares the published operating characteristics of a typical triode-type electrometer tube with the characteristics of a 3N98 MOS depletion-type transistor. Of particular significance in this comparison is the lower feedback capacitance exhibited by the MOS transistor. This, plus the higher voltage amplification factor, suggests that an improved first-stage signal-to-noise ratio can be used to offset the higher 1/f noise which is presently associated with the MOS field-effect transistor.

As pointed out by Munoz,[6] the operational-amplifier approach to current measurement is limited in sensitivity only by the thermal noise from the feedback resistor, R_f, of Fig. 10–20, if the operational amplifier has an infinite input resistance. The MOS transistor, with its insulated gate, approaches this infinite input resistance more closely than any other active device. In addition, the gate resistance of the MOS transistor is relatively insensitive to changes in temperature, as noted earlier.

Table 10–2   Comparison of a Typical Electrometer Tube and an MOS Transistor

	Tube	3N98 Transistor	Units
Filament voltage	1.25	none	v
Filament current	10.0	none	ma
Plate (or drain)-to-filament (or source) voltage	7.5	7.5	v
Grid (or gate)-to-filament (or source) voltage	−2.2	−4.5	v
Plate (or drain) current	95	90	μa
Transconductance, g_m	110	250	μmhos
Grid (or gate) current	5×10^{-14}	1×10^{-14}	a
Amplification factor, μ	2.1	100	
Output resistance, r_p (or r_d)	19	400	kilohms
Grid (or gate)-to-plate (or drain) capacitance	2	0.3	pf
Grid (or gate)-to-filament (or source) capacitance	2	5.0	pf
Plate (or drain)-to-filament (or source) capacitance	1.5	2.0	pf

In using the MOS transistor for the input stage of an electrometer, the circuit designer should:

1. Take precautions to assure that the transient and steady-state gate voltage ratings are not exceeded.
2. Maximize the stage gain to obtain the best signal-to-noise ratio.
3. Minimize the transistor dissipation to reduce thermal drift. Refer to Section 10–3.

Additional general considerations in electrometer design include the following:

1. Minimize input-circuit capacitance by careful placement of parts.

2. Maximize the current sampling or feedback resistor (for low-current measurements) to obtain higher signal voltages and to maintain a good signal-to-noise ratio.

3. Minimize input-circuit leakage paths so that large sampling or feedback resistors will be feasible.

4. Shield input circuit from hum and electrostatic voltages.

2. Phonograph amplifier

A phonograph amplifier illustrates the way in which a field-effect transistor can be used with a bipolar transistor to produce a simple, two-stage, high-input-impedance, solid-state power amplifier, shown in Fig. 10–21. The design of this phonograph amplifier is based on the following requirements:

1. High input impedance to match a ceramic cartridge such as the Sonotone 21T or its equivalent (voltage output, 0.56 v; element capacity, 775 pf).

2. One-watt power output at 10% total harmonic distortion.

3. Frequency response flat to within ± 3 db over the frequency range, 200 to 6000 cps. This requirement is compatible with a low-cost speaker.

4. Minimum number of components for low cost.

5. Operation at 117 v a-c.

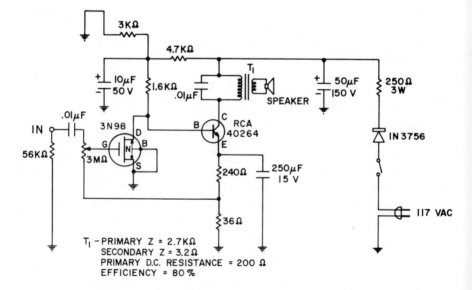

Figure 10–21. Line-operated class A one-watt phonograph amplifier.

The characteristics of the field-effect transistor match some of these requirements very well. These include a high input impedance and a linear transfer characteristic for low distortion at peak signal voltages. In addition, it is desirable to have (1) low gate leakage currents, so that the operating point is not shifted by a voltage drop across the large gate resistor, and (2) an insulated gate so that the gate may be operated at zero gate bias without causing distortion of large-peak signals. It is necessary to have an adequate device transconductance.

Adequacy is determined by the current gain of the second-stage power transistor. In this instance, an RCA 40264 high-voltage silicon power transistor with a current gain of 50 is used in the second stage. A first-stage transconductance of 1500 μmhos provides sufficient drive for the second stage.

CIRCUIT CONFIGURATION. There are four feasible circuit configurations for the phonograph amplifier using common-emitter operation of the power stage:

1. Common-source 1st stage RC-coupled to the base of the 2nd stage.

2. Same as (1) but direct-coupled from drain to base.

3. Source-follower 1st stage RC-coupled to the base of the 2nd stage.

4. Same as (3) but direct-coupled from source to base.

The arrangement of (3) accepts the widest range of first-stage drain current and transconductance but requires a large drain decoupling capacitor, a large source-to-base coupling capacitor, and two resistors for establishing the base bias.

The arrangement of (4) eliminates the source-to-base coupling capacitor and the two base bias resistors. However, the permissible drain-current spread is greatly reduced because the base bias becomes a direct function of drain current.

The amplifier performance was checked using both (4) and (2) configurations and was found to be essentially the same in both cases.

The volume control is placed in the gate circuit of the MOS transistor. See Fig. 10–21. The low side is returned to a d-c feedback voltage divider in the emitter circuit of the power transistor, and the wiper arm is connected directly to the gate. Because of the negligible leakage currents associated with the insulated-gate of the transistor, no significant gate-leakage-current noise voltage is developed across the multi-megohm potentiometer. The amplifier provides full power output with 0.25 v RMS at the input. Because the volume-control wiper arm is connected to the gate, the gate rarely "sees" more than 0.25 v. This means that distortion contributed by the first stage is a negligible factor in the over-all amplifier performance. This would not be the case if the volume-control potentiometer was placed in series with the source or if volume control was accomplished by variation of the d-c gate bias, because the transistor input would then be subjected to the peak output signal of the cartridge. At maximum input-signal levels, the peak-to peak voltage swing at the gate could be expected to exceed 5 v. The volume control, acting as a variable voltage divider ahead of the transistor input, provides a clear advantage in this application.

QUIESCENT OPERATING POINT. The second-stage bipolar power transistor presents a load impedance of approximately 200 ohms to the first-stage MOS transistor. Because of this low value of load resistance, we achieve maximum voltage gain in the first stage by maximizing its transconductance.

Reducing the drain resistance, r_d, has little effect until it drops to 2000 ohms or below. This can be seen by an examination of the voltage-amplification expression, Eq. (10–1). Since the transistor drain resistance, 4000 ohms, is much greater than the load resistance, 200 ohms, the voltage gain of the first stage is $g_m R_L$.

In general, the transconductance tends to increase with positive gate voltage if the quiescent drain voltage is large compared to the output-characteristic knee voltage. Therefore, in this application it is desirable to operate the MOS transistor at as high a drain voltage and enhancement-gate voltage as the ratings will allow.

COMPLETE AMPLIFIER. Figure 10–21 shows the complete circuit of the amplifier in which the drain of a 3N98 insulated-gate transistor was direct-coupled to the base of a RCA 40264 bipolar transistor. The d-c feedback from the emitter divider to the gate causes the 3N98 to operate in the enhancement region of its output characteristic. This feedback improves the device interchangeability. The use of a field-effect transistor having a higher transconductance, in conjunction with greater amounts of negative feedback by source degeneration, would further improve interchangeability. The upper-frequency response of this amplifier is limited by the 0.01 μf capacitor shunting the primary of the output transformer. This capacitor also serves to protect the output transistor from high-frequency transients in the 117-v line.

3. Voltage variable resistor

The linear output characteristic of the transistor in the low drain-to-source voltage region prior to channel pinch-off is referred to as the ohmic region. Varying the gate voltage of the transistor causes the drain-to-source resistance to increase or decrease, but the I_d vs. V_d characteristic remains linear. Thus, the device may be used as a low distortion, voltage-controlled attenuator. Chief advantages of the transistor in this application are the negligible gate-power requirements and the large dynamic range.

Figure 10-22 shows the drain resistance as a function of gate voltage for a typical n-channel depletion-type insulated-gate transistor. Units with higher pinch-off voltages will accept correspondingly greater peak signal voltage swings before waveform distortion occurs. However, the

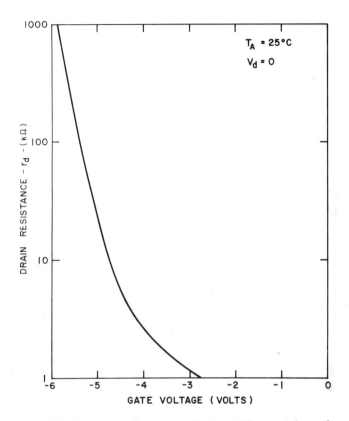

Figure 10-22. Drain resistance as a function of the gate voltage of an n-channel MOS transistor.

higher pinch-off voltage units require higher gate-voltage excursions to cover the resistance range from minimum to maximum. A typical silicon n-channel offset-gate depletion-type MOS transistor with $V_p = -6$ v will produce less than 2% total harmonic distortion in a 100-mv, 400 cps signal. Signal attenuation is illustrated in Fig. 10-23, which shows the output signal as a function of gate voltage for the circuit shown.

Figure 10-24 illustrates several possible circuit configurations using the field-effect transistor as a voltage variable resistor. Circuit (a) may be used when signal levels are high, so that the thermal noise of the one-megohm series resistor will not degrade the signal-to-noise ratio of the system to an objectionable degree. Circuit (a) is a simple *L*-pad configuration in which the transistor serves as the variable resistive element in the low side of the attenuator. In this circuit, the maximum attenuation is generally between 60 and 70 db, and the minimum attenuation is 1 to 2 db. This circuit must be followed by a high-impedance load such as a common-source transistor amplifier.

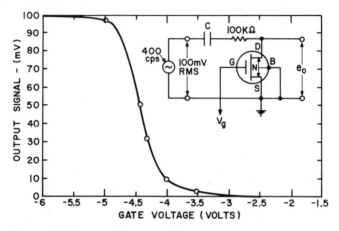

Figure 10–23. Signal attenuation as a function of the gate voltage of an *n*-channel MOS transistor.

Circuit (b) is the inverse of circuit (a) in that the transistor serves as the variable resistive element in the high side of the attenuator. Maximum useful attenuation in this circuit is also between 60 and 70 db, and the minimum attenuation is between 1 and 6 db. Circuit (b) is used to work into a low-impedance load such as a common-emitter bipolar transistor.

Circuit (c) demonstrates a method for providing simultaneous voltage control of both arms of an *L*-pad attenuator. In this circuit, a *p*-channel enhancement-type transistor is used in the upper arm, and an *n*-channel depletion-type transistor is used in the lower arm. Negative voltage applied to the gates causes the *n*-channel unit to increase in resistance while, at the same time, the resistance of the *p*-channel unit decreases. When the gate control is at 0 v, the drain resistance of the bottom unit is about 500 ohms and the upper unit is about 10 megohms. This produces a maximum attenuation of approximately 86 db. When the gate control is at −6 v, the drain resistance of the bottom unit is about 10 megohms and the upper unit is about 500 ohms. Under these conditions, the attenuation is essentially zero. This circuit must work into a high-impedance load.

Design considerations for utilizing a field-effect transistor as a linear attenuator include:

    1. Decouple the gate(s) adequately to prevent the introduction of unwanted signals.

2. Insert the transistor attenuator at a point in the system where the signal level is as high as the transistor can accept without excessive distortion.

3. In a-c systems, minimize d-c current flow through the transistor by the use of suitable blocking capacitors.

4. In a-c systems, provide proper layout to minimize stray shunt capacitance.

5. In a-c systems, take into account the effects of the capacitive elements of the transistor.

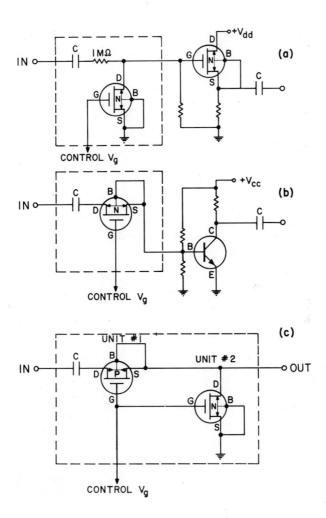

Figure 10–24. Attenuator circuits using MOS transistors.

REFERENCES

1. J. T. Wallmark, *RCA Rev.* **24**, 461 (1964).

2. L. J. Sevin, "Effect of Temperature on FET Characteristics," *Electro-Technology*, Apr., 1964, p. 103.

3. Amelco FG–37.

4. H. Wallman, A. B. Macnee, and C. P. Gadsden, *Proc. IRE* **36**, 700 (1948).

5. J. F. Keithley, *Instruments and Control Systems*, Jan., 1962.

6. R. Munoz, *Electronic Design,* May 11, 1964.

7. V. C. Rideout, *Active Networks,* (Englewood Cliffs, N. J.: Prentice-Hall, Inc., 1954), p. 189.

11

The Field-Effect Transistor in High-Frequency Linear Circuits

Paul E. Kolk and Harwick Johnson

11-1 INTRODUCTION

This chapter describes the use of insulated-gate field-effect transistors in linear amplifiers at frequencies into the ultra-high-frequency range. The transistors are characterized by their two-port admittances, and radio-frequency circuit designs are developed in terms of these admittances. The cross-modulation performance of the field-effect transistor is compared with that of bipolar transistors and vacuum tubes, and experimental confirmation of its superiority is presented. The linear circuit design is illustrated for two transistors. One is a high-frequency transistor described in Chapter 8 and discussed in linear circuit applications in Chapter 10. The other is an experimental uhf transistor designed for operation at higher frequencies.

The extensive development of the silicon bipolar transistor made possible the development of compact low-power receivers that operate at frequencies up to 1000 mc/s with noise figures of 6 db. When a bipolar transistor is used as a linear amplifier, its r-f selectivity and capability of handling interfering signals do not compare favorably with the performance of vacuum-tube circuits. However, the power gain and noise figure are better than those for germanium transistors and tubes.

On the other hand, the insulated-gate field-effect transistor does have characteristics which make possible the development of receivers with good r-f selectivity and an ability to withstand interfering signals; this compares favorably with vacuum tube circuits. These considerations are of considerable significance in communication system design, for the field-effect transistor offers the receiver designer the first solid-state device which attains the performance of the vacuum tube in this respect.

11-2 ADMITTANCE PARAMETERS

The two-port small-signal parameters provide the most convenient characterization of the transistor for linear circuit analyses. The admittance, or y-parameters, will be used here. A set of y-parameters can readily be converted to an impedance (z) set, a hybrid (h, g) set, or to other equivalent circuit representations. The choice is largely a matter of the designers preference or of the convenience of available measuring equipment.

The admittance specification of a two-port is illustrated in Fig. 11–1, where the relationship between the input and output currents and voltages is given by:

$$I_1 = y_{11}V_1 + y_{12}V_2$$
$$I_2 = y_{21}V_1 + y_{22}V_2$$

$$\text{(11–1)}$$

The input admittance, y_{11}, is the admittance of port 1 when port 2 is short-circuited ($V_2 = 0$). The reverse transfer admittance, y_{12}, is the transfer admittance from port 2 to port 1 when port 1 is short-circuited ($V_1 = 0$). The forward transfer admittance, y_{21}, is the transfer admittance from port 1 to port 2 when port 2 is short-circuited ($V_2 = 0$); it is also referred to as the forward transadmittance. The output admittance, y_{22}, is the admittance of port 2 when port 1 is short-circuited ($V_1 = 0$).

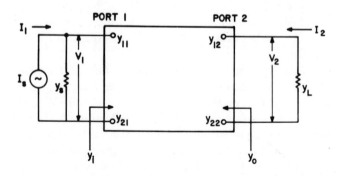

Figure 11–1 Two-port admittance representation of a network.

A three-terminal device such as a transistor has one electrode common to the input and output circuits, and this choice must be specified in stating the characteristic set of admittance parameters. The source is most frequently used as the common electrode in describing the field-effect transistor. The set of common-source admittances will be written as:

$$
\left.
\begin{aligned}
\text{input admittance} \qquad & y_{rs} = g_{rs} \times jb_{rs} \\
\text{reverse transfer admittance} \qquad & y_{rs} = g_{rs} + jb_{rs} \\
\text{forward transfer admittance} \qquad & y_{fs} = g_{fs} + jb_{fs} \\
\text{output admittance} \qquad & y_{os} = g_{os} + jb_{os}
\end{aligned}
\right\} \qquad \textbf{(11–2)}
$$

where the subscript, s, denotes the common source. Subscripts g and d will be used to denote common-gate and common-drain parameters, respectively. General relations will be written without the configuration subscript. A common-source admittance set can readily be converted to an equivalent common-gate or common-drain set by use of the indefinite matrix.[1] See Section 11–3.

The specification of transistor parameters in this way makes possible the use of matrix operations in circuit analyses. Thus, the common-source admittance matrix is:

$$
y_s = \begin{vmatrix} y_{is} & y_{rs} \\ y_{fs} & y_{os} \end{vmatrix} \qquad \textbf{(11–3)}
$$

While two-port admittance sets are convenient for circuit analyses, the transistor itself is frequently described by an equivalent circuit reflecting the physics of the device. The circuit elements of the equivalent circuit are usually independent of frequency over a wide range. An equivalent circuit for the field-effect transistor is shown in Fig. 11–2 and has been discussed in Chapter 10. By calculating the two-port admittances for this common-source circuit, we can express the frequency variation

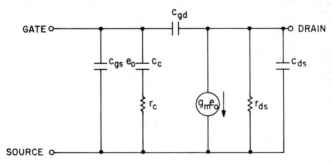

Figure 11–2. Common-source equivalent circuit representation of the insulated-gate field-effect transistor.

of the admittance parameters in terms of the equivalent circuit elements. These relations are:

$$y_{is} = \frac{r_c}{r_c^2 + (1/\omega C_c)^2} + j\omega\left\{C_{gs} + C_{gd} + \frac{C_c}{1 + (\omega r_c C_c)^2}\right\}$$

$$y_{rs} = -j\omega C_{dg}$$

$$y_{fs} = \frac{g_m}{1 + j\omega r_c C_c} - j\omega C_{dg}$$

$$y_{os} = \frac{1}{r_{ds}} + j\omega(C_{ds} + C_{dg})$$

(11–4)

11-3 THE FIELD-EFFECT TRANSISTOR AT HIGH FREQUENCIES

1. Transistor parameters

The two-port common-source admittances[2] of an insulated-gate field-effect transistor are shown in Figs. 11–3 through 11–6. The input

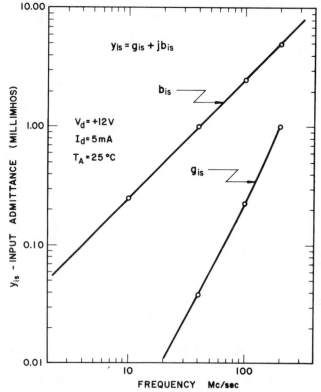

Figure 11–3. Common-source input conductance and susceptance as a function of frequency for a high-frequency MOS transistor.

admittance for this transistor remains susceptive up to several hundred mc/s, and the reverse transfer admittance is dominated by the feed-back capacitance from drain to gate. The forward transadmittance is essentially constant and real up to about 60 mc/s, so the low-frequency

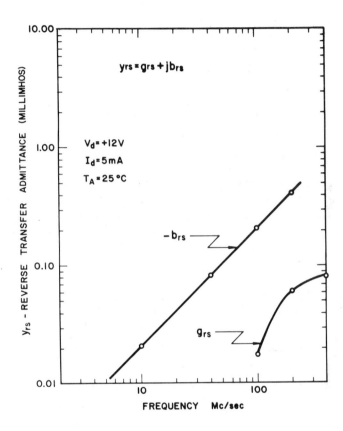

Figure 11–4. Common-source reverse transfer conductance and susceptance as a function of frequency for a high-frequency MOS transistor.

concepts of a real transadmittance (transconductance) are applicable up to this frequency. The real and imaginary components become equal in magnitude at about 200 mc/s. Because the output resistance of a field-effect transistor with its pentode-like characteristic is high, the conductive and susceptive components of the output impedance become equal near 10 mc/s. The susceptive components of y_{os} and y_{rs} vary linearly with frequency as expected from the model of Fig. 11–2 and Eq. (11–4). The susceptive components of y_{is} and y_{fs} vary slightly differently as would be

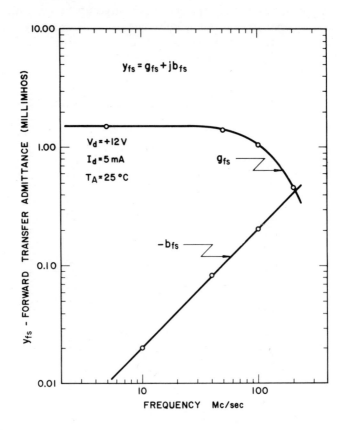

Figure 11–5. Common-source forward transfer conductance and susceptance as a function of frequency for a high-frequency MOS transistor.

expected from the presence of the r_c terms in Eq. (11–4). These observations are in accord with the equivalent circuit model of Fig. 11–2.

The two-port admittances of this transistor are given for the common-source, common-gate, and common-drain configurations at frequencies of 10, 20, 40, and 80 mc/s in Table 11–11.[2] The general characteristics of the different configurations are similar to those for similar vacuum-tube configurations. The transconductance, g_f, is essentially independent of the configuration. The common-gate shows a high input admittance analogous to a grounded-grid vacuum tube. The common-drain configuration shows the low input admittance and high output admittance of a cathode-follower. A detailed discussion of the particular properties of these configurations is given in Chapter 10.

Table 11–1 MOS Transistor Admittances (in μmhos) for Common-Source, Common-Gate, and Common-Drain Configurations

Admittance	$f=10$ mc/s		20 mc/s		40 mc/s		80 mc/s	
	g	b	g	b	g	b	g	b
y_{is}	2	150	7	300	25	600	86	1200
y_{ig}	1650	215	1650	390	1700	710	1750	1300
y_{id}	4	150	10	300	28	600	82	1150
y_{rs}	–	–8	–	–16	–	–32	–	–66
y_{rg}	60	55	72	97	93	180	140	320
y_{rd}	5	140	10	280	24	570	76	1120
y_{fs}	1600	–15	1600	–36	1600	–90	1500	–220
y_{fg}	1650	110	1650	110	1650	120	1600	160
y_{fd}	1600	150	1600	290	1600	540	1600	1000
y_{os}	60	65	72	115	94	215	140	390
y_{og}	60	62	70	110	92	210	140	380
y_{od}	1650	200	1650	390	1700	720	1750	1350

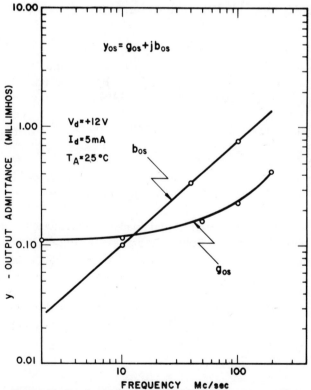

Figure 11–6. Common-source output conductance and susceptance as a function of frequency for a high-frequency MOS transistor.

2. High frequency circuit design

The transistor parameters described earlier will be utilized to discuss circuit design considerations and performance of the field-effect transistor at high frequencies. For illustration, an elementary circuit will be used first. Consider the operation of the transistor in the circuit of Fig. 11-7 at

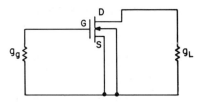

Figure 11-7. Elementary common-source amplifier circuit to illustrate the use of admittance parameters.

60 mc/s. From Figs. 11-3 through 11-6, the transistor y-parameters at this frequency are:

$$\left.\begin{array}{l} y_{is} = (0.08 + j2.0) \times 10^{-3} = 2 \times 10^{-3} \angle 87° \text{ ohm}^{-1} \\ y_{rs} = -j0.12 \times 10^{-3} = 0.12 \times 10^{-3} \angle -90° \text{ ohm}^{-1} \\ y_{fs} = (1.3 - j0.12) \times 10^{-3} = 1.3 \times 10^{-3} \angle -6° \text{ohm}^{-1} \\ y_{os} = (0.13 + j0.48) \times 10^{-3} = 0.49 \times 10^{-3} \angle 75° \text{ ohm}^{-1} \end{array}\right\} \quad \text{(11-5)}$$

The admittance matrix, Eq. (11-3), for this *circuit* is:

$$y = \begin{vmatrix} 0.08 + g_g + j2.0 & -j0.12 \\ 1.3 - j0.12 & 0.13 + g_L + j0.48 \end{vmatrix} 10^{-3} \text{ ohm}^{-1} \quad \text{(11-6)}$$

where g_g and g_L are the source and load conductances in millimhos, respectively. If $g_g = 2 \times 10^{-3}$ ohm^{-1} and $g_L = 10^{-5}$ ohm^{-1}, the admittance matrix becomes:

$$y = \begin{vmatrix} 2.08 + j2.0 & -j0.12 \\ 1.3 - j0.12 & 0.14 + j0.48 \end{vmatrix} 10^{-3} \text{ ohm}^{-1} \quad \text{(11-7)}$$

The forward voltage gain is:

$$-\frac{y_f}{y_o} = -0.496 + j2.56 = 2.6 \angle 101° \quad \text{(11-8)}$$

or a magnitude of 8.4 db. The reverse voltage gain is:

$$- \frac{y_r}{y_i} = 0.0288 + j0.03 = 0.0415 \angle 46°$$

(11-9)

or a magnitude of −28 db.

The ratio of the forward power gain to the reverse power gain of the transistor is a power-gain figure of merit of the transistor.[3] It is independent of the source and load admittances and is a characteristic of the transistor itself. For the field-effect transistor considered before, this ratio is:

$$\left| \frac{y_f}{y_r} \right|^2 = 118 \quad \text{or} \quad 21 \text{ db}$$

(11-10)

To check for short-circuit stability, a third row and column are added to the matrix of Eq. (11-7) to make the sum of the elements in each row and in each column equal to zero. This is the indefinite matrix[1] and, for the circuit example of Fig. 11-7, the indefinite matrix is:

$$y = \begin{vmatrix} 2.08+j2.0 & -j0.12 & -2.08-j1.88 \\ 1.3-j0.12 & 0.14+j0.48 & -1.44-j0.36 \\ -3.38-j1.88 & -0.14-j0.36 & 3.52+j2.24 \end{vmatrix} 10^{-3} \text{ohm}^{-1}$$ (11-11)

The elements on the main diagonal represent the driving-point admittances of the gate, drain, and source terminals, respectively, when the other two terminals are grounded. The conductances of the main diagonal, in this example, are all positive, hence, the circuit is short-circuit stable at this frequency. The appearance of a negative value would have indicated instability.

The indefinite matrix for a transistor is also a convenient method of obtaining the admittances for the different configurations of the transistor if the admittance matrix is known for one configuration. From the known matrix, the indefinite matrix for the transistor can be set up in the manner described earlier for the circuit example. Crossing out the row and column containing the driving-point admittance of the common electrode, we obtain the admittance matrix for that particular configuration. In our example, the lower right-hand end of the main diagonal is the source-terminal admittance. Therefore, crossing out the third row and column yields the common-source admittance matrix which was the starting point, Eq. (11-6).

A narrow-band transistor amplifier network will be neutralized if we connect it in parallel with a passive two-port network whose reverse transfer admittance is the negative of the reverse transfer admittance of the active two-port. This is essentially a method of making a nonunilateral active network unilateral. The resulting combination may be treated as a unilateral two-port network.

When a transistor amplifier is neutralized, the input and output admittances are independent of the source and load admittances. The input and output networks can therefore be designed independent of one another. The neutralizing, input, and output networks can be designed when the small-signal admittance parameters of the transistor are known. It can be shown that the amplifier gain will be a maximum if the source and load admittances are the conjugates of the transistor input and output admittances, respectively, after neutralization. The maximum power gain of the neutralized circuit under these conditions is given by:[3,5]

$$G_{max} = \frac{|y_f - y_r|^2}{4(g_i + g_r)(g_o + g_r)} \tag{11–12}$$

where the admittances and conductances are those of the transistor. For the transistor whose two-port admittances are given in Eq. (11–7) for a frequency of 60 mc/s, this becomes:

$$G_{max} = \frac{(1.3)^2}{4(0.08)(0.13)} = 41 \quad \text{or} \quad 16 \text{ db} \tag{11–13}$$

A 60 mc/s neutralized circuit utilizing field-effect transistors similar to that discussed earlier is shown in Fig. 11–8. Measured values of power

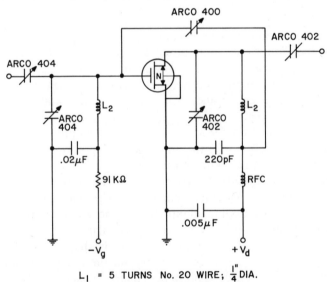

Figure 11–8. Amplifier circuit at 60 mc/s for an MOS transistor. $L_1 = 5$ turns No. 20 wire; 1/4 in. diameter $L_2 = 10$ turns No. 20 wire; 3/8 in. diameter.

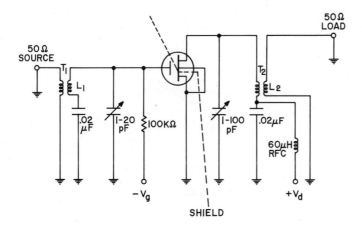

L$_1$ = 24μH COIL
T$_1$ = 5 TURNS WOUND ON 24μH COIL
L$_2$ = 10μH COIL
T$_2$ = 3 TURNS WOUND ON 10μH COIL

UNITS WERE MEASURED WITH V$_d$ = +15V
AND V$_g$ = 0 V

Figure 11-9. Field-effect transistor-amplifier circuit for 10 mc/s. $L_1 = 24$ μh coil; $T_1 = 5$ turns wound on 24 μh coil; $L_2 = 10$ μh coil; $T_2 = 3$ turns wound on 10 μh coil; $V_d = 15$ v; $V_g = 0$ v.

gain in this circuit are 12–14 db with a noise figure of 6 db. The circuit bandwidth was 2 mc/s and the generator impedance was 50 ohms.

The performance at 10 mc/s was evaluated in the circuit of Fig. 11–9. Measured values of power gain and noise figure were 18–20 db and 4.5 db, respectively. The generator impedance was 50 ohms and the circuit bandwidth was 1 mc/s.

A transistor designed for operation at higher frequencies and which will be discussed next yields a power gain of 22 to 24 db and a noise figure of 3.5 db in the circuit of Fig. 11–8.

11-4 THE FIELD-EFFECT TRANSISTOR AT UHF

1. Transistor parameters

The two-port common-source admittances of an experimental insulated-gate field-effect transistor designed to operate into the ultra-high-frequency range are shown in Figs. 11–10 through 11–13. At low frequencies, the behavior is similar to that described for the high-frequency

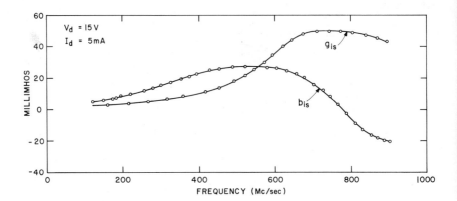

Figure 11-10. Common-source input conductance and susceptance of a uhf field-effect transistor as a function of frequency.

transistor; but above 400 mc/s, deviations from the simple low-frequency theory are evident in the input and forward transfer admittances, and at even lower frequencies in the case of the reverse transfer admittance. Some of this can be accounted for by small but significant inductances in the transistor assembly and measurement equipment. Nevertheless, the experimental data indicate that further refinement of the equivalent circuit is necessary at these frequencies. The output admittance is well-behaved over the measurement range.

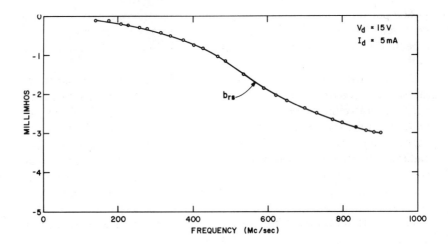

Figure 11-11. Common-source reverse transfer susceptance of a uhf field-effect transistor as a function of frequency.

The common-source admittance parameters at 400 mc/s for this transistor are:

$$y_{is} = (11 + j24) \times 10^{-3} = 26.4 \times 10^{-3} \angle 65° \text{ ohm}^{-1}$$
$$y_{rs} = -j0.7 \times 10^{-3} = 0.7 \times 10^{-3} \angle -90° \text{ohm}^{-1}$$
$$y_{fs} = (16 - j9) \times 10^{-3} = 18.3 \times 10^{-3} \angle -29° \text{ohm}^{-1}$$
$$y_{os} = (0.6 + j2.75) \times 10^{-3} = 2.8 \angle 78° \text{ ohm}^{-1}$$

$$(11\text{-}14)$$

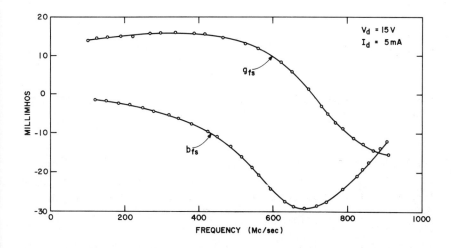

Figure 11-12. Common-source forward transfer conductance and susceptance of a uhf field-effect transistor as a function of frequency.

2. UHF circuit design

The condition that the real part of the driving-point admittances be greater than zero is a necessary but not sufficient condition to assure unconditional stability. Other considerations involving feedback may be operative to permit unlimited gain under some conditions. These effects generally become increasingly important at higher frequencies. The conditions for unconditional stability will be examined in greater detail and applied to the uhf field-effect transistor whose two-port admittances were described earlier. The stability relations have been expressed in many forms. The relations given by Linvill[6] will be used here.

The criterion for unconditional stability may be expressed in the form:

$$2g_i g_o - \mathscr{R}(y_r y_f) = \frac{1}{C} |y_r y_f|$$

$$(11\text{-}15)$$

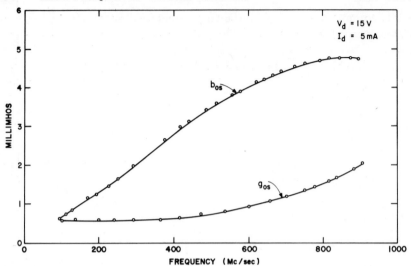

Figure 11–13. Common-source output conductance and susceptance of a uhf field-effect transistor as a function of frequency.

where C is the stability factor. If C is less than unity, the network is unconditionally stable. If C is greater than unity, the network is not necessarily unstable but may be stable under certain adjustments of source and load admittances.

When the output admittance of an active device is conjugately matched by the load admittance, the power gain is given by:

$$\frac{P_{oo}}{P_{io}} = \frac{|y_f|^2}{4g_i g_o - 2\mathscr{R}(y_r y_f)} \tag{11-16}$$

This differs from the maximum *available* gain by less than 3 db if the transistor is not potentially unstable. From Eqs. (11–15) and (11–16), C may be written as:

$$C = 2\frac{P_{oo}}{P_{io}}\frac{|y_r|}{|y_f|} \tag{11-17}$$

The maximum *available* gain, G_A, is related to P_{oo}/P_{io} by:

$$G_A = K_G\frac{P_{oo}}{P_{io}} \tag{11-18}$$

where K_G is defined as:

$$K_G = \frac{2(1 - \sqrt{1 - C^2})}{C^2} \tag{11-19}$$

If the stability factor, C, is less than unity, the expression is real, and the maximum available gain is finite. If C is greater than unity the maximum gain becomes infinite.

The optimum source admittance, y_S, and load admittance, y_L, for the maximum gain condition are given by Eqs. (11–20) and (11–21), respectively:

$$y_S = \left[y_i - \frac{y_r y_f}{2g_o} \left(1 - \frac{CK_g \exp j\theta}{2} \right) \right]^* \qquad \text{(11–20)}$$

where θ is the argument of $(-y_r y_f)^*$; and:

$$y_L = -y_o + \frac{2g_o}{1 - (CK_g \exp j\theta/2)} \qquad \text{(11–21)}$$

Utilizing these relations, we will design the circuit for a 400 mc/s amplifier using the uhf field-effect transistor.

From the power gain, Eq. (11–16), and the admittances of the transistor, Eq. (11–14):

$$\frac{P_{oo}}{P_{io}} = \frac{(18.3)^2}{4(11)(0.6) + 2(6.3)} = 8.7 \text{ or } 9.5 \text{db} \qquad \text{(11–22)}$$

The stability factor from Eq. (11–17) is:

$$C = 2(8.7)\frac{(0.7)}{18.3} = 0.66 \qquad \text{(11–23)}$$

Since C is less than unity, this transistor is unconditionally stable at this frequency. The maximum available gain from Eq. (11–18) is:

$$G_A = \frac{2(1 - \sqrt{1 - (0.66)^2})}{(0.66)^2}(8.7) = 10 \text{ or } 10 \text{ db} \qquad \text{(11–24)}$$

Calculating for the source and load admittances using Eqs. (11–20) and (11–21) gives:

$$y_S = (12.36 - j33.3) \times 10^{-3} \text{ ohm}^{-1} \qquad \text{(11–25)}$$

$$y_L = (0.67 - j3.2) \times 10^{-3} \text{ ohm}^{-1} \qquad \text{(11–26)}$$

At uhf, the input and output resonant circuits often take the form of modified quarter-wave coaxial resonators. The open end of the coaxial element is loaded by the transistor capacitance, and an additional variable capacitance may be added for tuning. In cylindrical or coaxial form, the outer diameter should be 3.6 times larger than the inner diameter to obtain minimum attentuation and high Q. The characteristic impedance, Z_o, of such a line is:

$$Z_o = 60 \ln \frac{d_o}{d_i} = 77 \text{ ohms} \tag{11-27}$$

An inductive reactance, X_L, is obtained by the use of a line length shorter than a quarter wavelength; the reactance is related to the length, l, by:

$$X_L = Z_o \tan \frac{2\pi l}{\lambda} \tag{11-28}$$

where λ is the wavelength.

For practical reasons, resonators are often constructed in the form of strip lines rather than coaxial lines, and such a construction will be described. The characteristic impedance of strip lines is shown in Fig. 11–14 for various dimensional relationships.

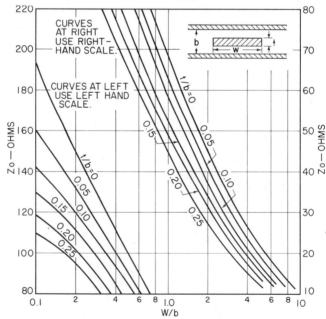

Figure 11–14. Characteristic impedance of strip transmission lines as a function of dimension ratios.

For the input resonator design, a strip thickness, t, of 0.05 in. is chosen as a practical thickness for a silver-plated brass strip. A cavity width, b, of 1 in. and a strip width, w, of 0.1 in. are selected. The characteristic impedance of a strip line of these dimensions, from Fig. 11–14, is 160 ohms. From Eq. (11–25), an inductive reactance of 30 ohms at 400 mc/s ($\lambda = 75$ cm) is required. The length of line from Eq. (11–28) is:

$$l = \frac{75}{2\pi} \arctan \frac{30}{160} = 2.3 \text{ cm} \approx 1 \text{ in.} \tag{11–29}$$

The output requires an inductive reactance of 310 ohms from Eq. (11–26). For a strip line having characteristic impedance of 160 ohms, this requires a length:

$$l = \frac{75}{2\pi} \arctan \frac{310}{160} = 12.5 \text{ cm} \approx 5 \text{ in.} \tag{11–30}$$

The construction of the 400-mc/s amplifier circuit according to these design guides is shown in Fig. 11–15. The circuit is shown schematically in Fig. 11–16. Measured amplifier power gains at 400 mc/s for the insulated-gate field-effect transistors designed for uhf operation range from 8.5–10 db. The transistor power gain is greater than this by 1.25 db due to insertion and output circuit losses of 0.5 and 0.75 db, respectively. The measured noise figures are 4 to 5 db.

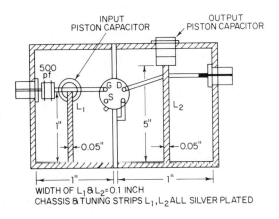

Figure 11–15.   Construction of 400 mc/s amplifier using strip lines.

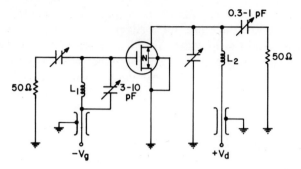

Figure 11–16. Schematic circuit diagram of 400-cm/s amplifier.

At uhf, lumped-constant circuits of conventional design are inefficient. Tuned circuits are still necessary, and the following three fundamental conditions are still required:

1. The interstage network should provide a good match for the terminal impedance of the transistor.

2. The interstage networks should have low losses.

3. The circuit configuration should provide adequate stability through mismatch or neutralization if it is otherwise unstable.

Although lumped-constant circuits can probably be used up to 600 mc/s, tank circuits designed with bar and strip stock in conjunction with

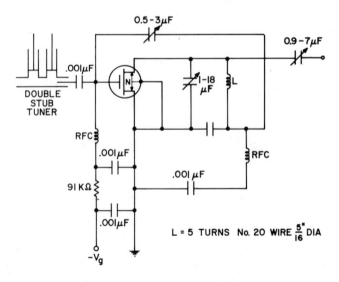

Figure 11–17. Test circuit for 200-mc/s operation of uhf field-effect transistor. $L = 5$ turns No. 20 wire $\frac{5}{16}$ in. diameter.

uhf capacitors provide circuit repeatability, low losses, and high unloaded Q's.

The uhf transistor tested at 200 mc/s in the circuit shown in Fig. 11–17 produced measured power gains of 16–18 db and a noise figure of 3.5 db. The circuit bandwidth was 6 mc/s, and the generator impedance was 50 ohms.

11–5   CROSS-MODULATION AND MODULATION DISTORTION IN FIELD-EFFECT TRANSISTORS

Cross-modulation is the transfer of modulation from an undesired radio-frequency signal, sometimes referred to as the undesired carrier, to a desired radio-frequency signal or carrier. This results in the undesired station or channel being heard on the desired station to which a radio receiver is tuned. Modulation distortion is the production of harmonics of the modulation of the desired carrier.

Both cross-modulation and modulation distortion are caused by the odd terms of the series expansion for the output current in terms of the input voltage. Thus, cross-modulation and modulation distortion can be described by the nonlinearities of the forward transadmittance of the device. They can also be related by the equation:[8]

$$\frac{V_2^2}{V_1^2} \times \frac{D_2}{K} = \frac{3}{8}m \qquad (11\text{--}31)$$

where: D_2 = modulation distortion of desired signal;
        K = cross-modulation factor;
        V_1 = voltage amplitude of desired carrier at input;
        V_2 = voltage amplitude of undesired carrier at input; and
        m = modulation of desired carrier.

At maximum gain, the cross-modulation and modulation distortion of the field-effect transistor is superior to conventional transistor and tube performance. With reverse-bias AGC, the g_m characteristic is sharp and the cross-modulation is comparable to that of sharp cutoff tubes. With forward-bias AGC, the g_m characteristic is remote and the cross-modulation and modulation distortion are comparable to that of tubes; but loading of the output tuned circuit is necessary to obtain a 45–50 db AGC range.

Cross-modulation is measured as shown in Fig. 11–18. The input of the transistor amplifier under test is broadband with a 50-ohm source. A tuned circuit with typical loading for a practical amplifier is used in the output. The undesired signal frequency is chosen to be far enough away

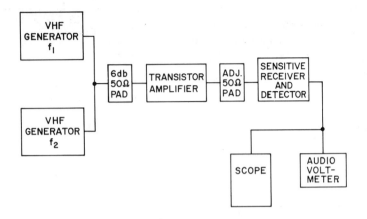

Figure 11–18. Circuit arrangement for the measurement of cross-modulation

from the desired signal frequency so that system selectivity prevents cross-modulation in the sensitive receiver following the transistor amplifier.

When comparing devices for cross-modulation, it is desirable to compare the devices in comparable systems. Unfortunately, the interfering signal voltage measured for a device is only part of the information required to compare system behavior. The other information needed is the input resistance of the device and the source that will be driving it. An approach to a system comparison can be made by converting to power. Thus:

$$\text{interfering signal power} = \frac{V_{is}^2}{R} \qquad \text{(11–32)}$$

where V_{is} is the voltage (at the input of the device) that causes 1% cross-modulation; and where:

$$R = \frac{R_s R_{in}}{R_s + R_{in}}$$

R_s is the source resistance and R_{in} is the input resistance of the device.

As the input resistance for both the transistor and tube increases with increased gain control, at some gain-control point, R approaches R_s.

The 1% cross-modulation vs. gain control is shown in Fig. 11–19 for a vacuum tube (6CW4), a silicon planar transistor, and a uhf field-effect transistor at 216 mc/s. The better performance of the insulated-gate field-effect transistor is evident.

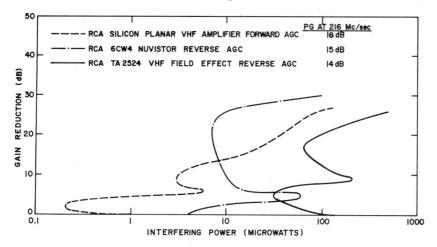

Figure 11–19. Comparison of the cross-modulation performance of an insulated-gate transistor, a bipolar transistor, and a vacuum tube.

REFERENCES

1. J. Shekel, *Proc. IRE* **40**, 1493 (1952).

2. D. M. Griswold, unpublished work.

3. R. F. Shea, *Transistor Applications,* (New York: John Wiley & Sons, Inc., 1964).

4. A. P. Stern, C. A. Aldridge, and W. F. Chow, *Proc. IRE* **43**, 838 (1955).

5. W. Gartner, *Transistors; Principles, Design, and Applications,* (Princeton, N.J.: D. Van Nostrand Co., 1960).

6. J. G. Linvill and L. G. Schimpf, *Bell Syst. Tech. J.* **35,** 813 (1956).

7. J. G. Linvill and J. F. Gibbons, *Transistors and Active Circuits,* (New York: McGraw-Hill Book Company, 1961).

8. B. G. Dammers, *Application of Electronic Valves in Radio Receivers and Amplifiers,* (Eindhoven, Netherlands: N. V. Philips Gloeilampenfabriken), 1960, **IV**, 308–335.

12

Applications of Field-Effect Transistors in Digital Circuits

A. Karl Rapp

12-1 THE FIELD-EFFECT TRANSISTOR AS A SWITCH

Electronic switches can only approximate the binary behavior of mechanical switches. While a mechanical switch is either open or closed, independent of the configuration of the circuit it controls, an electronic switch has a range of intermediate resistance values between its "open" and "closed" states. An electronic switch is, in fact, an active device, an amplifier, with significant gain nonlinearities in some region of its operating characteristics. It is the nature of these nonlinearities, in conjunction with the parameters of the controlled circuit, which determines performance.

A convenient tool for displaying the nonlinear gain of an electronic switch is the transfer-function curve. Because a field-effect-transistor switch, like a vacuum-tube switch, is voltage controlled, its behavior is best described by a plot of output voltage versus input voltage. Figure 12-1 illustrates a basic switch circuit and a typical voltage-transfer curve. The low-frequency, dynamic gain of the circuit for any selected input voltage is equal to the slope of the transfer curve at that voltage. At higher frequencies, the effective load impedance decreases, thereby decreasing the voltage gain. The two low-gain portions of the curve correspond to the binary states of the switch. Changes in input voltage over these portions produce relatively little change in output voltage.

312

The more closely the actual transfer curve approximates the ideal dashed curve in Fig. 12–1b, the more insensitive is the output voltage to spurious

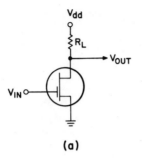

(a)

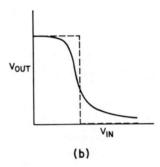

(b)

Figure 12–1. Basic field-effect transistor switch. (a) Circuit diagram. (b) Typical voltage-transfer curve. Dashed line portrays ideal curve.

(noise) voltages or to parameter variations. Circuit stability is more fully discussed in Section 12–3, in which methods are developed for designing digital circuits.

The transient behavior of a field-effect transistor switch depends both on the nonlinearity of the transistor conduction characteristic and on the values of the circuit elements. Circuit capacitance plays a particularly important role. The analysis in Section 12–4 indicates that the time required for switching increases with increasing circuit capacitance. Switching time is approximately inversely proportional to the voltage level and to the transistor parameter, β. For complementary-transistor switches (described later), these approximations become almost exact.

The transistor parameter, β, is one of the several parameters of field-effect transistors which are important for both the design and analysis of digital circuits. The basic current-voltage relation of the insulated-gate field-effect transistor given in Eq. (5–2) may be written:

$$I_d = \beta \left\{ (V_g - V_p)V_d - \frac{V_d^2}{2} \right\} \tag{12-1}$$

to define a transistor parameter, β, as:

$$\beta \equiv \frac{\epsilon_i \mu w}{d_i l} \tag{12-2}$$

where the pinch-off voltage, V_p, and the channel width, w, have been inserted in Eq. (5–2). As V_d approaches zero, it is seen that $\beta(V_g - V_p)$ represents the conductance of the channel as controlled by the field-effect mechanism. (See Chapter 2.) Relating β to the device physics, we see that it is the ratio of the field-effect conductance of the channel to the field-effect voltage (in the absence of drain voltage effects). It will be referred to as the field-effect conductance-to-voltage ratio. β is particularly useful for describing transistor behavior in large-signal circuits.

β used in this chapter is based on the *integrated channel conductance* of the transistor. In Chapter 6, β_s was based on the *surface or sheet conductivity* (the conductance of a unit square) of the channel. In both cases the dimensions are mhos/volt.

Other transistor parameters are shown in Fig. 12–2 which reviews the mathematical model derived in Chapter 5. The illustrated characteristics and equations portray an n-channel enhancement transistor. This chapter will assume n-type transistors unless otherwise indicated. Referring to Fig. 12–2, the drain leakage current, I_{du}, cannot be controlled by the gate voltage; it is produced by leakage paths in parallel with the channel. Its magnitude is typically in the nanoampere range. True channel current begins only as the gate voltage is increased beyond the channel pinch-off voltage, V_p. For a fixed gate voltage, V_g, the drain current, I_d, increases along an inverted parabola with drain voltage, V_d, until $V_d = V_g - V_p$. Beyond that voltage, the drain current saturates. The slope, G_o, at the origin of a constant-gate-voltage characteristic is a convenient approximation to the conductance of the transistor at small drain voltages. The validity of the mathematical model may be judged from Fig. 12–3, which presents a family of theoretical drain characteristics superimposed on a photograph of actual characteristics.

The electrical characteristics illustrated in Figs. 12–2 and 12–3 are those of enhancement transistors which are more useful in digital circuits than are the depletion type. Enhancement transistors permit the direct coupling of circuit stages without the necessity for voltage-level-shifting networks. Because of their superior properties for digital applications, enhancement transistors are discussed in this chapter. Except for special applications, such as nonlinear load resistors, depletion transistors will not be considered. Junction-gate field-effect transistors are inherently depletion devices and will not be discussed. Descriptions of digital applications will be limited to insulated-gate devices.

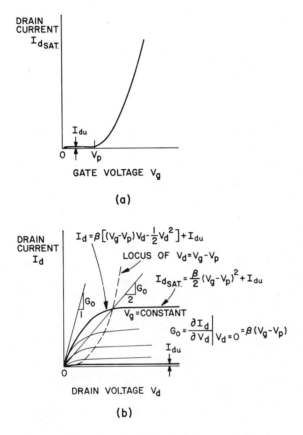

Figure 12–2. Theoretical electrical characteristics of an *n*-channel enhancement transistor. (a) Drain current vs. gate voltage for $V_d \geq V_g - V_p$. (b) Drain current vs. drain voltage for constant values of gate voltage.

Improved switch performance can be obtained with the use of nonlinear load resistors whose resistance increases with increasing current. Depletion transistors offer a convenient means for attaining this desired nonlinear characteristic. By connecting together the gate and source of a depletion transistor, we obtain the conduction characteristic of Fig. 12–4a. When this device is used as a load element, the load line shown in Fig. 12–4b results. One advantage of such a nonlinear load element

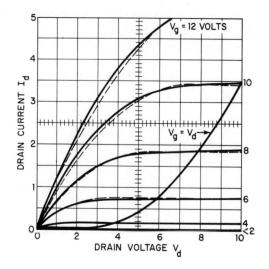

Figure 12–3. Theoretical drain characteristics superimposed on a photograph of the actual characteristics. $V_p = 2.4$v; $\beta = 1.2 \times 10^{-4}$ mhos/v.

over a resistor (dashed load line) is more equal "turn-on" and "turn-off" times of the switch. Other advantages are an improved voltage-transfer characteristic and greater circuit stability produced by the nonlinear load line. The voltage-transfer characteristic for the depletion-transistor load line of Fig. 12–4b is plotted in Fig. 12–5.

The load-current level, I_L, in Fig. 12–4 is fixed by the load-transistor properties and normally is not controllable. If, however, the load element is a transistor of the opposite conduction type, its gate-to-source voltage can independently be controlled, as indicated in Fig. 12–6a.

If transistors of both polarity types are available, a much more powerful configuration, the complementary-symmetry circuit, becomes possible.[1] This configuration, which, for brevity, is called the complementary circuit, is illustrated in Fig. 12–6b. It utilizes the input voltage, V_g, not only to control the lower transistor, Q_1, but also to control the upper transistor, Q_2. Both transistors in the complementary circuit are enhancement type. When V_g has a large positive value, say V_{dd}, n-channel transistor Q_1 is biased to a high-conductance state; p-channel transistor Q_2 then has zero gate-to-source bias and is cut off. For $V_g = V_{dd}$, the output voltage V_d is equal to zero (neglecting leakage current through Q_2). On the other hand, if V_g is brought to zero, Q_1 becomes cut off; p-channel transistor Q_2 has a large negative gate-to-source voltage and a high conductance. The output voltage for this condition is equal to supply voltage V_{dd} (again neglecting leakage current in the cut-off transistor). While

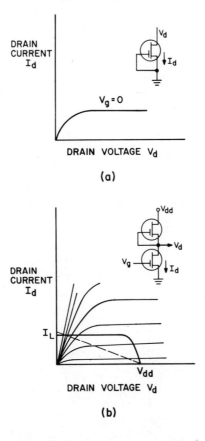

Figure 12–4. (a) Drain characteristic of a depletion transistor with zero gate-source voltage. (b) Depletion-transistor load-line on drain characteristics of an enhancement transistor.

most electronic switches function approximately as single-pole, single-throw switches (Fig. 12–7a), the complementary circuit provides single-pole, double-throw switching action (Fig. 12–7b). The effective load line resulting from the simultaneous changes in conductance which occur as V_g takes on intermediate values is shown in Fig. 12–8. A remarkable property of the complementary switch can now be seen. In either its "on" or "off" state, indicated in the figure as A and B, respectively, the switch conducts only leakage currents and dissipates very little power. This small static power dissipation does not change if the switch is used to control other insulated-gate stages, because they draw no average gate current. During switching transients, however, larger currents flow to charge and discharge circuit capacitance, thus producing dissipation. At high switching rates, the average dissipation can become appreciable. Power dissipation is discussed in Section 12–5.

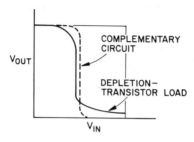

Figure 12–5. Typical voltage-transfer curves for a depletion-transistor load and the complementary circuit.

Other advantages of the complementary circuit result from its symmetry, i.e., the dual role of control unit and load element played by each transistor. Because of this symmetry, almost equal "turn-on" and

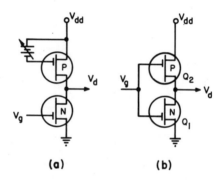

Figure 12–6. (a) Load consisting of a complementary-polarity transistor with an adjustable but constant bias. (b) Complementary-symmetry circuit.

"turn-off" switching times are obtained. For complementary transistors with similar characteristics of opposite polarity, exactly equal times result. Because of symmetry, the circuit stability of the complementary-transistor switch can greatly exceed that of the linear and depletion-transistor-loaded switches, as the symmetrical (dashed) transfer characteristic in Fig. 12–5 indicates. Less ideal characteristics for the complementary circuit result when unmatched p- and n-type units are used, or when parallel and series transistor connections are employed in logic circuits. This subject is discussed in Section 12–3.

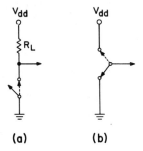

(a)   (b)

Figure 12–7. Mechanical-switch analogs of electronic switches. (a) Passive load element (single-pole, single-throw switch). (b) Active load element, complementary circuit (single-pole, double-throw switch).

12–2 LOGIC CIRCUITS USING FIELD-EFFECT TRANSISTORS

In several ways, field-effect transistors lack some of the advantages of bipolar transistors for logic circuits *when passive load elements are used.* The saturation voltage, i.e., the voltage drop across a transistor biased

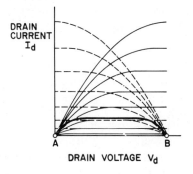

Figure 12–8. Effective load line for complementary circuit: the locus of the intersections of the drain characteristics of the n- and p-channel transistors, as gate voltage is varied. Points A and B correspond to $V_g = V_{dd}$ and $V_g = 0$, respectively.

into conduction, typically is an order of magnitude smaller for bipolar transistor circuits. Thus, the ratio of "off"-to-"on" output voltage may be five times greater for the bipolar transistor despite a smaller supply voltage. Also, the maximum switching speed of bipolar transistor circuits is about an order of magnitude greater than that of unipolar transistor circuits. However, field-effect transistors (and in particular, the insulated-gate transistor) contribute to logic circuits (1) general simplicity, and (2) the complementary circuit with all its concomitant advantages.

Simplicity results from the capability of field-effect transistor switches to be direct coupled. Such circuits, unlike direct-coupled bipolar transistor circuits, produce large voltage swings and are capable of almost infinite fan-out; i.e., one stage can drive an indefinite number of stages in parallel. The uneven distribution of driving current to paralleled bipolar transistor stages, has no counterpart in the voltage-controlled field-effect transistor circuit. The extremely high gate-input resistance of the driven stages presents essentially no static load to the driving stage. Although d-c conditions impose essentially no limitation on fan-out in field-effect transistor switches, transient requirements do restrict fan-out. Because the switching time of a stage is essentially proportional to the capacitance it must drive (see Section 12–4), fan-out and switching time can be interchanged. The simplicity of direct-coupled field-effect transistor logic circuits makes them particularly attractive for integrated structures (Section 12–6).

Complementary field-effect transistor circuits add other significant merits to the simplicity of direct coupling. These include the high circuit stability and low power dissipation already described in Section 12–1. In addition, the extremely low saturation voltage of complementary circuits (typically less than one millivolt)† gives rise to very large ratios of "off"-to-"on" output voltage.

1. Logic circuits with passive load elements

The simple field-effect transistor switch forms the most fundamental logic circuit, the inverter. The logical complement of the voltage at the input terminal of the switch appears at the output terminal. As with most digital devices, the inverter serves as the basis for the composite circuit structures which provide the basic operations of data storage and of performing logical AND and OR.

Two cross-coupled inverter stages become a bistable circuit or flip-flop (Fig. 12–9a). The connection of several transistors in parallel, as in Fig. 12–9b, produces a logical gate circuit whose output voltage is low if

---

†The quotient of the drain leakage current of the "off" transistor, typically a fraction of a microampere, and the conductance of the "on" transistor, typically 10^{-3} mhos.

the voltage at one or more input terminals is high. Series-connected transistors as in Fig. 12-9c, on the other hand, produce a gate circuit whose output voltage is low only if all input voltages are high.

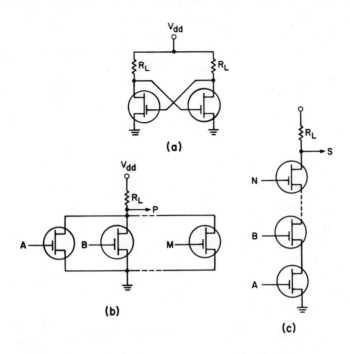

Figure 12-9. Basic logic circuits. (a) Flip-flop. (b) Parallel gate. (c) Series gate.

If logical ONE is defined to correspond to the high voltage level and logical ZERO to the low voltage level, then the circuit of Fig. 12-9b forms a NOR (NOT–OR) gate. The presence of a ONE signal at A, B, or any input terminal results in an inverted ONE (i.e., ZERO) at the output terminal P. The corresponding Boolean algebra equation is:

$$\bar{P} = A + B + C + \cdots + M \qquad (12\text{-}3)$$

where the bar superscript is used to denote logical inversion. Similarly, the circuit of Fig. 12-9c constitutes a NAND (NOT-AND) gate. ONE signals must be present at all input terminals to produce a NOT–ONE (i.e., ZERO) at the output S. The Boolean equation under these conditions is:

$$\bar{S} = A \cdot B \cdot C \cdots N \qquad (12\text{-}4)$$

Alternatively, logical ONE could be defined to correspond to the low voltage level and ZERO to the high level. The roles of the parallel and series-gate circuits are then interchanged, i.e., Fig. 12–9b represents a NAND gate, and Fig. 12–9c a NOR gate. This alternative logical system can have particular utility for complementary-transistor gates under some circumstances, as Section 12–3 indicates.

These basic circuit configurations can be combined to form more complex logic structures such as the shift-register stage of Fig. 12–10.

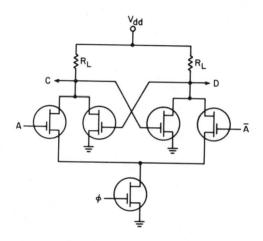

Figure 12–10. Shift-register stage, A and $\bar{A}$ are data inputs. C and D are data outputs. ϕ is the clock pulse.

In this circuit, data inputs A and $\bar{A}$ from the preceding stage affect the state of the illustrated stage only during the presence of clock pulse, ϕ. For logical ONE defined as the high voltage level, the Boolean equations for the circuit of Fig. 12–10 are:

$$\bar{C} = D + A\phi$$

$$\bar{D} = C + \bar{A}\phi$$

(12–5)

2. Complementary-transistor logic circuits

The use of complementary-transistor load elements does not alter the basic form of the inverter or flip-flop circuits. In forming logic gates of complementary transistors, care must be taken that the output voltage always is unambiguously determined. If several n-channel transistors are connected in parallel, in general it is necessary that an equal number of p-channel transistors be connected in series, with the gates of the two types of units connected together in pairs. Thus, in Fig. 12–11a, if any input signal (say *A*) is high, then the output is forced to be low. (Transistor Q_{nA} is turned "on" and transistor Q_{pA} is turned "off".) This circuit

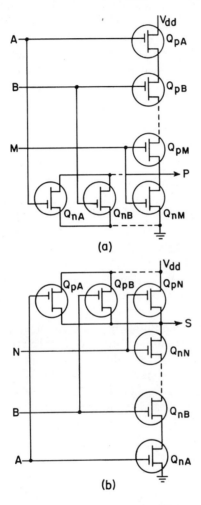

(a)

(b)

Figure 12–11. Composite complementary circuits. Under all static conditions, either the series portion or the parallel portion, but not both, are turned on.

configuration precludes the possibility of situations where the *p*- and *n*-portions of the circuit both are either "on" or "off". The output voltage in the latter situation would be dictated by the relative gains or relative leakage currents of the two transistor types and would lose all logical significance.

Figure 12–11a is analogous to the parallel-transistor circuit in Fig. 12–9b. Similarly, the series transistor circuit of Fig. 12–9c leads to the analogous complementary circuit in Fig. 12–11b. Neither of the dual complementary circuits is uniquely a parallel or series circuit; however, the first definition of logic levels will be assumed for the remainder of the chapter, except where the alternative definition is explicitly introduced. The circuits in Figs. 12–9b and 12–11a will be called NOR gates; those in Figs. 12–9c and 12–11b will be called NAND gates.

12–3 DIGITAL CIRCUIT DESIGN

1. General considerations

The simplicity of direct-coupled field-effect transistor circuits, although generally advantageous, imposes some restriction on design flexibility. At most, two circuit parameters are available: supply voltage, V_{dd}, and load resistance, R_L (or load characteristic if a nonlinear load element is used). For the complementary circuit, these reduce to supply voltage alone. Fortunately, one of the device parameters, the pinch-off voltage, lends itself to design for specific circuit performance. Other device parameters such as β, I_{du}, breakdown voltages, and terminal capacitances enter into design equations only as independent, performance limiting variables.

The design of circuits employing field-effect transistors or any other device invariably entails compromise. In digital circuits, the performance specifications involve circuit stability, noise immunity, speed, and power consumption. In this section, d-c criteria imposed by stability and noise-immunity requirements are examined. The following sections deal with factors that affect circuit speed and power dissipation.

2. The voltage-transfer curve

A rapid indication of circuit stability and noise immunity can be obtained from a voltage-transfer curve as in Fig. 12–1b. By super-imposing the transfer curve of an inverter and its image reflected about the line $V_{\text{out}} = V_{\text{in}}$, one can evaluate the effect of cascading inverter stages. This construction for the curve of Fig. 12–1b is shown in Fig. 12–12.

The transfer curve and its image intersect at three points. Points A and B are the two stable voltage states that inverters assume in a long chain of cascaded stages. Point C corresponds to unity static gain. A voltage, V_g^0, applied to the gate of the first stage theoretically forces each drain and gate to assume this same voltage. Dynamic gain, indicated by the slope of the transfer curve, usually is highest in the vicinity of point C. For a voltage other than V_g^0 applied to the gate of the first stage, the nonlinear gain of the inverters forces alternate stages to take on voltages which progressively diverge.[2] After a few stages, the voltages at points A and B are reached and maintained thereafter. The transfer-curve pair reveals this behavior quite conveniently, since each curve corresponds to

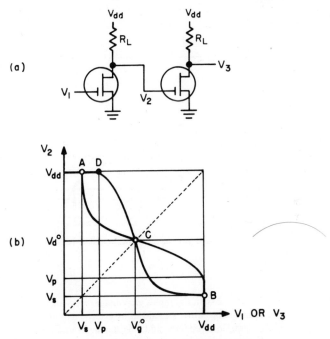

Figure 12–12. (a) Cascaded direct-coupled stages. (b) Corresponding pair of voltage-transfer curves, where the output of the first stage constitutes the input to the second stage.

one of the two sets of alternate stages of a cascade. In Fig. 12–13, for example, an input voltage $V_a < V_g^o$ follows the indicated succession of voltages in successive stages, finally reaching a value V_s (point A) at even-numbered drains and a value V_{dd} (point B) at odd-numbered drains. An input voltage $V_b > V_g^o$ follows the second progression indicated, ending in opposite voltage states. Since this behavior occurs for an applied voltage different from V_g^o by an arbitrarily small amount, it is evident that the voltage V_g^o can be propagated only in an ideal chain in which all components are perfectly matched and noise is completely absent.

The application of the transfer curve pair to flip flop stability follows directly from the preceding discussion. By connecting the second drain to the first gate in Fig. 12–12a, we obtain a flip-flop. Points A and B are points of stable equilibrium, and point C is a point of unstable equilibrium. A qualitative measure of the stability and recovery time of the flip-flop to disturbances which momentarily unbalance it may be obtained by considering the number of regenerative cycles required for recovery. The fewer voltage progressions of the type illustrated in Fig. 12–13 required, the more stable is the circuit.

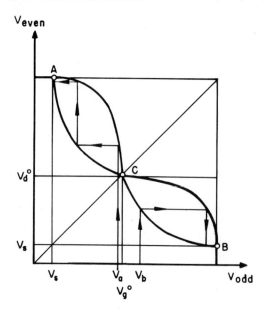

Figure 12–13. Examples of voltage progressions propagating down a chain of inverter stages. Two progressions are indicated, one starting from $V_{odd} = V_a$ and one starting from $V_{odd} = V_b$.

Noise voltages which disturb the state point of the flip-flop and drive it beyond V_g^o cause the circuit to change state. For maximum immunity to either polarity noise, the steep-slope transition region of the transfer curve at V_g^o should be centered between the input voltages which correspond to points A and B. The circuit becomes more stable and immune to noise as the transfer curve approaches the ideal dashed curve of Fig. 12–1b. The requirement that V_g^o be centered offers a convenient approach to the design of high-noise-immunity circuits.

CIRCUITS WITH LINEAR RESISTOR LOAD. The necessary conditions to assure equal immunity to noise voltages of both polarities are indicated in Fig. 12–14. The critical point C, where the output voltage, V_d^o, equals the input voltage, V_g^o, must always lie in the saturation region of the drain-current characteristics since $V_d > V_g - V_p$. From Fig. 12–2, the drain-current equation for this region is:

$$I_d = \frac{\beta}{2}(V_g - V_p)^2 + I_{du} \qquad (12\text{–}6)$$

The simultaneous solution of Eq. (12–6) with the equation for the load line and the introduction of the condition $V_d = V_g = V_g^o$ results in the following implicit equation for V_g^o.

$$\gamma(v_g^o - v_p)^2 = 2(1 - v_g^o) \tag{12-7}$$

where:

$$\gamma \equiv \beta R_L V_{dd}', \quad V_{dd}' \equiv V_{dd} - I_{du}R_L$$

$$v_g^o \equiv \frac{V_g^o}{V_{dd}'}, \quad v_p \equiv \frac{V_p}{V_{dd}}$$

The effect of the leakage current, I_{du}, has been absorbed in the definition of a modified supply voltage, V_{dd}'. The use of lower-case letters to designate voltages which have been normalized to the supply voltage is used throughout this chapter.

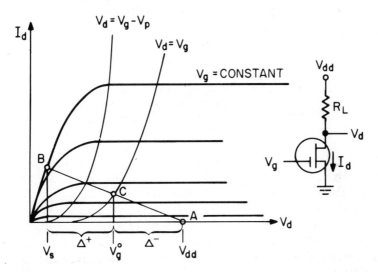

Figure 12-14. Condition for equal immunity to noise voltages of both polarities. V_g^o lies midway between V_s and V_{dd}; i.e., $\Delta^+ = \Delta^-$.

Centering of the transfer curve requires knowledge of the saturation voltage, V_s. For reliable circuit operation, this voltage is restricted to the region $V_d < V_g - V_p$. Hence, from Fig. 12-2, the pertinent drain current equation is:

$$I_d = \beta V_s\left(V_g - V_p - \frac{V_s}{2}\right) + I_{du} \tag{12-8}$$

where V_g must be set equal to V'_{dd}. Solving Eq. (12–8) simultaneously with the load-line equation, and introducing the balanced-noise-immunity requirement $\Delta^+ = \Delta^-$ (Fig. 12–14), we obtain a second implicit equation for V_g^o.

$$\gamma(1 - 2v_g^o)^2 + 2(\gamma - \gamma v_p + 1)(1 - 2v_g^o) + 2 = 0 \qquad (12\text{–}9)$$

The quantities defined in Eq. (12–7) also have been introduced into Eq. (12–9). The gate voltage, v_g^o, can be eliminated between Eqs. (12–7) and (12–9), leading to the useful design curve of Fig. 12–15a.

Acceptable values for the normalized pinch-off voltage, v_p, are indicated in Fig. 12–15a as lying in the range $0.227 < v_p < 0.500$. These limits are established by the general requirement $V_s < V_p$, i.e., a conducting inverter must be capable of holding off a following stage. The upper limit is set by the requirement that V_s be kept out of the current-saturation portion of the drain characteristics: $V_d < V_g - V_p$, or $V_s < V'_{dd} - V_p$. Introducing the limiting value for the saturation voltage $V_s = V_p$, $V_p < V'_{dd} - V_p$ or $v_p < \frac{1}{2}$. The lower limit is introduced by the balanced-noise-immunity restriction. This becomes clear if one plots v_g^o and v_s as a function of v_p (Fig. 12–15b). To meet the condition $v_s < v_p$, v_p must be greater than 0.227.

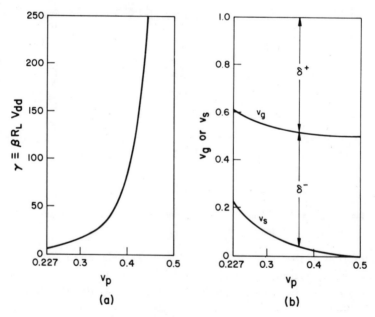

Figure 12–15. Design curves for resistor-loaded inverters with equal immunity to positive and negative noise voltage, δ. (a) γ vs. normalized pinch-off voltage v_p; (b) v_g^o and v_s vs. v_p.

Figure 12-15 constitutes a convenient set of design curves. Given the V_p of a transistor, one can select a value for the effective supply voltage, V'_{dd}; and thus determine v_p. From Fig. 12-15a, the proper value for $\gamma = \beta R_L V'_{dd}$ can be found. Knowledge of the field-effect conductance-to-voltage ratio, β, then enables calculation of the load resistance, R_L. We find the correct value for the actual supply voltage, V_{dd}, by augmenting V'_{dd} by $I_{du}R_L$. The normalized noise immunity $\delta = \delta^+ = \delta^-$ corresponding to the design can be read from Fig. 12-15b.

The normalized signal swing, i.e., the change in voltage as the inverter switches between its "on" and "off" states, is equal to 2δ. Figure 12-15b reveals that the supply voltage is more fully utilized with higher values of v_p. Higher values of v_p also produce transfer curves which more closely approach the ideal, as indicated by the several examples in Fig. 12-16. In general, for inverters with linear-resistor loads, stability and noise immunity improve with increasing v_p. The use of supply voltages not much greater than twice the transistor pinch-off voltage V_p is suggested.† Large values of v_p, however, lead to very large load-resistance values. It is shown in Section 12-4 that high load resistances produce long turn-off time constants. Fast switching speed dictates selection of the highest supply voltage that the transistor can withstand. Thus, compromise is required.

COMPLEMENTARY-TRANSISTOR CIRCUITS. Gibson[3] has pointed out the ease of sketching the transfer curve for complementary circuits. The salient points are illustrated in Fig. 12-17. The arcs which join the linear segments are sections of rotated parabolas, and the slope of the transfer curve is continuous where these sections meet.

The gate voltage, v_g^o, which produces an equal output voltage, v_d^o, can readily be found for the complementary circuit. Figure 12-17 reveals that the drain characteristics for the n- and p-channel transistors ‡ both lie in the current saturation region at $v_g = v_g^o$, i.e., $v_g^o + v_{pp} > v_d^o > v_g^o - v_{pn}$. As v_g moves through this range, these drain characteristics very rapidly cross each other, the one rising as the other falls. (See Fig. 12-8.) Thus the pertinent equations are:

$$I_d = \frac{\beta_n}{2}(V_g - V_{pn})^2 + I_{dun} = \frac{\beta_p}{2}(V_{dd} - V_g - V_{pp})^2 + I_{dup} \qquad \text{(12-10)}$$

†This choice for V_{dd} maximizes the *normalized* noise immunity. The circuit then is highly tolerant of noise generated *within* the digital system, where the maximum voltage is V_{dd}. If the circuit is to function in high *external* noise ambients, higher values for the supply voltage may be advisable.

‡The additional subscript p is used to denote a parameter of a p-channel transistor, and n denotes a parameter of an n-channel transistor. The pinch-off voltages, V_{pp} and V_{pn}, are assumed to be positive quantities.

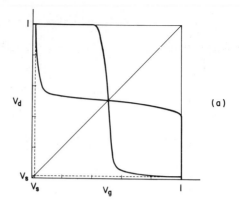

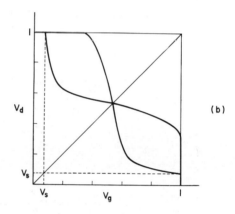

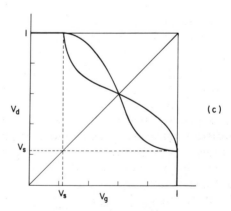

Figure 12–16. Effect of v_p on the shape of the voltage-transfer curves, when $\delta^+ = \delta^-$. (a) $v_p = 0.41, \gamma = 100$; (b) $v_p = 0.32, \gamma = 20$; (c) $v_p = 0.227, \gamma = 6$.

Neglecting leakage currents, we can solve Eq. (12–10) for the normalized gate voltage $v_g = v_g^o$:

$$v_g^o = \frac{v_{pn} + \beta_r^{1/2}(1 - v_{pp})}{1 + \beta_r^{1/2}} \qquad (12\text{–}11)$$

where $\beta_r \equiv \beta_p/\beta_n$. Equation (12–11) is valid if $v_{pn} \leqslant v_g^o$ and $v_{pp} \leqslant 1 - v_g^o$.

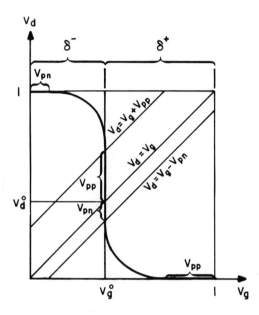

Figure 12–17. Sketch of voltage-transfer characteristic for a complementary circuit.

The design requirement for centering the transfer curve is easily found since the normalized signal swing of a complementary-transistor inverter always is equal to one (neglecting the effect of leakage currents). Setting $v_g^o = \frac{1}{2}$ in Eq. (12–11), we find that the pinch-off voltages of the n-type, and p-type transistors must satisfy the relationship plotted in Fig. 12–18. So long as this relationship is satisfied, the noise immunity $\delta^+ = \delta^- = \frac{1}{2}$.

If the p- and n-type transistors have equal pinch-off voltages $(V_{pn} = V_{pp} = V_p)$ and field-effect conductance-to-voltage ratios $(\beta_n = \beta_p)$, then the ideal transfer curve is achieved with $V_{dd} = 2V_p$, i.e., for $v_p = \frac{1}{2}$ (Fig. 12–19a). For normalized pinch-off voltages greater than $\frac{1}{2}$, ideally abrupt, but translated transfer curves result. These curves exhibit hysteresis as Fig. 12–19b illustrates. Throughout the gate voltage range $(1 - v_{pp}) < v_g < v_{pn}$, neither transistor conducts. The charged drain capacitance, however, maintains the drain voltage.

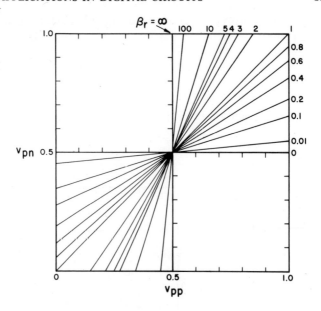

Figure 12-18. Necessary relationship between normalized pinch-off voltages v_{pp} and v_{pn} to ensure equal noise immunity ($\delta^+ = \delta^-$). The relative field-effect conductance-to-voltage ratio $\beta_r = \beta_p/\beta_n$ appears as a parameter.

3. Leakage currents and circuit design

Drain leakage currents typically lie in the nanoampere range and need not be considered a first-order design variable. Leakage currents can assume a more fundamental role in worst-case designs. Integrated circuit designs must often be made more tolerant to accommodate the inevitable variation in parameters. Leakage current also establishes the lower limit to permissible voltage-supply values in very-low-power circuits.

Leakage currents affect the design of many-element, mixed combinational gates, which are circuits formed of series-parallel combinations of transistors, such as each half of the shift-register stage in Fig. 12–10. Although independent load-resistor values can be selected for individual NOR and NAND gates to satisfy their individual stability requirements, a single value must be selected to simultaneously satisfy both the parallel and series portions of mixed gates. In analyzing mixed gates, it is convenient first to consider separately the restrictions imposed by these two portions, then to consider their composite effect.

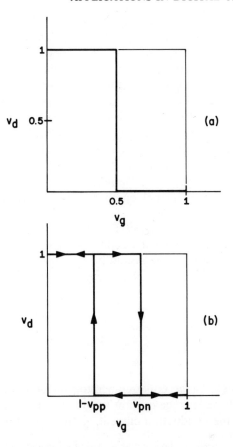

Figure 12–19. Special-case voltage-transfer curves. (a) $v_{pp} = v_{pn} = \frac{1}{2}$; (b) $v_{pp} > \frac{1}{2}$, $v_{pn} > \frac{1}{2}$.

4. Mixed gates with linear resistor load

NOR (PARALLEL) GATE CRITERION. For a fixed supply voltage, the maximum number of transistors which may be connected in parallel to form a NOR gate (Fig. 12–9b) is limited by the transistor leakage current. It is convenient to introduce a *circuit-design parameter, k,* which is the fraction of the supply voltage appearing at the output in the presence of leakage current. To ensure that the output voltage of the nonconducting gate will be at least equal to kV_{dd} when M parallel transistors each contribute a leakage current, I_{du}, the load resistance must satisfy the condition:

$$R_{Lp} \leq (1 - k)\frac{V_{dd}}{MI_{du}} \qquad (12\text{–}12)$$

Subscript p denotes a restriction imposed by the parallel circuit. The most difficult condition which a conducting parallel gate must meet occurs when only one transistor conducts. This condition may be considered a special case of the criterion for the following series-connected gate.

NAND (SERIES) GATE CRITERION. Appreciable current can flow in the series circuit, Fig. 12–9c, only if all gate potentials are made positive. The composite conduction characteristic of the series circuit when all gates are at the same potential can readily be derived. The series connection effectively produces a transistor with N times the channel length of an individual transistor, neglecting parasitic series resistance. Since the transistor field-effect conductance-to-voltage ratio, β, is inversely proportional to channel length, the effective ratio of the composite structure is β/N.†

When the N gate terminals of Fig. 12–9c are raised to the potential kV_{dd}, the output voltage must become sufficiently small to hold off a following stage. Inserting the condition which marginally meets this requirement, $V_s = V_p$, into the drain current equation, Eq. (12–8), we obtain, for $V_g = kV_{dd}$:‡

$$I_d = \frac{\beta}{N}V_p(kV_{dd} - \tfrac{3}{2}V_p), \quad kV_{dd} \geqslant 2V_p \tag{12–13}$$

The effective field-effect conductance-to-voltage ratio, β/N, has been introduced, and the leakage-current term has been considered negligible compared with the conduction current. Combining Eq. (12–13) with the

---

†The critical reader may prefer a mathematical proof. Applying the drain-current equation (Eq. 12–8) to each of *two* series transistors with equal external gate voltages, we can derive the equation for the combination and show that it has the same form as Eq. 12–8. However, the effective β of the combination is:

$$\beta_{\text{eff}} = \frac{\beta_1\beta_2}{\beta_1 + \beta_2}$$

where β_1 and β_2 are the individual field-effect conductance-to-voltage ratios. For $\beta_1 = \beta_2 = \beta$, the effective ratio becomes $\beta/2$. If three identical transistors are connected in series, two of them have a combined ratio of $\beta/2$. Thus, $\beta_1 = \beta/2$, $\beta_2 = \beta$, and the effective over-all ratio is $\beta_{\text{eff}} = \beta/3$. Generalizing, if $\beta_1 = \beta/(N - 1)$ and $\beta_2 = \beta$, the effective field-effect conductance-to-voltage ratio becomes β/N.

‡No solution for $V_d > V_g - V_p$ is considered since this condition corresponds to the current saturation region. Although it is possible to design a family of circuits with both stable points confined to this region, it is better to restrict the "on"-current point to smaller drain voltages. The "on"-current point, then, is much less sensitive to fluctuations in gate voltage. In addition, the total power dissipation and particularly the transistor power dissipation are kept smaller for a given value of V_{dd}. This restriction of the stable "on"-current point imposes the relationship $kV_{dd} \geqslant 2V_p$, as Eq. (12–13) indicates.

load-line relationship and introducing an inequality sign to indicate the stable region for R_L, we obtain:

$$R_{LS} \geq \frac{N(V_{dd} - V_p)}{\beta V_p(kV_{dd} - \frac{3}{2}V_p)}, \quad kV_{dd} \geq 2V_p \tag{12-14}$$

Subscript s denotes a restriction imposed by the series circuit.

COMPOSITE-GATE CRITERION. Equations (12–12) and (12–14) together define the range of values for R_L which will permit the indefinite cascading of composite gate circuits without progressive amplitude attenuation. The specific choice of R_L within that range may be dictated by other design criteria. Among these are circuit speed, power consumption, and stability margin. Lower resistance values provide higher circuit speed (Section 12–4). Higher values reduce power dissipation (Section 12–5). Intermediate values provide higher circuit stability.

A measure of circuit stability is the decrease in supply voltage which can be tolerated before circuit instability is reached. Figure 12–20 illustrates a typical decrease in the permissible range for R_L as the supply

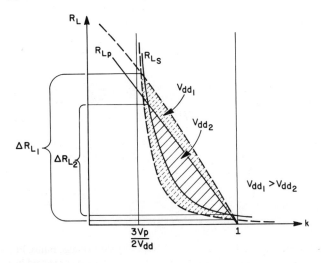

Figure 12–20. Decrease in the permissible range for R_L (crosshatched area) as the supply voltage is decreased. Solutions exist only for $k \geq 2(V_p/V_{dd})$.

voltage is decreased. The curves are sketches of Eqs. (12–12) and (12–14), where R_L is drawn as a function of the circuit-design parameter k, and all transistor parameters are held constant. As the supply voltage is decreased from V_{dd_1} to V_{dd_2}, the cross-hatched permissible-design area decreases, reducing the design range for R_L from ΔR_{L_1} to ΔR_{L_2}. The reduction in the R_L design range does not generally progress uniformly for high and low values of resistance. Hence, the optimum value of R_L for stability does not lie in the center of the design range.

DESIGN FOR MAXIMUM STABILITY. An optimum value for R_L can be found. It corresponds to the limiting resistance as the cross-hatched area in Fig. 12-20 shrinks to zero, i.e., as the two curves become tangent. Circuit stability is then maintained over the widest possible range of V_{dd}. To find the optimum load resistance, R_L^*, and its associated optimum circuit-design parameter, k^*, we equate the resistances R_{Lp} and R_{Ls} [Eq. (12-12) and (12-14)] and solve the resulting expression for k. The quadratic expression obtained indicates that the requirement:

$$\frac{16MNI_{du}(V_{dd}-V_p)}{\beta V_p(2V_{dd}-3V_p)^2} \leq 1 \qquad (12\text{-}15)$$

must be satisfied for *any* stable design to be possible, i.e., for intersection of the R_{Lp} and R_{Ls} curves to occur. Expression (12-15) exists as an equality when the curves intersect in only one place and are tangent. The corresponding value for k is:

$$k^* = \frac{2V_{dd}+3V_p}{4V_{dd}} \qquad (12\text{-}16)$$

This optimum value for k and the minimum supply voltage which satisfies Eq. (12-15) can be substituted into either Eq. (12-12) or (12-14) to obtain:

$$R_L^* = \frac{N}{\beta V_p}\left[1+\left(1+\frac{\beta V_p^2}{2MNI_{du}}\right)^{1/2}\right] \qquad (12\text{-}17)$$

The supply voltage producing marginal stability can then be put into the form:

$$(V_{dd})_{min} = 2MI_{du}R_L^* + \tfrac{3}{2}V_p \qquad (12\text{-}18)$$

Equation (12-16) denotes the fractional reduction in output voltage due to leakage current *only* when $V_{dd} = (V_{dd})_{min}$ [Eq. (12-18)]. For selection of the supply voltage to be used, $(V_{dd})_{min}$ must be increased by the desired marginal-stability voltage. The effective value for k, then, is closer to unity. Equation (12-16) and the inequality condition of Eq. (12-13) impose an upper limit on the values of V_p which permit realization of R_L^* :

$$V_p \leq \tfrac{2}{5}V_{dd} \qquad (12\text{-}19)$$

Additional design flexibility becomes possible if the transistor pinch-off voltage can be independently selected, or, as in the MOS transistor, adjusted by application of substrate bias. (See Chapter 5.) An optimum value V_p^* can be found which will still further minimize $(V_{dd})_{min}$ and increase the stability margin for a given supply voltage. Minimizing V_{dd} with respect to V_p in Eq. (12–15), we find that:

$$V_p^* = 0.271(V_{dd})_{min} = 1.50\left(\frac{MNI_{du}}{\beta}\right)^{1/2} \tag{12-20}$$

Because of the uncertainty with which this critical pinch-off voltage can be precisely achieved and maintained, it is expedient to introduce a tolerance factor in calculating the absolute minimum supply voltage $(V_{dd})^*_{min}$. If V_p can be held to within $\pm x$ per cent:

$$(V_{dd})^*_{min} = 5.54A(x)\left(\frac{MNI_{du}}{\beta}\right)^{1/2} \tag{12-21}$$

where $A(x)$ is plotted in Fig. 12–21.

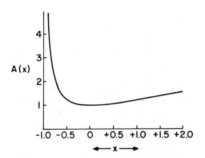

Figure 12–21. Value of coefficient $A(x)$ in Eq. (12–21) as a function of the tolerance x on V_p^*. $A(x) = 2/5.54(1 + x)$ $[\frac{2}{3}(1 + \sqrt{1 + \frac{9}{8}(1 + x)^2}) + \frac{9}{8}(1 + x)^2]$

EXAMPLE: Design a compatible set of mixed-gate circuits in which the maximum values for M and N are 5 and 4, respectively. Design for minimum supply voltage, allowing a 25% stability margin. Assume that the pinch-off voltage can be selected and held to within $\pm 50\%$. The worst-case transistor parameters are $\beta = 1 \times 10^{-4}$ mhos/v and $I_{du} = 5 \times 10^{-6}$ amp.

SOLUTION: From Eq. (12–20), $V_p^* = 1.50$ v. The maximum value for $A(x)$ (Fig. 12–21) corresponds to $x = -0.50$ and is equal to 1.22. Equation (12–21) then indicates that $(V_{dd})^*_{min} = 6.8$ v. This must be increased by 25% to provide the required stability margin; thus $V_{dd} = 8.5$ v.

The optimum load resistance is found from Eq. (12–17) to be $R_L^* = 6.6 \times 10^4$ ohms. This large load resistor will limit the circuit speed. However, this design was directed toward low-voltage, low-power operation.

COMPLEMENTARY TRANSISTOR CIRCUITS. The dual complementary circuits of Fig. 12–11 must provide compatible NOR and NAND functions. Positive M-input NOR and N-input NAND logic is assumed. Each circuit must satisfy two stability criteria. When the p-channel units conduct (Fig. 12–11a), they must produce a sufficiently positive output voltage to hold off the p-channel transistors in a succeeding stage. Thus, V_d must be greater than $V_{dd} - V_{pp}$. When the n-channel units conduct (Fig. 12–11b), they must produce a sufficiently small output voltage to hold off succeeding n-channel transistors, and V_d must be less than V_{pn}.

The most difficult circuit condition occurs when the series transistors conduct. They must present a sufficiently low resistance to the multiple leakage currents, MI_{dun} or NI_{dup}, of the parallel transistors to satisfy the preceding requirements. The circuits of Figs. 12–11a and b give rise to the dual requirements:†

$$MI_{dun} \leqslant \frac{\beta_p}{M} V_{pp}\left(V_{dd} - V_{pn} - \frac{3}{2} V_{pp}\right) \qquad (12\text{–}22)$$

and

$$NI_{dup} \leqslant \frac{\beta_n}{N} V_{pn}\left(V_{dd} - V_{pp} - \frac{3}{2} V_{pn}\right) \qquad (12\text{–}23)$$

In these equations, the drain voltages have been set equal to their permissible-limit values. β_p/M and β_n/N are the effective field-effect conductance-to-voltage ratios of equivalent single transistors.

To minimize power consumption, we select the minimum supply voltage that satisfies Eqs. (12–22) and (12–23). This requirement is conveniently stated by the equations rearranged in the form:

$$V_{dd} \geqslant \frac{M^2 I_{dun}}{\beta_p V_{pp}} + V_{pn} + \frac{3}{2} V_{pp} \qquad (12\text{–}22a)$$

$$V_{dd} \geqslant \frac{N^2 I_{dup}}{\beta_n V_{pn}} + V_{pp} + \frac{3}{2} V_{pn} \qquad (12\text{–}23a)$$

If all transistor parameters are fixed, the more stringent of these requirements determines the minimum voltage.

An optimum design is possible if transistor pinch-off voltages can be selected or adjusted as in the MOS transistor with substrate bias. Particular values for V_{pp} and V_{pn} can be found to minimize the right-hand

†The restrictions $V_{dd} \geqslant 2V_{pn} + V_{pp}$ and $V_{dd} \geqslant 2V_{pp} + V_{pn}$ must be applied to Eqs. (12–22) and (12–23), respectively, to assure that conducting transistors statically are kept out of the current-saturation region of their drain characteristics.

sides of Eqs. (12–22a) and (12–23a). The absolute minimum for V_{dd} occurs when both equations impose the same limit. While a simultaneous solution is possible, it is unwieldy. It is more convenient to minimize Eq. (12–22a) with respect to V_{pp}, and Eq. (12–23a) with respect to V_{pn}. The resulting optimum values for the pinch-off voltages are:

$$V_{pp}^* = M\left(\frac{2I_{dun}}{3\beta_p}\right)^{1/2} \tag{12-24}$$

and

$$V_{pn}^* = N\left(\frac{2I_{dup}}{3\beta_n}\right)^{1/2}$$

A tolerance factor again should be introduced, specifying the accuracy with which the pinch-off voltages can be achieved and maintained. Thus, $V_{pp} = (1 \pm x)V_{pp}^*$ and $V_{pn} = (1 \pm x)V_{pn}^*$. The minimum stable supply voltage is given by the more restrictive of the two equations:†

$$(V_{dd})_{\min}^* = 3B(x)V_{pp}^* + (1+x)V_{pn}^* \tag{12-26}$$

$$(V_{dd})_{\min}^* = 3B(x)V_{pn}^* + (1+x)V_{pp}^* \tag{12-27}$$

where x can assume both positive and negative values; $B(x)$ is plotted in Fig. 12–22.

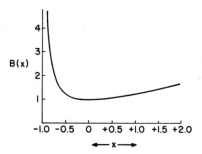

Figure 12–22. Value of coefficient $B(x)$ in Eqs. (12–26) and (12–27) as a function of the tolerance x on V_{pp}^* and V_{pn}^* $B(x) = \frac{1}{2}[(1+x) + 1/1 + x)]$.

†In general, these restrictions will not be identical. The optimum pinch-off voltages are independent of each other. Hence, the pinch-off voltage which appears only linearly in the basic equation, Eq. (12–22a) or (12–23a), can be progressively decreased until a match occurs.

A simpler method, leading to a slightly more conservative design, consists of merely accepting the larger value for $(V_{dd})_{\min}^*$ from Eqs. (12–26) and (12–27).

Equations (12–26) and (12–27) always are more restrictive than the conditions necessary to keep conducting transistors out of the current-saturation region. Hence, they always are applicable.

EXAMPLE: Design a compatible set of complementary gates to operate with the minimum supply voltage that will provide a 25% stability margin. Provision is to be made for NOR-gate fan-ins $M = 5$ and NAND-gate fan-ins $N = 4$. Assume that the pinch-off voltages can be set and held to within $\pm 50\%$. The worst-case transistor parameters are $\beta_p = 3.2 \times 10^{-5}$ mhos/v, $\beta_n = 1 \times 10^{-4}$ mhos/v, $I_{dup} = 6 \times 10^{-6}$ amp, and $I_{dun} = 3 \times 10^{-6}$ amp.

SOLUTION: From Eqs. (12–24) and (12–25), V_{pp}^* and V_{pn}^* are found to be 1.25 and 0.80, respectively. Figure 12–22 indicates that the maximum value for $B(x)$ corresponds to $x = -0.5$ and is equal to 1.25. The two values for $(V_{dd})^*_{\min}$, from Eqs. (12–26) and (12–27) are:

$$(V_{dd})^*_{\min_1} = 3(1.25)(1.25) + (1 - 0.5)(0.80) = 5.1 \text{ v}$$
$$(V_{dd})^*_{\min_2} = 3(1.25)(0.80) + (1 - 0.5)(1.25) = 3.6 \text{ v}$$

A choice of $(V_{dd})^*_{\min}$ of 5.1 v is indicated. The stability-margin requirement raises the actual supply voltage to $V_{dd} = 6.4$ v.

A considerably better match (in this case, an exact match) between the values for V_{pp}^* and V_{pn}^* can be obtained if we arrange the circuit so that the higher-gain n-channel transistors provide the limitation in the fan-in-of-five circuit, instead of the p-channel transistors. This arrangement amounts to reinterpreting the circuits in Fig. 12–11. Figure 12–11a becomes an M-input, negative-NAND gate, and Fig. 12–11b becomes an N-input, negative-NOR gate. The values for M and N become interchanged. Pursuing a new design on this basis, we obtain a matched value for $(V_{dd})^*_{\min}$ of 4.25 v, with $V_{pp}^* = V_{pn}^* = 1.0$ v; V_{dd} then equals 5.3 v.

A convenient criterion for choosing between positive and negative logic, when $M = N$ and the transistors have different characteristics, is to use that logic which results in the best match between the initial optimum pinch-off voltages, V_{pp}^* and V_{pn}^*.

12–4 TRANSIENT PERFORMANCE OF FIELD-EFFECT TRANSISTORS

A simple circuit model (Fig. 12–23) can be used to calculate the transient response of field-effect-transistor switches. Circuit capacitance and the resistance through which it is charged and discharged constitute the predominant limitation on switching speed. Charge transit time in the transistor is negligible. The nonlinear resistance of the transistor prevents the problem from reducing to that of the calculation of simple RC transients.

For the circuit model, the gate-to-channel capacitance is approximated as a lumped element, contributing both to the input capacitance, C_i, and to the lumped feedback capacitance, C_f. The input capacitance and the output capacitance, C_o, include the capacitances of the driving source and the driven load, respectively. Stray capacitances associated with the transistor package and circuit wiring contribute to all three capacitances.

A general analysis of the response of the circuit of Fig. 12–23 to an arbitrary driving function is an ambitious undertaking. This chapter

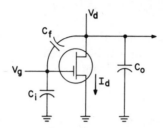

Figure 12-23. Circuit model for transient analysis.

concentrates on transient calculations applicable to digital logic circuits, where the amplitude of the driving signal is equal to the output-signal swing. Tractable solutions are obtained by the utilization of step-voltage drives for both linear and nonlinear load elements.

1. Transient analysis; step drive

The use of a low-impedance drive eliminates the effect of C_i and the degenerative effect of the feedback capacitance. However, C_f does couple some of the drive signal to the output. In the following analysis, the effect of C_f is first neglected and corrections are subsequently made. Two cases are considered: linear-resistor load and complementary-transistor load.

The analysis requires the use of segmented load lines. To avoid solutions with many segments, it is convenient to approximate the transistor drain characteristic by a single parabolic arc over the required zero-to-V_{dd} voltage range. Curve (A) in Fig. 12–24, which has the equation:

$$I_d = \begin{cases} \beta[(V_{dd}-V_p)V_d - \tfrac{1}{2}V_d^2], & 0 \leqslant V_d \leqslant V_{dd}-V_p \\[2mm] \dfrac{\beta}{2}(V_{dd}-V_p)^2, & V_d \geqslant V_{dd}-V_p \end{cases} \tag{12-28}$$

is approximated by curve (B):

$$I_d = \beta\left(\frac{V_{dd}-V_p}{V_{dd}}\right)^2\left(V_{dd}V_d - \frac{1}{2}V_d^2\right), \quad 0 \leqslant V_d \leqslant V_{dd} \tag{12-29}$$

All voltages will be normalized with respect to the supply voltage, V_{dd}. Since the drain voltage is the only voltage variable, it is convenient to omit the subscript d. Equation (12–29) becomes:

$$I_d = \beta V_{dd}^2 \ (1 - v_p)^2 (v - \tfrac{1}{2}v^2), 0 \leqslant v \leqslant 1 \qquad \text{(12–29a)}$$

The error introduced into the analysis by the use of curve (B) to approximate curve (A) (Fig. 12–24), increases for increasing (normalized) threshold voltage, v_p. An indication of the error can be obtained by

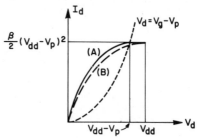

Figure 12–24. Approximation (B) to actually segmented drain characteristic (A).

comparison of the areas under the curves for $0 \leqslant v \leqslant 1$. The area is an integrated measure of the current available for discharging circuit capacitance, and it is related to switching speed. The difference in area under the two curves, expressed as a fraction of the area under curve (A), is equal to $v_p/(2 + v_p)$.

CIRCUIT WITH LINEAR-RESISTOR LOAD. Figure 12–25 illustrates the net current available both for discharging the circuit capacitance during "turn-on" of the transistor and for charging the capacitance during "turn-off."

1. *"Turn-on"*: The pertinent equation is:

$$C\frac{dV_d}{dt} = I_R - I_d$$

$$= \frac{V_{dd} - V_d}{R_L} - \beta\left(\frac{V_{dd} - V_p}{V_{dd}}\right)^2\left(V_{dd}V_d \quad \frac{1}{2}V_d^2\right) \qquad \text{(12–30)}$$

with the boundary condition $V_d = V_{dd}$ at $t = 0$. Normalizing Eq. (12–30) with respect to V_{dd} and solving for normalized time τ:

$$\tau = \int_1^v \frac{dv}{v^2 - 2(1 + 1/\alpha) + 2/\alpha} \qquad \text{(12–31)}$$

where:

$$\alpha \equiv \beta R_L V_{dd}(1 - v_p)^2 \tag{12-32}$$

$$\tau \equiv \frac{\alpha t}{2R_L C} = \frac{\beta V_{dd}(1 - v_p)^2}{2C}t \tag{12-33}$$

Integrating and employing the identity for $\tanh(x + y)$, we find that:

$$v = \frac{\sqrt{\alpha^2 + 1} - (\alpha - 1)\tanh\left[(\sqrt{\alpha^2 + 1}/\alpha)\tau\right]}{\sqrt{\alpha^2 + 1} + \tanh\left[(\sqrt{\alpha^2 + 1}/\alpha)\tau\right]} \tag{12-34}$$

This equation can be simplified if we note that the condition $\alpha^2 \gg 1$ usually is satisfied. Then:

$$v_{on} \approx 1 - \frac{\alpha \tanh \tau}{\alpha + \tanh \tau}, \quad \alpha^2 \gg 1 \tag{12-35}$$

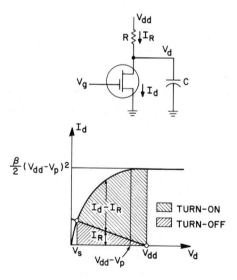

Figure 12–25. Current available for charging and discharging the circuit capacitance. (Resistor load.)

2. *"Turn-off"*: The "turn-off" transient is a simple RC charging function with $v = v_s$ at $t = 0$. Hence:

$$v = (v_s - 1)e^{-t/R_t C} + 1 \tag{12-36}$$

The value of the saturation voltage, v_s, can most easily be determined if we let $\tau \to \infty$ in Eq. (12–35). Then:

$$v_s \approx \frac{1}{1+\alpha} \tag{12-37}$$

Inserting this into Eq. (12–36), and introducing the normalized time variable, τ, we obtain:

$$v_{\text{off}} = 1 - \frac{\alpha}{1+\alpha} e^{-(2/\alpha)\tau} \tag{12-38}$$

COMPLEMENTARY-TRANSISTOR CIRCUIT. The current available for charging and discharging circuit capacitance is illustrated in Fig. 12–26 for a complementary-transistor inverter. Because voltage steps are assumed for the driving functions, only one transistor conducts current at any given time. During "turn-on," the n-channel unit conducts and the p-channel unit is cut off. During "turn-off," the reverse is true. Analysis of the complementary inverter reduces to a special case of the linear-resistor load, the case where the load resistance becomes infinitely large.

1. *"Turn-on"*: From Eq. (12–35), in the limit as $R_L \to \infty$, α also $\to \infty$, and the equation becomes:

$$V_{\text{on}} = 1 - \tanh \tau \tag{12-39}$$

2. *"Turn-off"*: Because of the symmetry of the complementary circuit, the "turn-off" transient has the same shape as the "turn-on" transient. "Turn-off" begins with a voltage of zero for the circuit of Fig. 12–26. The transient solution is:

$$V_{\text{off}} = \tanh \sigma\tau \tag{12-40}$$

where:

$$\sigma \equiv \frac{\beta_p(1 - v_{pp})^2}{\beta_n(1 - v_{pn})^2} \tag{12-41}$$

The coefficient σ accounts for the dependence of the "turn-off" transient on parameters of the *load* (p-channel) transistor. In effect, σ renormalizes the time variable to these parameters.

2. Corrections for the effect of feedback capacitance

The preceding analysis neglected the effect of C_f (Fig. 12–23). Because of the high-impedance level of field-effect transistor output circuits, C_f can couple a significant fraction of the drive signal to the output. This produces an initial reverse-polarity transient and prolongs the total switching transient. Correction can readily be made for this effect.

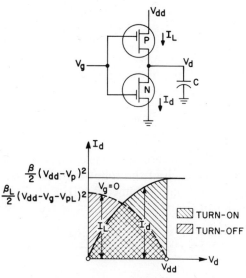

Figure 12–26. Current available for charging and discharging the circuit capacitance. (Complementary circuit.)

Figure 12–27 illustrates the reverse-polarity transient produced at the drain. The amplitude of the feed-through voltage, ΔV, depends on the relative size of the capacitance, C_f, and the output capacitance, C_o. The magnitude of ΔV can be calculated if we note that the instantaneous changes in charge of C_f and C_o must be equal, since the transistor and load element can conduct only finite currents and do not affect the

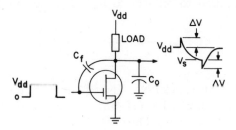

Figure 12–27. Reverse-polarity transient signals produced by the feed-through capacitance.

momentary charge redistribution. Alternatively, ΔV may be viewed as a voltage step produced by a capacitive voltage divider. In either case, the result is:

$$\Delta V = \pm \frac{C_f}{C_f + C_o} V_{dd} \tag{12–42}$$

when the input signal changes by $\pm V_{dd}$. It is convenient to define $f = C_f/C_o$. Introducing f and normalizing with respect to V_{dd}, we have:

$$\Delta v = \frac{f}{1+f} \tag{12–43}$$

The duration of the feed-through transient now can be determined for each type of load. For each of the following solutions, the capacitance factor in the normalized-time parameter, τ [Eq. (12–33)] consists of the parallel combination of C_f and C_o, i.e., τ must be redefined as:

$$\tau \equiv \frac{\beta V_{dd}(1 - v_p)^2}{2C_o(1+f)} t \tag{12–44}$$

CIRCUIT WITH LINEAR-RESISTOR LOAD. Figure 12–28 illustrates the current available for charging or discharging the circuit capacitance and allowing the drain voltage to recover to its initial value. Thereafter, the problem is identical to that of Fig. 12–25.

1. "*Turn-on*": ΔV is positive. The transistor current is constant for $V_d \geq V_{dd}$, and the transient is a simple exponential. Its equation in normalized form is:

$$v_{\text{on}} = 1 - \frac{\alpha}{2} + \left(\frac{f}{1+f} + \frac{\alpha}{2}\right)e^{-(2/\alpha)t}, \quad v_{\text{on}} \geq 1 \tag{12–45}$$

and the time required to recover to $V_d = V_{dd}$, i.e., $v = 1$, is given by:

$$\tau_{dd} = \frac{\alpha}{2}\ln\left\{1 + \frac{2f}{\alpha(1+f)}\right\} \tag{12–46}$$

2. "*Turn-off*": ΔV is negative. The equation for the entire "turn-off" transient is an extension of Eq. (12–38), where now the boundary conditions are $v = v_s - \Delta v$ at $t = 0$. Thus:

$$v_{\text{off}} = 1 - \left(\frac{\alpha}{1+\alpha} + \frac{f}{1+f}\right)e^{-(2/\alpha)\tau}, \quad v_{\text{off}} \geq v_s - \Delta v \tag{12–47}$$

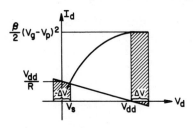

Figure 12-28. Current available for recovering from reverse-polarity feed-through transients. (Resistor load.)

The duration of the feed-through transient τ_s is found if we set $v_{off} = v_s = 1/(1 + \alpha)$. Then:

$$\tau_s = \frac{\alpha}{2} \ln \left\{ 1 + \frac{f}{\alpha} \left(\frac{1 + \alpha}{1 + f} \right) \right\} \tag{12-48}$$

COMPLEMENTARY-TRANSISTOR CIRCUIT

1. *"Turn-on"*: Figure 12-29 indicates that a constant current discharges the capacitance. The feed-through transient has a linear decay represented by the equation:

$$v_{on} = \frac{1 + 2f}{1 + f} - \tau, \quad v_{on} \geq 1 \tag{12-49}$$

This transient persists until $v_{on} = 1$, or until τ reaches:

$$\tau_{dd} = \frac{f}{1 + f} \tag{12-50}$$

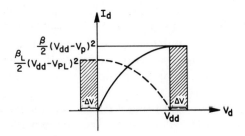

Figure 12-29. Current available for recovering from reverse-polarity feed-through transients. (Complementary circuit.)

2. *"Turn-off"*: A constant current again is available and the "turn-off" equation has the same general form as Eq. (12–49). However, the time variable must be normalized to the parameters of the *p*-channel transistor. Then:

$$v_{off} = \sigma\tau - \frac{f}{1+f}, \quad v_{off} \leqslant 0 \tag{12-51}$$

The feed-through transient ends at $v_{off} = 0$, or:

$$\tau_o = \frac{1}{\sigma}\frac{f}{1+f} \tag{12-52}$$

3. Summary: response to step-voltage drive

The transient-response equations derived in the preceding sections are summarized in Table 12–1. Solutions of these equations for the 0%–10% delay times and 10%–90% rise (fall) times are summarized in Table 12–2.

Comparisons of measured and calculated transient responses for the two types of load elements are shown in Figs. 12–30 and 12–31. Circuit inductance, not accounted for in the calculated waveform, causes a rounding of the feed-through transient in the measured waveform. The calculated waveforms are slower than the measured ones, due to the non-segmented approximation used for the theoretical drain characteristics.

It is of interest to note the dependence of switching time on transistor and circuit parameters. Although no straight-forward dependence can be cited for the "turn-on" of a resistor-loaded inverter, "turn-off" time is clearly proportional to α and, hence, to the $R_L C_o$ time constant.

The case is quite clear for the complementary circuit. Switching time is directly proportional to output capacitance, C_o, and inversely proportional to supply voltage, V_{dd}, and transistor field-effect conductance-to-voltage ratio, β. The ratio β/C_o is a large-signal analog to the small-signal gain-bandwidth, g_m/C and is inversely related to switching time. Switching time increases with increasing normalized pinch-off voltage, v_p.

In Section 12–5, it is shown that the power consumed by insulated-gate-transistor circuits is approximately proportional to V_{dd}^2. Since switching speed (reciprocal of switching time) rises only linearly with V_{dd}, there is advantage in operating the circuits at moderately low supply voltages to maximize the switching speed per unit power dissipation.

Transient signal feed-through is important only in response-time measurements, where step voltages with small rise time are used. In actual cascaded digital circuits, where the driving waveform has a rise time in the same range as that of the output response, feed-through

Table 12-1 Transient Response to Step Voltage Drive

	"Turn-on"	"Turn-off"
Linear resistor ($\alpha^2 \gg 1$)		
$1 + \Delta v \geq v \geq 1$	$v = 1 - \dfrac{\alpha}{2} + \left[\dfrac{f}{1+f} + \dfrac{\alpha}{2}\right] e^{-(2/\alpha)\tau}; \quad \tau_{dd} = \dfrac{\alpha}{2}\ln\left[1 + \dfrac{2f}{\alpha(1+f)}\right]$	$v = 1 - \left[\dfrac{\alpha}{1+\alpha} + \dfrac{f}{1+f}\right] e^{-(2/\alpha)\tau}$
$V_s - \Delta v \leq v \leq 1$	$v = 1 - \dfrac{\alpha \tanh(\tau - \tau_{dd})}{\alpha + \tanh(\tau - \tau_{dd})}$	
Complementary Circuit		
$1 + \Delta v \geq v \geq 1$	$v = \dfrac{1+2f}{1+f} - \tau; \quad \tau_{dd} = \dfrac{f}{1+f}$	$v = \tanh(\sigma\tau - \tau_o)$
$0 \leq v \leq 1$	$v = 1 - \tanh(\tau - \tau_{dd})$	
$-\Delta v \leq v \leq 0$		$v = \sigma\tau - \dfrac{f}{1+f}; \quad \tau_o = \dfrac{f}{1+f}$

Definitions: Lower-case $v \equiv$ voltage normalized to V_{dd}

$$\alpha \equiv \beta_n R_L V_{dd}(1 - v_{pn})^2$$

$$\tau \equiv \frac{\beta_n V_{dd}(1 - v_{pn})^2}{2C_o(1+f)} t = \frac{\alpha}{2R_L C_o(1+f)} t$$

$$\sigma \equiv \frac{\beta_p}{\beta_n} \times \frac{(1 - v_{pn})^2}{(1 - v_{pn})^2}$$

$$f \equiv \frac{C_f}{C_o}$$

Table 12-2 Normalized Switching Times for Step Voltage Drive

	"Turn-on"	"Turn-off"
Linear resistor ($\alpha^2 \gg 1$)		
Delay time, τ_{0-10}	$\tanh^{-1}\left[\dfrac{\alpha}{9+10\alpha}\right] + \dfrac{\alpha}{2}\ln\left[1+\dfrac{2f}{\alpha(1+f)}\right]$	$0.052\alpha + \dfrac{\alpha}{2}\ln\left[1+\dfrac{f(1+\alpha)}{\alpha(1+f)}\right]$
Rise (fall) time, τ_{10-90}	$\tanh^{-1}\left[\dfrac{80\alpha}{91\alpha+9}\right] \approx 1.37$	1.10α
Complementary Circuit		
Delay time, τ_{0-10}	$0.10 + \dfrac{f}{1+f}$	$\dfrac{1}{\sigma}\left(0.10+\dfrac{f}{1+f}\right)$
Rise (fall) time, τ_{10-90}	1.37	$\dfrac{1.37}{\sigma}$

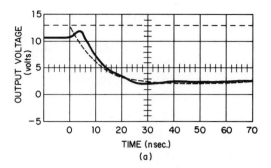

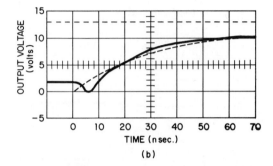

Figure 12–30. Comparison of calculated (dashed-line) transient response with measured transient response (resistor load). (a) "Turn-off." $V_{dd} = 10.5$v, $R_L = 1$ kilohm, $V_{pn} = 3.2$v, $\beta_n = 7.84 \times 10^{-4}$ mhos/v, $C_o = 17$pf, $C_f = 6$pf. (b) "Turn-on."

becomes insignificant. The signal feed*back* which occurs under cascaded-circuit conditions can become appreciable. Measurements indicate that the effect of the Miller feedback capacitance, C_f, on the response time of cascaded stages can very closely be simulated by an additional capacitance of $3C_f$ shunting the output capacitance of each stage and no feedback capacitance. The coefficient 3 was obtained, within $\pm 20\%$, for inverters with linear-resistor, depletion-transistor, and complementary-transistor loads.

4. Transient analysis; non-ideal drive

Analysis of the transient response of field-effect transistor switches to drive-waveforms which are functions of time leads to nonlinear differential equations. Solutions to problems of this type are best carried out graphically or with the aid of a computer.

Burns[4] has used a digital computer to analyze one class of particular interest. He studied the case of cascaded complementary-transistor inverters. Transient waveforms at the drains of six successive inverter stages were found for various combinations of pinch-off voltages and transistor β for n-channel and p-channel transistors. For each solution all n-type units were assigned the same characteristics, as were all p-type

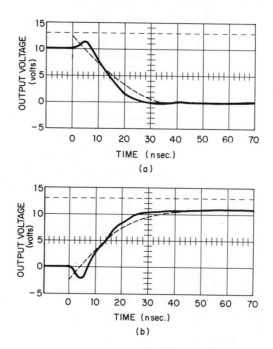

Figure 12–31. Comparison of calculated (dashed-line) transient response with measured transient response. (Complementary circuit.) (a) "Turn-on." (b) "Turn-off." $V_{dd} = 10.5$v, $V_{pn} = 3.2$v, $V_{pp} = 2.8$v, $\beta_n = 7.84 \times 10^{-4}$ mhos/v, $\beta_p = 6.72 \times 10^{-4}$ mhos/v, $C_o = 24$pf, $C_f = 7$pf.

units. The six inverter stages proved more than adequate for converting the step voltage applied to the first stage to a *standardized signal*, i.e., the signal waveform which propagates unchanged in shape through each pair of stages of a chain. In all cases, Burns found that the waveform became standardized after three stages. He also found that the pair delay (the time delay between corresponding points of alternate-stage waveforms) was the same for rising and falling output transients. A convenient empirical expression for this pair delay was found to be:

$$\tau_d \approx 0.9 \left(1 + \frac{1}{\sigma}\right) \tag{12–53}$$

where τ_d is normalized to the transistor and circuit parameters according to Eq. (12-53), and σ is defined in Eq. (12-41). Equation (12-53) was found to be useful for $v_{pn}, v_{pp} < 0.5$, and $\beta_p/\beta_n > 0.2$.

Useful approximations to the 10%-90% rise and fall times were expressed as functions of the response of the circuit to a step drive. These equations are:

$$T_r = (T_r)_{\text{step}} + 0.35 \frac{(T_f)_{\text{step}}}{(T_r)_{\text{step}}} \tag{12-54}$$

and

$$T_f = (T_f)_{\text{step}} + 0.35 \frac{(T_r)_{\text{step}}}{(T_f)_{\text{step}}} \tag{12-55}$$

where T_r and T_f are the *unnormalized* rise and fall times, respectively. Computations of these times can be made with the aid of Table 12-2.

Plots of transient waveforms and of the dependence of τ_d, T_r, and T_f on the transistor parameters are given by Burns.[4]

12-5 POWER DISSIPATION

Three effects contribute to the power dissipated in field-effect transistor switching circuits. They are: (1) the transient losses which accompany each charging or discharging of the circuit capacitance; (2) the constant dissipation associated with the current drawn by a switch in the "on" state, and (3) the constant dissipation produced by leakage currents. Slow-rise-time driving voltages produce transient currents which give rise to additional losses. It will be assumed that the critical range of the applied pulse is traversed quickly, so that negligibly short transients occur. The two types of load element, the linear resistor and the complementary-transistor load, again are considered.

1. Circuits with linear-resistor load

During the "turn-off" transient, as the voltage across the circuit capacitance increases from its initial value, V_s, to the supply-voltage, V_{dd}, an energy, $E = \frac{1}{2}C(V_{dd} - V_s)^2$ is supplied to the capacitance. An equal energy is dissipated in the resistance of the charging circuit, independent of the linearity of this resistance. Thus, in Fig. 12-32a, the energy:

$$E = \frac{C}{2}(1 - v_s)^2 V_{dd}^2 \tag{12-56}$$

is dissipated. The normalized initial voltage, v_s, is the saturation voltage of the switch (Fig. 12–25). In Eq. (12–37), this voltage was shown to be approximately equal to $1/(1 + \alpha)$, where α is defined in Eq. (12–32). Thus, Eq. (12–56) may be approximated as:

$$E \approx \frac{C}{2}\left(\frac{\alpha V_{dd}}{\alpha+1}\right)^2 \tag{12-57}$$

During "turn-on" of the switch (Fig. 12–32b), the incremental energy which has been stored in the capacitance during the "turn-off" transient

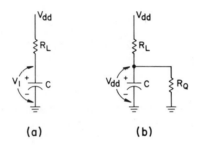

(a)   (b)

Figure 12-32. Equivalent circuits for calculating power dissipation. (a) Circuit capacitance charged to V_s prior to "turn-off." (b) Circuit capacitance charged to V_{dd} prior to "turn-on."

is dissipated. This energy also is given by Eq. (12–57). Thus, a transient energy, $2E$, is dissipated during each complete switching cycle. If switching cycles occur at a repetition frequency F, the average transient power dissipation is given by:

$$P_{\text{trans}} = CF\left(\frac{\alpha V_{dd}}{\alpha+1}\right)^2 \tag{12-58}$$

In addition to the capacitive discharge current, a current simultaneously flows through R_L and the transistor. Because the transistor resistance, R_Q, is not linear, superposition is not valid. Its application, however, results in an adequate approximation. Thus, a steady-state power

$$P_{ss} = \frac{V_{dd}^2}{R_L + R_Q} \tag{12-59}$$

is dissipated during the conduction portion of the switching cycle. Using the approximation for v_s, R_Q can be shown to equal R_L/α. Equation (12–59) becomes:

$$P_{ss} \approx \frac{\alpha}{\alpha+1}\left(\frac{V_{dd}^2}{R_L}\right) \tag{12-60}$$

Finally, if the switch conducts during a fraction, θ, of each cycle, and the transistor has leakage current I_{du}, the total power dissipation is given by:

$$P = CF\left(\frac{\alpha V_{dd}}{\alpha + N}\right)^2 + \frac{\theta}{R_L}\left(\frac{\alpha}{\alpha + N}\right)V_{dd}^2 + MI_{du}V_{dd} \tag{12–61}$$

The factors M and N have been introduced to account for multiple-transistor circuits. One of them normally would be set equal to unity, depending on the type of logic gate under analysis.

2. Complementary-transistor circuits

The steady-state term drops out of the dissipation equation for the complementary circuit since only leakage currents flow during steady state. In addition, the transient term is simplified because the saturation-voltage drop across a conducting transistor is zero. The resulting dissipation equation for a NOR circuit (Fig. 12–11a) is:

$$P = CFV_{dd}^2 + [\theta_n I_{dup} + (1 - \theta_n)MI_{dun}]V_{dd} \tag{12–62}$$

The duty factor, θ_n, is the fraction of the cycle during which the n-channel transistors conduct. A similar equation can be written for a NAND circuit.

3. Effect of non-ideal drives

Complementary circuits in which v_{pn} and v_{pp} both are greater than 0.5 can never conduct resistive currents, since each type transistor is cut off when the other type conducts. Appreciable currents can flow in transistors with normalized pinch-off voltages of less than 0.5. In transistors of this type, drive waveforms with slow voltage transitions can introduce significant transient resistive currents. The adequacy of Eq. (12–62), which does not account for this effect, becomes questionable when finite-rise-time drives are considered.

Burns[4] has investigated this question. In his computer analysis of cascaded complementary inverters, he found no combination of values for v_{pn} and v_{pp} which caused deviation from a linear power-frequency relationship by more than 11%. Similar data for linear-resistor loads Eq. (12–61) are not available.

12–6 INTEGRATED DIGITAL CIRCUITS

Several significant properties of insulated-gate field-effect transistors commend them for use in integrated digital circuits. Their structural simplicity and the fewer processing steps required for their fabrication lead to high on-wafer yields, a primary requirement of integrated devices. Their electrical characteristics permit the direct coupling of digital stages. This eliminates the need for a secondary processing technology to produce coupling elements. Finally, the low-dissipation complementary-symmetry circuit enables complete digital networks to be fabricated of only transistors and connecting leads. As with bipolar integrated circuits, the leads can be applied as part of the vacuum deposition and photo-lithographic process used to make the transistors.

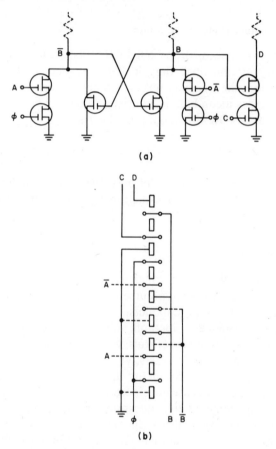

Figure 12–33. (a) Typical digital circuit. (b) Possible intraconnection pattern using ladder-like array of transistors.

One example of an integrated digital structure based on the thin-film transistor is the scanning generator described in Chapter 9. While direct coupling was not employed for this application, direct-coupled

MOS transistors have been investigated under an approach which has been called *integrated logic nets.*[5] The thesis of this approach is that digital subsystems can be realized economically as arrays of identical switching elements with superimposed connections fabricated en masse. The ladder-like array of MOS transistors described in Figs. 8-2 and 8-4 was developed as part of this integrated-circuit concept. Because the transistors in this type of array are completely symmetrical, each diffused region can serve as either source or drain. Many of the series-circuit connections required· to implement a digital function are inherently present. Sections of such a transistor ladder are isolated by grounding a source-drain or gate electrode. The circuit in Fig. 12-33a, for example, can be realized by the connection pattern in Fig. 12-33b.

Although circuit *intra*connections (connections between transistors on the same substrate) can readily be evaporated onto an array, means also must be available for *inter*connecting substrates to one another and to nonintegrated parts of a system. A technique to connect terminals on a semiconductor wafer to lands on a ceramic board is illustrated in

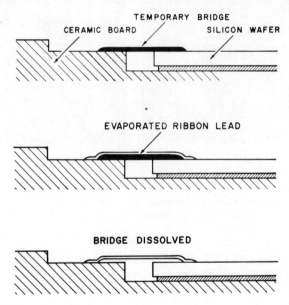

Figure 12-34. A method for fabricating terminal inter-connections.

Fig. 12-34.[6] This technique utilizes a temporary bridge as a base for evaporating a ribbon lead. Dissolution of the bridge then leaves the ribbon free to flex and follow thermal expansions and contractions. This bridging technique has been employed in the fabrication of the 16-transistor logic-block illustrated in Fig. 12-35.

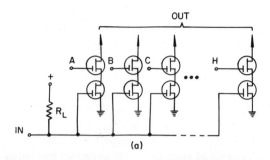

(a)

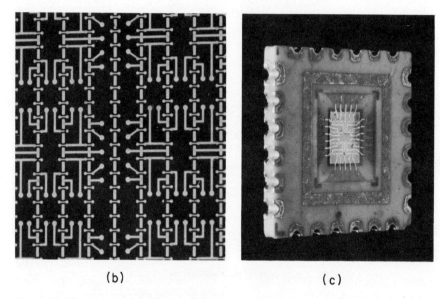

(b)   (c)

Figure 12–35. 16-transistor logic block. (a) Circuit schematic diagram. (b) Array of MOS transistors with superimposed wiring pattern, thus forming a group of logic blocks. (c) Single logic block packaged in $\frac{1}{2}$ in. $\times$ $\frac{1}{2}$ in. $\times$ $\frac{3}{64}$ in. ceramic container.

REFERENCES

1. F. M. Wanless and C. T. Sah,. "Nanowatt Logic Using Field-Effect Metal-Oxide-Semiconductor Triodes," *Digest of Technical Papers,* 1963 International Solid-State Circuits Conference, Philadelphia, p. 32.

2. A. W. Lo, *IRE Trans. on Electronic Computers* **EC–10,** 416 (1961).

3. J. J. Gibson, private communication.

4. J. R. Burns, "Switching Response of Complementary Symmetry MOS Logic Circuits," *RCA Review.* **25,** 627 (1964).

5. A. K. Rapp, "MOS Integrated Logic Nets," *Proceedings of the Symposium on Microelectronics and Large Systems,* 1964, Spartan Books.

6. J. H. McCusker, private communication.

Bibliography

This bibliography contains in chronological order a fairly complete list of published papers on the subject of field-effect transistors and their applications. Trade journals and other journals which usually do not contain primary information have been omitted. Digests from technical meetings which usually reappear in a more complete form as published papers also have been omitted with a few exceptions. Particularly useful references are marked with an asterisk.

The second half of the bibliography is devoted to (United States) patents (one British patent is included) describing field-effect devices. This part of the bibliography is of particular interest to research and development groups in tracing the history of the device and for describing various modifications designed for special purposes.

FIELD-EFFECT TRANSISTORS

1948   1. Shockley, W. and G. L. Pearson, "Modulation of Conductance of Thin Films of Semiconductors by Surface Charges," *Phys. Rev.,* Vol. 74 (1948), p. 232.

1952   *2. Shockley, W. "A Unipolar Field-Effect Transistor," *Proc. IRE,* Vol. 40 (November, 1952), p. 1365.

1953   3. Pearson, G. L., "A High Impedance Silicon Field-Effect Transistor," *Phys. Rev.,* Vol. 90 (April 15, 1953), p. 336.

       4. Dacey, G. C. and I. M. Ross, "Unipolar 'Field-Effect' Transistor," *Proc. IRE,* Vol. 41 (August, 1953), p. 970.

       5. Prim, R. C. and W. Shockley, "Joining Solutions at the Pinch-Off Point in 'Field-Effect' Transistor," *IRE Trans. on Electron Devices,* Vol. ED-4 (December, 1953), p. l.

1955 *6. Dacey, G. C. and I. M. Ross, "The Field-Effect Transistor," *Bell Syst. Tech. J.*, Vol. 34 (November, 1955), p. 1149.

1956 7. Huang, C., M. Marshall, and B. White, "Field-Effect Transistor Applications," *Comm. and Electronics*, Vol. 3 (July, 1956), p. 323.

1958 8. Teszner, S., "A New High Frequency Amplifier" (in French), *Comptes Rendus*, Vol. 246 (January 6, 1958), p. 72.

9. Aisberg, E., "The Tecnetron – Competitor of the Transistor," *Radio-Electronics*, Vol. 29 (May, 1958), p. 60.

1959 10. Warner, Jr., R. M., W. H. Jackson, G. I. Doucette, and H. A. Stone, "A Semiconductor Current Limiter," *Proc. IRE*, Vol. 47 (January, 1959), p. 44.

11. Stone, Jr., H. A., "Theory and Use of Field-Effect Tetrodes," *Electronics*, Vol. 32, (May 15, 1959.) p. 66.

12. Wallmark, J. T. and S. M. Marcus, "Integrated Devices Using Direct-Coupled Unipolar Transistor Logic," *IRE Trans. on Electronic Computers*, Vol. EC–8 (June, 1959), p. 98.

13. Wegener, H. A. R., "The Cylindrical Field-Effect Transistor," *IRE Trans. on Electron Devices*, Vol. ED–6 (October, 1959), p. 442.

1960 14. Schwartz, B. and M. Levy, "Field Effect on Silicon Transistors," *Proc. IRE*, Vol. 48 (March, 1960), p. 317.

15. Martin, A. V. J., "The Alcatron," *Electronic Industries*, Vol. 19 (October, 1960), p. 98.

16. Beale, J. R. A., D. E. Thomas, and T. B. Watkins, "Field Effect on Silicon Transistors," *Proc. IRE*, Vol. 48 (December, 1960), p. 2038.

1961 17. Terman, L. M., "An Investigation of Surface States at a Silicon/Silicon-Oxide Interface Employing MOS Diodes," Tech. Rep. 1655–1, Stanford University, Stanford Electronics Laboratories, Solid-State Electronics Laboratory (February 23, 1961).

18. Babcock, R. V., "Radiation Damage to Unipolar Transistors," *Trans. Am. Nucl. Soc.*, Vol. 4 (June, 1961), p. 60.

19. Stone, H. A., and R. M. Warner, "The Field-Effect Tetrode," *Proc. IRE*, Vol. 49 (July, 1961), p. 1170.

20. Ihantola, H. K. J., "Design Theory of a Surface Field-Effect Transistor," Stanford Electronics Laboratories, Tech. Rep. 1661–1 (August 17, 1961).

21. Kulp, B. A., J. P. Jones, and A. F. Vetter, "Electron Radiation Damage in Unipolar Transistor Devices " (letter), *Proc. IRE*, Vol. 49 (September, 1961), p. 1437

22. Sah, C. T., "A New Semiconductor Tetrode – The Surface-Potential Controlled Transistor," *Proc. IRE*, Vol. 49 (November, 1961). p. 1623.

1962   23. Martin, T. B., "Circuit Applications of the Field-Effect Transistor," *Semiconductor Products*, Vol. 5 (February, 1962), p. 33 (March, 1962), p. 30.

  *24. Weimer, P. K., "The TFT—A New Thin-Film Transistor," *Proc. IRE*, Vol. 50 (June, 1962), p. 1462.

   25. Kauffman, A. B , "Do Field-Effect Transistors Resist Nuclear Radiation?" *Electronics*, Vol. 35 (July 13, 1962), p. 94.

   26. Onodera, G. G., W. J. Corrigan, and R. M. Warner, Jr., "Silicon Field-Effect Transistor With Internal Epitaxial Channel" (letter), *Proc. IRE*, Vol. 50 (August, 1962), p. 1824.

   27. van der Ziel, A., "Thermal Noise in Field-Effect Transistors," *Proc. IRE*, Vol. 50 (August, 1962), p. 1808.

   28. Etter, P. J. and B. L. H. Wilson, "Inductance from a Field-Effect Tetrode," *Proc. IRE*, Vol. 50 (August, 1962), p. 1828.

   29. Parmer, W. F., "Four Ways to Pair Field-Effect and Conventional Transistors," *Electronic Design*, Vol. 10 (August 16, 1962), p. 44.

   30. Highleyman, W. H. and E. S. Jacob, "An Analog Multiplier Using Two Field-Effect Transistors," *IRE Trans. on Communications Systems*, Vol. CS–10 (September, 1962), p. 311.

   31. van der Ziel, A., "Shot Noise in Thin Film Transistors" (letter), *Proc. IRE*, Vol. 50 (September, 1962), p. 1985.

   32. Alford, D., F. Garrett, and L. J. Sevin, "Germanium Field-Effect Transistors," *IRE Trans. on Broadcast and Television Receivers*, Vol. BTR–8 (November, 1962), p. 106.

   33. Bergstrom, J. W., "CdSe Photoconductive Field-Effect Transistors" (letter), *Proc. IRE*, Vol. 50 (November, 1962), p. 2376.

   34. Glover, V., "Using a New Device: Field-Effect Transistor Oscillators," *Electronics*, Vol. 35 (December 21, 1962), p. 44.

1963   35. Bockemuehl, R. R., "Analysis of Field-Effect Transistors with Arbitrary Charge Distribution," *IEEE Trans. on Electron Devices*, Vol. ED–10 (January, 1963), p. 31.

   36. Latham, D. C., D. J. Hamilton, and F. A. Lindholm, "New Modes of Operation for Field-Effect Devices" (letter), *Proc. IEEE*, Vol. 51. (January, 1963), p. 226.

   37. Olsen, D. R., "Equivalent Circuit for a Field-Effect Transistor" (letter), *Proc. IEEE*, Vol. 51 (January, 1963), p. 254.

   38. Cohen, J. M., "Generating Linear Waveforms with Field-Effect Transistors," *Electronic Design*, Vol. 11 (January 4, 1963), p. 66.

   39. Burns, R. C. and E. D. Crawfis, "Try Field-Effect Transistors for Redundancy," *Electronic Design*, Vol. 11 (January. 18, 1963), p. 74.

40. Grosvalet, J., C. Metsch, and R. Tribes, "Physical Phenomenon Responsible for Saturation Current in Field-Effect Devices," *Solid-State Electronics,* Vol. 6 (January-February, 1963), p. 65.

41. Bruecke, W. C., "Noise Measurements in Field-Effect Transistors" (letter), *Proc. IEEE,* Vol. 51 (February, 1963), p. 378.

42. Lindholm F. A. and D. C. Latham, "Junction Capacitance of Field-Effect Transistors" (letter), *Proc. IEEE,* Vol. 51 (February, 1963), p. 404.

43. Wallmark, J. T. and A. G. Revesz, "Redundancy in Unipolar Transistor Circuits" (letter), *IEEE Trans. on Electronic Computers,* Vol. EC–12 (February, 1963), p. 23.

44. Wanlass, F. M. and C. T. Sah, "Nanowatt Logic Using Field-Effect Metal-Oxide-Semiconductor Triodes," 1963 International Solid-State Circuit Conference, Philadelphia, Pa., February 20–22, 1963.

45. Kauppila, J. E., "Cadmium Sulfide Unipolar Surface Transistor" (letter), *Proc. IEEE,* Vol. 51 (March, 1963), p. 472.

46. van der Ziel, A., "Gate Noise in Field-Effect Transistors at Moderately High Frequencies," *Proc. IEEE,* Vol. 51 (March, 1963), p. 461.

47. Evans, A. D., "Characteristics of Unipolar Field-Effect Transistors," *Electronic Industries,* Vol. 22 (March, 1963), p. 99.

48. Bignell, T. R., "How to Get Maximum Input Impedance with Field-Effect Transistors," *Electronics,* Vol. 36 (March 8, 1963), p. 44.

49. Zuleeg, R., "CdS Thin-Film Electron Devices," *Solid-State Electronics,* Vol. 6 (March-April, 1963), p. 193.

50. Bechtel, G. N., "A Circuit and Noise Model of the Field-Effect Transistor," Stanford Electronics Laboratories, Tech. Rep., 1612–1 (April, 1963).

51. Fleenor, E. G., "Low-Noise Preamplifier Uses Field-Effect Transistors," *Electronics,* Vol. 36 (April 12, 1963), p. 67.

52. Shallcross, F. V., "Cadmium Selenide Thin-Film Transistors" (letter), *Proc. IEEE,* Vol. 51 (May, 1963), p. 851.

53. Warner, R. M., "Epitaxial FET Cutoff Voltage" (letter), *Proc. IEEE,* Vol. 51 (June, 1963), p. 939.

54. Borkan, H. and P. K. Weimer, "An Analysis of the Characteristics of Insulated-Gate Thin-Film Transistors," *RCA Rev.,* Vol. 24 (June, 1963), p. 153.

55. Csanky, G. and R. M. Warner, Jr., "Put More Snap in Logic Circuits with Field-Effect Transistors," *Electronics,* Vol. 36 (June 14, 1963), p. 43.

56. Beneteau, P. J. and E. G. Fleenor, "FET Amplifier," *Electronics,* Vol. 36 (June 21, 1963), p. 4.

57. Hoerni, J. A. and B. Weir, "Conditions for a Temperature Compensated Silicon Field-Effect Transistor" (letter), *Proc. IEEE*, Vol. 51 (July, 1963), p. 1058.

58. Roosild, S. A., R. P. Dolan, Jr., and D. O'Neill, "A Unipolar Structure Applying Lateral Diffusion" (letter), *Proc. IEEE*, Vol. 51 (July, 1963), p. 1059.

*59. Hofstein, S. R. and F. P. Heiman, "The Silicon Insulated-Gate Field-Effect Transistor," *Proc. IEEE*, Vol. 51 (September, 1963), p. 1190.

60. Richer, I. and R. D. Middlebrook, "Power-law Nature of Field-Effect Transistor Experimental Characteristics" (letter), *Proc. IEEE*, Vol. 51 (August, 1963), p. 1145. Also *Proc. IEEE*, Vol. 52 (March, 1964) p. 314.

61. Middlebrook, R.D., "A Simple Derivation of Field-Effect Transistor Characteristics" (letter), *Proc. IEEE*, Vol. 51 (August, 1963), p. 1146.

62. Richer, I., "Input Capacitance of Field-Effect Transistors," *Proc. IEEE*, Vol. 51 (September, 1963), p. 1249.

63. Halladay, H. E. and W. C. Bruncke, "Excess Noise in Field-Effect Transistors," *Proc. IEEE*, Vol. 51 (November, 1963), p. 1671.

64. van der Ziel, A., "Carrier Density Fluctuation Noise in Field-Effect Transistors," *Proc. IEEE*, Vol. 51 (November, 1963), p. 1670

65. Zuleeg, R., "Electrical Evaluation of Thin-Film CdS Diodes and Transistors," *Solid-State Electronics*, Vol. 6 (November–December, 1963), p. 645.

66. Wallmark, J. T., "The Field-Effect Transistor — A Review," *RCA Rev.* Vol. 24 (December, 1963). p. 641. Also *IEEE Spectrum*, Vol. 1 (March, 1964), p. 182.

67. Shallcross, F. V., "Evaluation of Cadmium Selenide Films for Use in Thin-Film Transistors," *RCA Rev.*, Vol. 24 (December, 1963), p. 676.

68. Bosenberg, W., "Transfer Characteristics of Field-Effect Transistors," *RCA Rev.*, Vol. 24 (December, 1963), p. 688.

*69. Walston, J. A. and J. R. Miller, eds., "Field-Effect Transistors," chapter in *Transistor Circuit Design,* (New York: McGraw-Hill Book Company, 1963).

1964 70. Haering, R. R., "Theory of Thin-Film Transistor Operation," *Solid-State Electronics*, Vol. 7 (January, 1964), p. 31.

71. Miksic, M. G., E. S. Schlig, and R. R. Haering: "Behavior of CdS Thin-Film Transistors," *Solid-State Electronics*, Vol. 7 (January, 1964), p. 39.

72. Hodges, D. A., "High-Performance Field-Effect Transistors formed by Redistribution," *Proc. IEEE*, Vol. 52 (January, 1964), p. 89.

73. Kaufman, A. B., "Field-Effect Transistors Under Nuclear Radiation," *Electronic Industries*, Vol. 23 (March, 1964), p. 94.

74. LeMée, J., A. V. J. Martin, I. Richer, and R. D. Middlebrook, "Power-Law Nature of Field-Effect Transistor Characteristics" (letter), *Proc. IEEE*, Vol. 52 (March, 1964), p. 314.

75. Goldberg, C., S. R. Hofstein, and F. P. Heiman, "Pinch-Off in Insulated-Gate Field-Effect Transistors" (letter and reply), *Proc. IEEE*, Vol. 52 (April, 1964), p. 414.

76. Abraham, D. and T. O. Poehler, "A Modified Representation for Thin-Film Triodes" (letter), *Proc. IEEE*, Vol. 52 (April, 1964), p. 416.

77. Muller, R. S. and B. G. Watkins, "Hall-Effect Studies in Deposited CdS Thin Films" (letter), *Proc. IEEE*, Vol. 52 (April, 1964), p. 425.

78. van der Ziel, A. and J. W. Ero, "Small-Signal, High-Frequency Theory of Field-Effect Transistor Characteristics" *IEEE. Trans, on Electron Devices*, Vol. ED–11 (April, 1964), p. 128.

79. Gutierrez, W. A. and H. L. Wilson, "The Effects of Rectifying Contacts on the Characteristics of the TFT" (letter), *Proc. IEEE,* Vol 52, (May, 1964), p. 607.

80. Weimer, P. K., "A p-type Tellurium Thin-Film Transistor" (letter), *Proc. IEEE*, Vol. 52 (May, 1964), p. 608.

81. Winslow, J., "Space-Charge Effects in the Insulated-Gate Field-Effect Triode" (letter), *Proc. IEEE*, Vol. 52 (May, 1964), p. 618.

82. Root, C. D. and L. Vadasz, "Design Calculations for MOS Field-Effect Transistors," *IEEE Trans. on Electron Devices,* Vol. ED–11 (June, 1964), p. 294.

83. Latham, D. C., F. A. Lindholm, and D. J. Hamilton, "Low-Frequency Operation of Four-Terminal Field-Effect Transistors," *IEEE Trans. on Electron Devices*, Vol. ED–11 (June, 1964), p. 300.

84. Fowler, A. B., "Thin-Film Circuit Technology, Part III – Active Thin-Film Devices," *IEEE Spectrum,* Vol. 1 (June, 1964), p. 102.

85. Weimer, P. K., "The Insulated-Gate Thin-Film Transistor," chapter in *Physics of Thin Films* Vol. 2, G. Hass, R. Thun, eds., (New York: Academic Press, 1964).

86. Radeka, V., "The Field-Effect Transistor – Its Characteristics and Applications," *IEEE Trans. on Nuclear Science*, Vol. NS–11 (June, 1964), p. 358.

87. Blalock, T. V., "A Low-Noise Charge-Sensitive Preamplifier with a Field-Effect Transistor in the Input Stage," *IEEE Trans. on Nuclear Science,* Vol. NS–11 (June, 1964), p. 365.

88. Reinhartz, K. R., V. A. Russell, D. L. Stockman, W. J. van der Grinten and W. L. Willis, "Aging Characteristics of Field-Effect Thin Film Active Devices," *IEEE Trans. on Component Parts,* Vol. CP–11 (June, 1964), p. 27.

89. Sah, C. T., "Characteristics of the Metal-Oxide-Semiconductor Transistors," *IEEE Trans. on Electron Devices,* Vol. ED–11 (July, 1964), p. 324.

90. Sah, C. T., "Theory of Low-Frequency Generation Noise in Junction-Gate Field-Effect Transistors," *Proc. IEEE,* Vol. 52 (July, 1964), p. 795.

91. Hofstein, S. R., K. H. Zaininger, and G. Warfield, "Frequency Response of the Surface Inversion Layer in Silicon," (letter), *Proc. IEEE,* Vol. 52 (August, 1964), p. 971.

92. Zaininger, K. H., and G. Warfield, "Hydrogen Induced Surface States at a $Si-SiO_2$ Interface" (letter), *Proc. IEEE,* Vol. 52 (August, 1964). p. 972.

93. Chopra, A., and L. Vadasz, "Silicon MOS Field-Effect Transistors Using Impurity Redistribution During Oxidation," *Proc. IEEE,* Vol. 52 (August, 1964), p. 985.

94. Gosling, W., *Field-Effect Transistor Applications,* (London; Temple Press Ltd., 1964).

95. Hayashi, T., and T. Niimi, "Observations of Negative-Resistance Phenomena and Oscillations in the MOS Diode," *Proc. IEEE,* Vol. 52 (August, 1964), p. 986.

96. "Mos Surface Effects"; 9 papers in *IBM J. Res. and Dev.,* Vol. 8 (September, 1964).

97. Cobbold, R. S. C., and F. N. Trofimenkoff, "Field-Effect Transistor with Forward Biased Gate-Channel Junction" (letter), *Proc. IEEE,* Vol. 52 (September, 1964), p. 1073.

98. Zuleeg, R. and V. O. Hinkle, "A Multichannel Field-Effect Transistor" (letter), *Proc. IEEE,* Vol. 52 (October, 1964), p. 1245.

99. Gutierrez, W. A. and H. L. Wilson, "An Analysis of the CdSe Thin-Film Triode as a Current Limiter," *IEEE Trans. on Electron Devices,* Vol. ED–11 (October, 1964), p. 466.

100. Abstracts from the Solid-State Device Research Conference July 1–3, 1964, Boulder, Colorado, *IEEE Trans. on Electron Devices,* Vol. ED–11 (November, 1964), p. 530.

101. Buchanan, B., S. Roosild and R. Dolan, "Silicon Current Amplifier for Microampere Current Levels" (letter), *Proc. IEEE,* Vol. 52 (November, 1964), p. 1364.

102. Cobbold, R. S. C. and E. N. Trofimenkoff, "Breakdown Phenomena in Double-Gate Field-Effect Transistors" (letter), *Proc. IEEE,* Vol. 52 (November, 1964), p. 1375.

103. "The Field-Effect Transistor," Part I, II and III; 15 papers in *Electronics*, Vol. 37 (November 30, December 14 and December 28, 1964).

104. Weimer, P. K., H. Borkan, G. Sadasiv, L. Meray-Horvath and F. V. Shallcross, "Integrated Circuits Incorporating Thin-Film Active and Passive Elements," *Proc. IEEE*, Vol. 52 (December, 1964), p. 1479.

105. Mueller, C. W. and P. H. Robinson, "Grown-Film Silicon Transistors on Sapphire," *Proc. IEEE*, Vol. 52 (December, 1964), p. 1487.

106. Teszner, S. and R. Gicquel, "Gridistor – A New Field-Effect Device," *Proc. IEEE*, Vol. 52 (December, 1964), p. 1502.

107. Ruegg, H. W., "An Integrated FET Analog Switch," *Proc. IEEE*, Vol. 52 (December, 1964), p. 1572.

1965   108. Gutierrez, W. A. and H. L. Wilson, "Shelf and Operating Life Studies on SiO Protected CdSe Thin-Film Triodes" (letter), *Proc. IEEE*, Vol. 53 (January, 1965), p. 92.

109. Josephs, H. C., "Conditions for Optimizing FET Operation," (letter) *Proc. IEEE*, Vol. 53 (February, 1965), p. 199.

110. Hofstein, S. R. and G. Warfield, "The Insulated-Gate Tunnel Junction Triode," *Trans. on Electron Devices*, Vol. ED–12 (February, 1965), p. 66.

111. Middlebrook, R. D. and I. Richer, "Nonreactive Filter Converts Triangular Waves to Sines," *Electronics*, Vol. 38 (March 8, 1965) p. 96.

112. White, M. H. and R. C. Gallagher, "Metal-Oxide-Semiconductor (MOS) Small Signal Equivalent Circuit," (letter) *Proc. IEEE*, Vol. 53 (March, 1965), p. 314.

113. Chang, L. L. and H. N. Yu, "The Germanium Insulated-Gate Field-Effect Transistor (FET)" (letter), *Proc. IEEE*, Vol. 53 (March, 1965), p. 316.

114. Trofimenkoff, F. N., "Field-Effect Transistor Transient Analysis" *Int. J. of Electronics*, Vol. 18, No. 4, (1965), p. 301.

115. Snow, E. H., A. S. Grove, B. E. Deal and C. T. Sah, "Ion Transport in Insulating Films," *J. Appl. Phys.*, Vol. 36 (1965), p. 1664.

116. Special issue on Metal-Oxide-Semiconductor (MOS) Devices; *IEEE Trans. on Electron Devices*, Vol. ED–12 (March, 1965).

117. Heiman, F. P. and G. Warfield, "The Effects of Oxide Traps on the MOS Capacitance," *IEEE Trans. on Electron Devices*, Vol. ED–12 (April, 1965), p. 167.

118. Zaininger, K. H. and G. Warfield, "Limitations of the MOS Capacitance Method for the Determination of Semiconductor Surface Properties," *IEEE Trans. on Electron Devices*, Vol. ED–12 (April, 1965), p. 179.

119. Tarnay, K., "Temperature Dependence of the Current of the Field-Effect Transistors in the Pinch-off Region" (letter), *Proc. IEEE*, Vol. 53 (May, 1965), p. 485.

120. Todd, C. D., "Presence of Negative Resistance in FET Output Characteristics" (letter), *Proc. IEEE*, Vol. 53 (May, 1965), p. 508.

121. Osterfjells, S., "Analog Multiplier with Field-Effect Transistors" (letter), *Proc. IEEE*, Vol. 53 (May, 1965), p. 521.

FIELD-EFFECT TRANSISTOR PATENTS

P1. J. E. Lilienfeld: Method and apparatus for controlling electric currents
                            U.S. Pat. 1,745,175
                            January 28, 1930

P2. J. E. Lilienfeld: Amplifier for electric currents
                            U.S. Pat. 1,877,140
                            September 13, 1932

P3. J. E. Lilienfeld: Device for controlling electric current
                            U.S. Pat. 1,900,018
                            March 7, 1933

P4. H. C. Weber: Electronic device
                            U.S. Pat. 1,949,383
                            February 27, 1934

P5. O. Heil: Improvements in or relating to electrical amplifiers and other control arrangements and devices
                            Brit. Pat. 439,457
                            December 6, 1935

P6. G. Holst *et al.*:   Electrode system of unsymmetrical conductivity
                            U.S. Pat. 2,173,904
                            September 26, 1939

P7. A. Glaser *et al.*:   Dry-plate electrode system having a control electrode
                            U.S. Pat. 2,208,455
                            July 16, 1940

P8. W. C. Van Geel: Blocking-layer cells comprising one or more grids embedded in the blocking layer
                            U.S. Pat. 2,428,400
                            October 7, 1947

P9. W. C. Van Geel: Blocking-layer electrode system
                            U.S. Pat. 2,456,758
                            December 21, 1948

P10. E. H. G. Spenke *et al.*:   Controllable electric resistance device
U.S. Pat. 2,648,805
August 11, 1953

P11. H. Welker: Semiconductor for control purposes
U.S. Pat. 2,683,840
July 13, 1954

P12. W. Shockley: Semiconductor signal-translating devices
U.S. Pat. 2,744,970
May 8, 1956

P13. L. D. Armstrong *et al.*:   Unipolar Semiconductor devices
U.S. Pat. 2,750,542
June 12, 1956

P14. W. Shockley: Semiconductor signal-translating devices
U.S. Pat. 2,756,285
July 24, 1956

P15. W. Shockley: Semiconductor signal-translating devices
U.S. Pat. 2,764,642
September 25, 1956

P16. W. Shockley: Semiconductor signal-translating devices
U.S. Pat. 2,778,885
January 22, 1957

P17. G. C. Dacey *et al.*:   Semiconductor signal-translating devices
U.S. Pat. 2,778,956
January 22, 1957

P18. W. Shockley: Semiconductor signal-translating devices
U.S. Pat. 2,790,037
April 23, 1957

P19. D. H. Looney: Semiconductive-translating device
U.S. Pat. 2,791,758
May 7, 1957

P20. I. M. Ross: Semiconductive translating device
U.S. Pat. 2,791,760
May 7, 1957

P21. I. M. Ross: Semiconductor signal-translating devices
U.S. Pat. 2,805,397
September 3, 1957

P22. J. Kurshan: Semiconductor devices
U.S. Pat. 2,820,154
January 14, 1958

P23. J. I. Pankove: Field-controlled semiconductor devices and methods of making them
U.S. Pat. 2,829,075
April 1, 1958

P24. V. Ozarow: Multi-electrode field-controlled germanium
                              devices
                                        U.S. Pat. 2,836,797
                                        May 27, 1958

P25. G. L. Tucker: Unipolar transistor
                                        U.S. Pat. 2,869,054
                                        January 13, 1959

P26. R. N. Noyce: Field-effect transistor
                                        U.S. Pat. 2,869,055
                                        January 13, 1959

P27. J. T. Wallmark: Field-effect transistor
                                        U.S. Pat. 2,900,531
                                        August 18, 1959

P28. O. M. Stuetzer: Semiconductor amplifier
                                        U.S. Pat. 2,918,628
                                        December 22, 1959

P29. S. Teszner: Very-high-frequency field-effect transistors
                                        U.S. Pat. 2,921,265
                                        January 12, 1960

P30. S. Teszner: High-power field-effect transistor
                                        U.S. Pat. 2,930,950
                                        March 29, 1960

P31. S. Teszner: Unipolar field-effect transistors
                                        U.S. Pat. 2,939,057
                                        May 31, 1960

P32. J. I. Pankove: Semiconductor devices
                                        U.S. Pat. 2,940,022
                                        June 7, 1960

P33. H. F. Matare: Semiconductor oscillator
                                        U.S. Pat. 2,944,167
                                        July 5, 1960

P34. G. B. Herzog: Semiconductor devices
                                        U.S. Pat. 2,951,191
                                        August 30, 1960

P35. J. I. Franke: Plane concentric field-effect transistors
                                        U.S. Pat. 2,952,804
                                        September 13, 1960

P36. E. I. Doucette *et al.*: Semiconductor resistance element
                                        U.S. Pat. 2,954,486
                                        September 27, 1960

P37. W. Shockley *et al.*:   Transistor structure
U.S. Pat. 2,967,985
January 10, 1961

P38. R. N. Noyce: Transistor structure and method of making the same
U.S. Pat. 2,968,750
January 17, 1961

P39 H. F. Matare *et al.*:   Temperature-independent transistor with grain boundary
U.S. Pat. 2,970,229
January 31, 1961

P40. H. A. R. Wegener: Semiconductor field-effect device
U.S. Pat. 2,975,344
March 14, 1961

P41. L. J. Giacoletto: Unipolar transistors
U.S. Pat. 2,984,752
May 16, 1961

P42. H. Nelson: Semiconductor devices
U.S. Pat. 2,985,805
May 23, 1961

P43. S. Teszner: Unipolar field-effect transistor
U.S. Pat. 2,987,659
June 6, 1961

P44. K. Lehovec: Transistor combinations
U.S. Pat. 2,993,998
July 25, 1961

P45. J. I. Franke: Manufacture of field-effect transistors
U.S. Pat. 2,997,634
August 22, 1961

P46. M. A. Chappey: Structures for a field-effect transistor
U.S. Pat. 3,001,111
September 19, 1961

P47. J. T. Wallmark *et al.*:   Semiconductor signal-translating devices
U.S. Pat. 3,005,937
October 24, 1961

P48. I. F. Barditch: Modulating circuit and field-effect semi-conductor structure for use therein
U.S. Pat. 3,007,119
October 31, 1961

P49. R. N. Noyce: Field-effect transistor
U.S. Pat. 3,010,033
November 21, 1961

P50. E. M. Pell: Semiconductor devices and methods of making
                                the same
                                          U.S. Pat. 3,016,313
                                          January 9, 1962

P51. J. F. Dewald *et al.*:   Signal-translating device
                                          U.S. Pat. 3,017,548
                                          January 16, 1962

P52. W. Ruppel: Electric contacts
                                          U.S. Pat. 3,018,426
                                          January 23, 1962

P53. S. R. Morrison: Asymmetrically conductive device employing
                                semiconductors
                                          U.S. Pat. 3,021,433
                                          February 13, 1962

P54. H. A. R. Wegener: Field-effect transistor
                                          U.S. Pat. 3,025,438
                                          March 13, 1962

P55. E. I. Doucette: Semiconductor switching apparatus
                                          U.S. Pat. 3,035,186
                                          May 15, 1962

P56. E. G. Linder: Semiconductor modulator
                                          U.S. Pat. 3,048,797
                                          August 7, 1962

P57. E. M. Davis: Photosensitive field-effect unit
                                          U.S. Pat. 3,051,840
                                          August 28, 1962

P58. C. A. Mead: Solid-state electron devices
                                          U.S. Pat. 3,056,073
                                          September 25, 1962

P59. R. M. Warner, Jr.:   Temperature-compensated field-effect resistor
                                          U.S. Pat. 3,056,100
                                          September 25, 1962

P60. M. M. Atalla: Semiconductor triode
                                          U.S. Pat. 3,056,888
                                          October 2, 1962

P61. H. A. Stone, Jr. *et al.*: Multiple-channel field-effect semiconductor
                                          U.S. Pat. 3,061,739
                                          October 30, 1962

P62. E. G. Roka: Unipolar transistor
                                          U.S. Pat. 3,081,421
                                          March 12, 1963

P63. D. Kahng: Electric field-controlled semiconductor device
                        U.S. Pat. 3,102,230
                        August 27, 1963

P64. C. R. Cook, Jr., *et al.*: Ring counter utilizing bipolar field-effect devices
                        U.S. Pat. 3,112,411
                        November 26, 1963

P65. M. E. Szekely: Unipolar transistors and assemblies therefor
                        U.S. Pat. 3,114,867
                        December 17, 1963

P66. E. M. Pell: Asymmetrically conductive device
                        U.S. Pat. 3,116,183
                        December 31, 1963

P67. W. Shockley: Field-effect transistor having grain boundary
                        therein
                        U.S. Pat. 3,126,505
                        March 24, 1964

Index